D1483259

Whistlers
and Related Ionospheric
Phenomena

Whistlers
and Related Ionospheric
Phenomena

Robert A. Helliwell

1965

Stanford University Press, Stanford, California

© 1965 by the Board of Trustees of the
Leland Stanford Junior University
Printed and bound by Stanford University Press
Stanford, California, U.S.A.
L.C. 63-14128

JOINT UNIVERSITY
LIBRARIES
NASHVILLE. TENN.

QC
973
,H4

Science

480272

Preface

The aim of *Whistlers and Related Ionospheric Phenomena* is to present a comprehensive treatment of this new and rapidly growing aspect of radio science. Research on these remarkable natural phenomena has continually been stimulated by the International Scientific Radio Union (URSI), with at least sixteen different countries now participating. Studies expanded greatly during the International Geophysical Year (IGY), and a large quantity of data in various stages of interpretation is now available. The rapid growth of the field is illustrated by the number of references, which was less than 50 before 1956 and now exceeds 500. The reader should be cautioned that this book contains much original material, generated in the author's group in the Radioscience Laboratory at Stanford University, that has not yet been subjected to the tests of journal publication and public discussions.

The results of whistler studies have been applied to problems in other fields, including very low frequency (VLF) propagation, the outer ionosphere, nuclear detection and satellite communications. The phenomena described in the book appear to be a vital aspect of solar–terrestrial relationships, and therefore their study should contribute substantially to the solution of problems in this area.

This book covers both theoretical and experimental aspects of the subject. An introductory chapter presents a general, qualitative description of the phenomena that can be understood by nearly everyone. Chapter 2 traces the history of whistlers and related phenomena from the early work of Barkhausen through the IGY. In Chap. 3 an attempt is made to present a first-order theory of whistlers, including the calculation of the intensity of whistler-mode signals. The characteristics of whistlers are described in Chap. 4, which includes a comprehensive atlas of various kinds of whistlers. Chapter 5 reports the results of fixed-frequency whistler-mode studies, based primarily on experiments conducted by Stanford University. The chapter includes a discussion of the first results of satellite observation of fixed-frequency whistler-mode propagation. Application of whistler data to the study of the distribution of electron density in the magnetosphere is given in Chap. 6. The book is planned so that Chaps. 4, 5, and 6 can be read with relatively little reference to the theory given in Chap. 3. However, every effort is made to interpret the experimental results in terms of the theory.

The characteristics of VLF emissions, or ionospheric noise, are described in Chap. 7, which also has a comprehensive atlas of the spectra of various types of emissions. The chapter concludes with an outline of the several theories of generation of this noise. The appendix contains a new chart of the dipole field of the earth, including gyro-frequencies and the lengths of field lines.

In the preparation of this book I have recieved substantial and valuable help from the students and staff engaged in VLF research at Stanford. I am especially indebted to R. L. Smith (Chap. 3), D. L. Carpenter (Chap. 4), and J. P. Katsufrakis (Chap. 7). Valuable assistance was also given by T. F. Bell, N. M. Brice, G. B. Carpenter, J. H. Crary, W. J. Helms, K. E. Marks, L. H. Martin, H. M. Morozumi, M. L. Trimpi, and E. E. Ungstrup. Preparation and checking of the bibliography were expertly handled by P. J. Flanagan and A. D. Calhoun. Very helpful comments on the manuscript were provided by J. O. Thomas. Most of the editorial supervision and many of the calculations, including the absorption calculations of Chap. 3, were provided, most competently, by N. Dunckel. I am grateful to Elaine Lasky of Stanford University Press for her patience and care in the editing of the text.

The atlas illustrations were derived mainly from the recordings of the stations of the "Whistlers-West" network of the IGY (Helliwell and Carpenter, 1961) and other associated stations. Thanks are due to the individuals and the institutions who cooperated in the operation of these stations.

Tape recordings from Norwich, Vermont, were kindly loaned by M. G. Morgan, Director of the "Whistlers-East" network, Dartmouth College, and tape recordings of Vanguard III whistlers by J. C. Cain of the National Aeronautics and Space Administration. Transmissions of VLF data from the Alouette I satellite to Stanford as well as whistler tapes from Ottawa were provided through the courtesy of J. S. Belrose of the Defence Research Telecommunication Establishment of Canada.

Many of the illustrations and computations were made available by projects under the sponsorship of agencies of the U.S. Government, including the National Science Foundation, the Air Force Office of Aerospace Research, the Office of Naval Research, and the National Aeronautics and Space Administration.

R. A. H.

Contents

Whistlers
and Related Ionospheric Phenomena

Chapter One

Introduction

Among the many accidental discoveries of science are whistlers, which, with related phenomena, comprise a group of complex and fascinating natural events that can be heard on very low frequencies with the simplest of audio-frequency equipment.

Whistlers are remarkable bursts of very-low-frequency (VLF) electromagnetic energy produced by ordinary lightning discharges. These bursts travel into the ionosphere, where their interaction with free electrons forces them to follow approximately the lines of force of the earth's magnetic field. Traveling many earth radii beyond the earth's surface, they bring back information about the distribution of ionization in the outer atmosphere and form the basis for a new and novel means of communication.

Noises similar to whistlers, called VLF emissions, appear to originate within the earth's ionosphere, possibly on streams of charge that flow in from the sun or are trapped in the earth's magnetic field. They, too, carry information about sun–earth relationships, but the interpretation of this information is a problem that remains to be solved.

To many first-time observers these phenomena seem almost unbelievable. To others they suggest supernatural origins. During the early phases of research on whistlers at Stanford University, the subject was of great interest to newspaper reporters. Articles entitled "Voices from Outer Space" stimulated a substantial flow of fan mail from many parts of the world. One correspondent, gratified to learn that research in this field had at last begun at Stanford, wrote at length about his own investigations during which, he said, he was able to hear without benefit of any special equipment the weird sounds described in the newspaper report. Moreover, he stated, he had identified the producers of these strange sounds as the people on Mars. Others found close connections between the whistler phenomena and flying saucers. One contributor reported that she had heard whistlers on a three-quarter-ton Admiral air conditioner. As the occult aspects of the subject faded away, ordinary scientific curiosity began to produce information that has resulted in a fairly complete and understandable picture of whistlers.

1.1 Whistlers

Nature and occurrence of whistlers. Whistlers are radio signals in the audio-frequency range that "whistle." Usually a whistler begins at a high frequency and in the course of about one second drops in frequency to a lower limit of about 1000 cycles per second. Some whistlers are very pure gliding tones; others sound "swishy"—much like air escaping from a punctured

1

balloon tire. Some whistlers are very short, lasting a fraction of a second; others are long, lasting two or three seconds. Often whistlers occur in groups. In one type of group the whistler appears to echo several times with an equal time lapse between different members of the train of echoes. In each whistler of the group the rate of decrease of frequency is less than that in the preceding whistler. These groups are called "echo trains." Sometimes two or more distinct, similar whistlers appear to overlap in time; these are called multiple whistlers. The amplitude of whistlers is greatest at a frequency usually near 5000 cps, but sometimes as high as 15,000 cps. On rare occasions whistlers have been observed to sweep all the way from 35,000 down to 300 cps.

Many whistlers are preceded by a sharp impulse that usually sounds like a click in the reproducer. These impulses, called "atmospherics," or sometimes "spherics" for short, are produced by strokes of lightning which may be many thousands of miles away. The radiation from the lightning stroke travels at approximately the speed of light in the space between the earth and the lower edge of the ionosphere, called the earth–ionosphere waveguide. At times when the reflection efficiency of the ionosphere is high this radiation may echo back and forth between the boundaries of the waveguide many times before disappearing into the background noise. Then the received disturbance consists of a series of impulses, which produces a faintly musical or chirping sound. This particular type of atmospheric is usually called a "tweek."

During a period of high whistler activity, there is usually no uncertainty about the relation between whistlers and the sharp clicks preceding them. However, many whistlers appear without an associated sharp click. These latter whistlers are believed to originate in lightning flashes in the opposite hemisphere of the earth, which explains why the atmospheric from the source is often not an identifiable event at the receiver. Occasionally, however, these atmospherics are strong enough to be clearly identified in recordings made in the opposite hemisphere.

The variable occurrence of whistlers is understood in broad terms. Whistlers tend to be more common during the night than during the day, mainly because of the relatively high absorption in the daytime ionosphere, and they are more frequent at locations and times where lightning storms are common, or at points magnetically conjugate to regions of lightning activity, i.e., points that have a common magnetic field line with the active regions but that lie in the opposite hemisphere. As a result of the dependence of whistlers on lightning as well as on propagation factors, the day-to-day variation in whistler occurrence is great. Many days may pass without the observation of a single whistler. On other occasions whistlers may occur at rates exceeding one per second.

Synoptic data on the occurrence of whistlers show that whistler activity tends to be greatest at middle latitudes, reaching a maximum in the vicinity of 50 degrees geomagnetic latitude. At the geomagnetic equator whistlers are virtually unknown, and in polar regions their rate is significantly lower than in middle latitudes.

Recordings made simultaneously at spaced stations show that a whistler may spread over an area typically about 1000 km in diameter. On occasion very strong whistlers have been detected at stations spaced as much as 7000 km apart.

From these observations we can characterize the whistler as a local phenomenon that is concentrated at middle latitudes and that shows marked variations in occurrence even from day to day.

Methods of observation. Man has no sense that enables him to detect radio waves of ordinary intensity. (Very strong radio waves, however, can produce a noticeable or even dangerous increase in body temperature.) For the detection of whistlers it is necessary simply to employ a transducer that converts electromagnetic waves to sound waves. Perhaps because of this simplicity of observation, whistlers were observed early in the history of radio. One method of detection is to listen to a telephone receiver connected to a long, rural telephone line or to a submarine cable. The telephone line or cable acts as an antenna, and the telephone receiver converts the weak electrical currents into sound waves. An ordinary high-fidelity audio amplifier connected to 50 feet or so of wire makes another excellent detector of whistlers. It is also possible to detect whistlers by inserting metallic probes in the earth at some distance from each other and connecting these to a high-gain audio amplifier. The earth-probe circuit acts like a loop antenna in picking up electromagnetic waves.

The basic requirement for the detection of whistlers is that a voltage be induced in an electrical circuit by the very-low-frequency electromagnetic waves of the whistler. This voltage must be amplified and converted into a form suitable for observation. Whistlers may be reproduced with earphones or a loudspeaker for direct detection by ear, they may be recorded on magnetic tape for later reproduction, or they may be displayed directly on an oscilloscope or chart recorder for visual observation.

Modern methods of observation are basically the same as those used originally, except that antennas are smaller, frequency ranges are wider, and accurate timing is provided. A typical whistler antenna consists of a single-turn loop of copper wire in the shape of a delta with an elevation of about thirty feet. This loop is connected through a transformer to a high-gain, low-noise, wideband audio amplifier. The output of the amplifier is recorded on a conventional magnetic-tape recorder together with time marks from a local clock or from a radio time-standard station. Networks of whistler stations of this general design are scattered over the surface of the earth to provide data on the geographic variations of whistlers and related phenomena.

Sources of whistlers. As we have stated, whistlers and lightning are closely associated. A few visual observations of lightning and aural observations of the associated whistlers have been made, but most of the data have been obtained from radio recordings. Relatively little is known about the spectra of lightning discharges that precede whistlers. It appears that any strong lightning discharge can excite a whistler. However, there is also evidence that many whistlers originate in unusually intense lightning discharges with peaks in their energy spectra in the vicinity of 5 kc/s. From direction-finder studies it is clear that the causative lightning discharges can be located thousands of kilometers from the receiver or from the receiver's conjugate point. Intense electromagnetic impulses that can excite ordinary whistlers are also produced by nuclear bombs.

Dispersion. Energy from a lightning discharge enters the ionosphere and is guided by the lines of force of the earth's magnetic field into the opposite hemisphere. As the radio waves travel along this path they are dispersed. This means that the different frequency components of the wave travel with different velocities. Usually the high frequencies travel faster than the low. Since the causative impulse from the lightning discharge excites all frequencies simultaneously, the signal at the end of the path consists of a gliding tone in which the high frequencies arrive first. The length of the path and the velocity differences are such that the energy is stretched out over a period of about one second.

The waveform of a whistler is sketched in Fig. 1-1a with all frequencies divided by 400 to give better definition. The actual variation of frequency (f) with time is shown in Fig. 1-1b, and is called the dynamic spectrum of the whistler. By plotting $1/\sqrt{f}$ versus t, one obtains a straight line as in Fig. 1-1c; the reciprocal of the slope of this line is called the dispersion D and is equal to the time of propagation multiplied by the square root of the frequency (see p. 32 for further discussion). This law describes most whistlers at middle latitudes and at low frequencies rather closely. The dispersion of a whistler depends on the length of the path over which it travels and on the electron density along the path. Hence at high latitudes, where the paths are very long, dispersion is high, and conversely at low latitudes dispersion is low. When electron density is high, as it is during the years near sunspot maximum, the dispersion is also high. During magnetic storms the electron density in the whistler medium is lowered and the dispersions are correspondingly reduced. In satellites, where the path can be very much shorter than that observed between points on the ground, the dispersion can be very small indeed. In fact, whistlers observed from satellites at heights of 1000 to 2000 km are so short that it is difficult to distinguish them from ordinary atmospherics.

Since dispersion is closely related to electron density, it becomes an important quantity in the study of the variations of electron density in the ionosphere and magnetosphere.

Paths of propagation. Perhaps the most interesting and puzzling feature of whistler propagation is the path of propagation. Although the law of dispersion described above has been known for many years, the path followed by a whistler was discovered comparatively recently. Even now the picture is not complete because the actual path has not been observed experimentally but has only been inferred from the experimental data.

From the discrete traces of multipath whistlers, from the precise integral relationship of the members of an echo train, and from related data, it has been concluded that the paths must be fixed in the ionosphere. This conclusion has led to the hypothesis of a field-aligned enhancement of ionization that acts as a waveguide or "duct" to trap the whistler energy and produce discrete traces. Figure 1-2 shows such a path beginning at the earth's surface (at point A) and following a typical dipole line of force of the earth's magnetic field to point

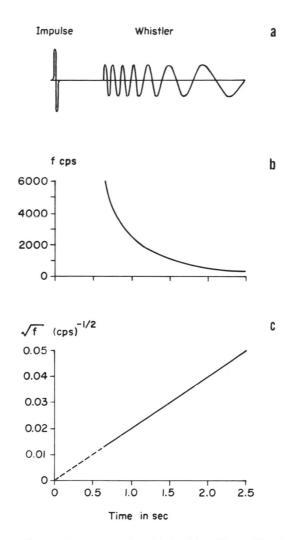

Fig. 1-1. Idealized waveform and spectrum of a whistler ($D = 50$). *a*, Waveform with each cycle representing 400 cycles on the original; *b*, curve of actual frequency with time; *c*, curve of $1/\sqrt{f}$ with time.

B in the opposite hemisphere. The diagram is drawn roughly to scale, so that the bottom edge of the ionosphere (labeled E layer) is shown properly in relation to the length of the field-line path. Energy from a lightning source near the earth's surface travels in the earth–ionosphere waveguide and enters the ionosphere continuously along the lower surface. Wave components that enter the ionosphere at the location of a duct are then trapped and conveyed to the opposite hemisphere along the same line of force, where they emerge from the ionosphere and enter the earth–ionosphere waveguide.

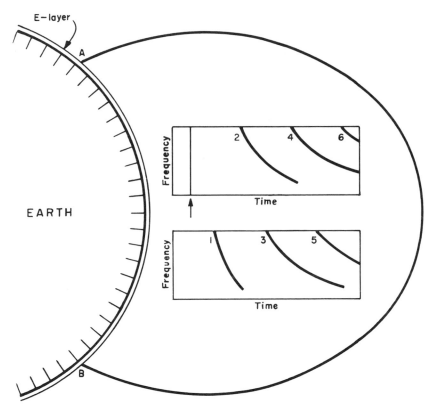

FIG. 1-2. Field-line path followed by a ducted whistler. Inset diagrams show idealized spectra of whistler echo trains at conjugate points A and B.

Wave components entering elsewhere through the lower boundary also follow curved paths of propagation, but these paths do not coincide exactly with the lines of force of the earth's magnetic field. Furthermore, this second type of wave, upon arriving at the lower boundary of the ionosphere in the opposite hemisphere, does not readily cross the boundary, and so is not easily detected on the ground. However, a satellite-borne receiver can pick up this type of wave. Because of the relatively small number of ducts present at one time, most of the whistlers observed by a satellite-borne receiver will probably not have followed field-aligned paths.

Let us now return to the properties of the ducted signals. Because of dispersion, the impulse entering at point A (Fig. 1-2) is gradually lengthened as it travels until it becomes a gliding tone, as shown in Fig. 1-1. If we assume that the energy per unit frequency interval is constant, and that there are no energy losses along the path, the amplitude of the wave will decrease as the frequency decreases, since the spread in time per unit frequency interval increases as the frequency is reduced. Hence for this case the leading edge of the whistler shows the strongest amplitude, and the envelope of the whistler gradually decreases in strength with decreasing frequency.

The inset diagrams of Fig. 1-2 show the dynamic spectra of the whistlers observed at receivers near the source and near the conjugate point. The first whistler observed is one that has passed once over the path and is picked up in the opposite hemisphere. This is called a "one-hop" or "short" whistler and is labeled 1 in the lower inset diagram. Since the exit boundary of the magnetospheric path is sharp, some of the energy is reflected. This energy travels back along the same path and becomes further dispersed, until it emerges from the "two-hop" path. The curve of frequency versus time for the two-hop whistler is labeled 2 in the upper inset diagram. At each frequency the delay is twice that observed in the one-hop whistler on the lower diagram. This echoing process continues, resulting in trains of whistlers at the two ends of the path. One can see from the diagram that the ratio between the delays of the members of the echo train will be 1, 3, 5, and so forth at the one-hop end of the path, and 2, 4, 6, and so forth at the source end of the path.

Although only one path is shown in Fig. 1-2 for purposes of explanation, the ionosphere often contains a number of such paths, which can be excited approximately simultaneously by the signal radiated from a lightning source. Because the lengths of these paths are different, and because the distribution of electron density and magnetic-field strength along them is different, the delays will be different.

Often when multiple ducts are present some whistlers appear to result from propagation over a combination of these ducts. These "mixed-path" whistlers are not well understood; it is probable that conditions for coupling between the ends of the ducts are fairly good on certain occasions. A possible explanation is that the ducts terminate well above the F layer, permitting energy to spread out, be reflected from the lower boundary, and enter any other ducts that are present.

Nose whistlers. During the preparation period for the International Geophysical Year, observations of whistlers were extended to higher latitudes and to higher frequencies. At high latitudes and at frequencies below 10 kc/s, and at middle latitudes and higher frequencies, a new type of whistler was observed. This whistler had the frequency–time shape sketched in Fig. 1-3, showing a distinct nose at which the delay was a minimum. The frequency of this nose was called the "nose" frequency and these whistlers were called "nose" whistlers. At frequencies above the nose, the frequency of the whistler increased with time. Simultaneously, below the nose, the frequency decreased with time. From an extension of the dispersion theory, it was found that this type of whistler was to be expected. Further study showed that all ordinary whistlers were simply the lower-frequency parts of nose whistlers. The discovery that the frequency of minimum time delay was dependent on the strength of the earth's magnetic field along the path of propagation was of particular interest, since it provided for the first time a means of determining the latitude of the path of propagation. When this frequency is known, it is possible to calculate the distribution of electron density in the magnetosphere from roughly one earth radius to six earth radii. But since the nose whistler occurs relatively infrequently, it is not particularly satisfactory for statistical studies, and a new method was developed for obtaining the nose frequency and nose delay from whistlers that do not show a nose. With this technique it has been possible to obtain statistically satisfactory quantities of data at different times and places.

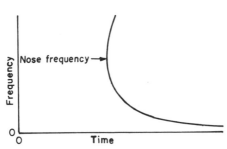

FIG. 1-3. Idealized spectrum of a nose whistler.

Electron density. The discovery of the nose whistler led rapidly to methods for systematic study of the electron density of the outer atmosphere. A number of results have already been obtained from these studies. Among them are the following:

(1) An average model of the density of the ionosphere out to six earth radii has been defined. The density appears to drop off roughly in proportion to the strength of the earth's mangetic field, and at sunspot maximum it has a value of roughly 100 electrons per cubic centimeter at a distance of five earth radii from the center of the earth.

(2) Data for the electron-density model revealed that there is a regular annual variation in the effective electron-density values. Densities at solar maximum appear to be nearly twice as high in December as in June. This effect, as yet unexplained, holds for both hemispheres.

(3) During a magnetic storm the apparent electron density in the magnetosphere, as measured by whistlers, drops greatly. Densities may range all the way from two-thirds to one-tenth of their normal quiet-day values. The explanation of this effect, when it is found, promises to affect theories of the F region and the magnetosphere significantly.

Artificially generated whistler-mode signals. The understanding of the phenomenon of whistlers has led naturally to a new means of communication. Signals generated by very-low-frequency transmitters can be launched into the whistler mode and received in both hemispheres, sometimes with remarkably great strength. The combination of propagation in the earth–ionosphere waveguide and whistler-mode propagation provides a unique method for transmitting from the earth to a satellite around the curve of the earth. At the same time, however, the existence of the whistler mode introduces the possibility of interference with proposed VLF navigation systems, since the whistler-mode signal may sometimes approach in amplitude the signal that is transmitted normally between the lower boundary of the ionosphere and the earth. In such cases, the whistler-mode signal is delayed by appreciable fractions of a second and shows wide variations in phase.

Studies of the interaction of the whistler mode with the charged particles of the upper atmosphere have indicated that it may be possible to accelerate electrons or protons by means of man-made whistler-mode signals. It has been found that the relativistic electrons spiraling around the earth's magnetic field can in theory be locked into a whistler-mode wave. Because the gyro-frequency of the particles varies with their mass, the interaction process is stable, much as in a synchrocyclotron. By reducing the frequency of the exciting wave appropriately, it is possible to increase the rotational energy of the electron to a relatively high value. This idea is the basis of a tentative proposal to simulate the Argus experiment, in which energetic particles were injected into the upper atmosphere by nuclear explosions. The successful performance of such an experiment would make possible a systematic study of the orbits and lifetimes of particles trapped in the earth's magnetic field.

1.2   VLF Emissions

Nature and occurrence of VLF emissions.   Using the equipment described for the reception of whistlers, one often observes other unusual sounds. With the exception of the sounds normally produced by lightning energy traveling in the earth–ionosphere waveguide, these other natural noises are called VLF emissions, or VLF ionospheric noise.

Perhaps the most common type of VLF emission is the so-called "dawn chorus," which sounds like a multitude of birds waking up in the morning. Other types of emissions include hissing sounds, rising tones (called "risers"), warbling tones, and combinations of these. They sometimes occur in distinct bands, and are often associated with strong whistlers. The sounds of these naturally occurring events are quite remarkable—often as distinct and clear as those one would get from a laboratory oscillator. A more detailed discussion of the types of VLF emissions will be given in Chap. 7.

Although VLF emissions occur under circumstances similar to those associated with whistlers, there are some important differences. First, emissions tend to be concentrated at higher latitudes than whistlers and show a greater dependence on magnetic activity. Second, the diurnal occurrence of these two phenomena tends to differ. Furthermore, certain types of emissions show a correlation with visual and optical auroral phenomena.

Sources of VLF emissions.   The evidence is strong that VLF emissions originate in the ionosphere, but the complex generation mechanisms are not yet understood. The various theories that have been advanced to explain them are similar in one respect. They all postulate the presence of streams of charged particles in the outer ionosphere. These particles are presumed to travel along the lines of force of the earth's field and to create electromagnetic waves as they move. Among the mechanisms that have been suggested are Čerenkov radiation, traveling-wave-tube amplification, and cyclotron radiation. Difficulties in applying these mechanisms to VLF emissions arise because the medium is dispersive and hence the conditions for synchronizing particles and waves depend on frequency. Furthermore, the medium is highly anisotropic and hence the characteristics of the waves vary with the direction of their propagation. The study of emissions shows promise of producing a valuable key to the quantitative analysis of the dynamic processes of the magnetosphere.

The association of VLF emissions with whistlers suggests that it may be possible to generate emissions artificially by radiating a wave that has the essential properties of a whistler in a region where emissions are known to occur.

Indeed it has recently been discovered that strong discrete emissions are on occasion triggered by the Morse code dashes, but not the dots, transmitted by high-power fixed-frequency VLF stations in the 10- to 20-kc/s range. The extension of this experiment to lower frequencies should greatly increase the occurrence of these man-made emissions and lead eventually to an understanding of their mechanism. From understanding may come new methods for measuring the dynamical properties of streams of charged particles trapped in the earth's field.

Chapter Two

History

The study of whistlers and related phenomena is divided into two principal periods, the early period, from 1894 to 1935, and the modern period, beginning in 1951. The recent growth of interest in the field is illustrated by the fact that before 1951 there were only about fifteen publications on whistlers and related phenomena, but since 1951 over three hundred publications have appeared. The suspension of activity between 1935 and 1951 can be attributed mainly to World War II. At the time of the outbreak of the war, whistlers and VLF emissions were unexplained oddities of nature and were of little apparent use. Hence the urgencies of wartime research displaced any investigation of these phenomena. After the war the widespread use of tape recorders and the development of spectrum analyzers undoubtedly helped to revive interest in whistlers. With the International Geophysical Year came more complete understanding of the phenomena and an appreciation of the possibilities for their use in research on the earth's environment. Current progress, theoretical as well as experimental, indicates that the investigation of these VLF phenomena is becoming one of the most active new areas of research in radioscience. Much of the progress in this field can be attributed to the stimulation provided by the International Scientific Radio Union (URSI). A brief review of URSI's activities in this field is given in Chap. IV of the *U.R.S.I. Golden Jubilee Memorial* (1963).

Early period—1894 to 1935. The beginnings of whistler research are obscure indeed. For many years the first known report on a phenomenon resembling whistlers was a paper by Preece (1894). At the Twelfth General Assembly of URSI held at Boulder, Colorado, in 1957, J. Fuchs of Austria reported on observations of whistlers in Austria dating back to 1886, when whistlers were heard on a 22-km telephone line without amplification (Fuchs, 1938). The observations described in Preece's paper were made by operators at the British government post office, who listened to telephone receivers connected to telegraph wires during a display of aurora borealis on March 30 and 31, 1894. The descriptions suggest that the observers had heard tweeks and possibly whistlers and dawn chorus. At the same time sunspot activity and earth currents were noted. These observations were the result of an examination of photographic records of earth currents taken during the previous large magnetic storm. This work could not be extended, since there were no suitable recording and analyzing devices with which quantitative information could readily be obtained.

The next known work on whistlers was reported by Barkhausen (1919). During World War I amplifiers were used on both sides of the front to overhear enemy telephone conversations. Because of inductive action and poor insulation, signal currents extended into the ground in the vicinity of the telephone cables. Although weak, they could be made audible by means of high-gain amplifiers. These induced signals were usually detected by inserting metallic probes into the ground at points several hundred meters apart. The probes were connected to the amplifier, which in turn was connected to the telephone.

According to Barkhausen's paper, a strange whistling sound could be heard on the telephone at certain times. Soldiers at the front would say, "You can hear the grenades fly." As far as identification by letters was possible, it sounded almost like "piou." To Barkhausen it appeared to be a constant-amplitude signal whose frequency decreased through the complete tonal scale and ended with the deepest audible sounds or tones. The whole process lasted almost a full second. Because of the characteristics of the amplifier, the sounds or tones around the frequency of 1000 cycles per second were especially prominent. On some days these whistling sounds were so strong and frequent that for periods of time they made it impossible to hear any other signals. Barkhausen suggested that they were correlated with meteorological influences. They occurred especially frequently during the mornings of warm days in May and June, but were completely different from the normal atmospheric disturbances, which produced only a crackling or bubbling noise in the telephone. The ground electrodes, which could sometimes have produced sounds, were ruled out as the cause of the whistling.

Barkhausen considered that the amplifier itself, perhaps excited by an especially strong atmospheric disturbance, could produce the characteristic oscillations. However, in the laboratory he tried in vain to evoke whistling noises in such an amplifier by using strong impulsive currents and direct spark gaps. Moreover, never during his experiments had he encountered such sounds. He concluded that the phenomenon was unexplainable at that time.

A few years after Barkhausen's first paper appeared, Eckersley (1925) described disturbances of a musical nature that had been known to workers in "radio" for some years. They were heard when a telephone or any other "audio-recorder" system was connected to a large aerial. He described the disturbances as varying considerably in duration, at times being a very small fraction of a second and at others up to a fifth of a second. From this description we might conclude that he was observing ordinary tweeks. However, he indicated that the pitch of the note invariably started above audibility and rapidly decreased, ending with a low note of virtually constant frequency on the order of 300 to 1000 cps. If the phenomenon was the tweek, as its duration strongly suggests, and not a whistler, then Eckersley's estimate of the terminating frequency was low, since tweeks normally terminate at a frequency of about 1600 cps. If both tweeks and whistlers were included, the distinction between the two is certainly not clear. Eckersley attributed the musical nature of these disturbances to dispersion of an electrical impulse in a medium loaded with free ions.

In a second paper Eckersley (1926) discussed experiments performed a year and a half earlier in which he found that the characteristic frequency was between 300 and 500 cps. In the later tests he reported that the prevailing characteristic frequency was two or three times the value previously reported, and suggested a fourfold to tenfold increase in the ionic density. Eckersley attributed this increase in frequency to increased solar activity. However, since no correlation of this nature has since been observed, and since the higher characteristic frequency would lie close to the normally observed tweek cutoff of about 1600 cps, the presumption is strong that his first estimate of the limiting frequency was simply too low. In both papers Eckersley attempted to develop the idea that the dispersion of the signals was related to dispersion in an ionized medium. We know now that the dispersion exhibited by tweeks is caused simply by the earth–ionosphere waveguide, and does not relate directly to the electron density of the ionosphere.

In later papers by Eckersley (1928, 1929) the reference to whistlers is unmistakable. He distinguished two types of whistlers, the short and the long. In the first type, which Eckersley had described in 1925, the disturbance started with a note of high pitch and dropped rapidly to about 200 to 500 cps. In the second class the frequency dropped more slowly. From the similarity in characteristics, Eckersley concluded that the mechanism was the same in both classes. If it were not for the low value of the lowest frequency, we might conclude that the first class consisted of tweeks. But although whistlers themselves may decrease to frequencies as low as 200 to 300 cps, tweeks do not.

Eckersley summarized his observations on long whistlers, which had been carried out over a period of nine months. He found that whistlers were associated with magnetic storms, occurring much more frequently during magnetic disturbances than on quiet days, and that whistlers sometimes occurred in groups of echoes preceded by a violent click. The time between the click and the first echo was approximately 3 seconds, but that between succeeding echoes was about 3.8 seconds. As many as seven echoes were heard. Each succeeding whistler was spread over a longer time than the one before. His description is sufficiently complete to identify what he observed as a bona fide whistler echo train. We can understand the difference in the period between successive echoes and the period between the click and the first echo on the basis of the fact that at higher frequencies the first whistler of an echo train is often relatively stronger than later components. Hence to the ear, the time delay of the first whistler would appear to be somewhat less than the time between successive echoes, whose intensities would be relatively greater at lower frequencies, which have a longer echoing period.

In this note Eckersley attempted to link whistlers with the short-wave echoes with long delay reported by Størmer (1928). Eckersley postulated that the original pulse was produced by a group of charged atoms emitted by the sun and abruptly stopped at the earth's atmosphere. The resulting pulse spread into the toroidal ring and circulated around it perhaps five or six times before being extinguished. The region within the ring was assumed to be slightly dispersive, with an electron density of about one electron per cubic centimeter, which was sufficient to spread the pulse into its spectrum of frequencies. It is not surprising that subsequent research did not confirm the existence of this postulated mechanism. In none of Eckersley's papers up to this date was there any mention of Barkhausen's observations that had been published in 1919.

The next publication on whistlers came in July 1930 from Barkhausen (1930). He reviewed the facts that he had reported in 1919, and offered two possible explanations of whistlers. The first of these, which involves multiple reflections between earth and ionosphere as diagrammed in Fig. 3-37, is identical to the mechanism for the production of tweeks. Barkhausen showed that this mechanism produced a decrease in pitch with time and was thus qualitatively in agreement with observations. He noted, however, that the minimum frequency would be about 1500 cps—too high to explain the observed results. He expressed doubt that a tone lasting almost a second could be produced by a mechanism like this. In his second explanation Barkhausen introduced the idea of a dispersive medium of propagation, as Eckersley had done in 1925. Clearly, this explanation was due to his knowledge of transmission networks, certain types of which have the property of transmitting higher frequencies more quickly than lower frequencies. He suggested that a remote lightning stroke acts as a direct-current impulse that contains all frequencies. He considered possible dispersion in the ground and in the space between the earth and the ionosphere, but saw no way to account for both the long duration and the lack of appreciable attenuation. He concluded by suggesting that much more observational data would be needed, and that it could best be obtained in sites far from cities, which produce disturbance. Even today the search for such sites continues.

In a report on developments in the study of radio-wave propagation, Eckersley (1931) noted that interest had been revived in whistlers and related atmospheric disturbances. He reported a connection between whistler storms and the earth-current variation usually associated with magnetic storms. In particular, he reported an observation by K. Tremellen that isolated whistlers were definitely caused at certain times by local lightning flashes, and a suggestion by Schelleng, similar to that of Barkhausen (1930), that whistlers are caused by multiple reflections between earth and the Heaviside layer. Eckersley also mentioned his own work on the escape of wireless waves into outer space through the Heaviside layer. This appears to be the first reference to the essential features of the magneto-ionic theory, which accounts for the transmission of whistler-mode energy into the ionosphere.

Burton (1930) and Burton and Boardman (1933a,b) reported on various types of audio-frequency atmospherics, particularly those we now call tweeks and whistlers. They noted that confusion existed in Eckersley's early descriptions of musical atmospherics, and that Barkhausen's attempt to explain the whistler could, in fact, explain tweeks.

Burton and Boardman also described swishes observed in Newfoundland. They compared them to "musical sounds such as made by thin whips when lashed through the air." These sounds were ordinarily distinctly musical in character, the frequency varying sometimes downward and other times upward, which suggests that they were so-called "risers." At times, simultaneous upward and downward progressions were observed. These might have been nose whistlers. The duration of the observed swishes varied from one quarter of a second to more than a second. In Ireland, somewhat similar swishes were observed, but a more usual type was longer and much clearer in tone. These swishes were audible from half a second to possibly 4 seconds and covered a frequency range from below 800 to above 4000 cycles per second. To the ear the frequency appeared to progress steadily, with perhaps a slight lingering near the termination of the descending variety. On a few occasions whistlers were observed to hesitate and "wobble" slightly before disappearing. Of particular interest are series of swishes with almost perfectly regular spacing of a few seconds between each swish, the train persisting on occasion for as long as a few minutes. Some of these trains were observed successively to increase in intensity, terminating abruptly, while other trains were reduced gradually until submerged in the static.

Quasi-musical sounds, frequently audible as a subdued jumble or as hollow rustling or murmuring sounds, were observed between 500 and 1500 cps. These sounds often increased regularly in strength for some time, after which faint swishes began to appear in the same frequency range. The swishes sometimes increased in intensity and length, and eventually submerged the murmuring sounds. Occasionally the murmuring continued for a short time after the swishes decreased in amplitude or disappeared. This description is much like one that might be applied to high-latitude "chorus" observed at frequencies near 1000 cps. Burton and Boardman also note that on a few occasions musical high frequencies, similar in general character to the murmuring, were observed. The sound took the form of a continual "chirping" or "jingling" in the vicinity of 3200 cps. This phenomenon is similar to the typical "chorus," since it was composed of large numbers of short, overlapping, high-frequency swishes.

It is particularly interesting to note that variations of intensity were found in the swishes, with maxima and minima spaced at irregular intervals of possibly a few minutes. Burton and Boardman note that swishes could sometimes be observed without amplifying apparatus, with a 12-mile telegraph line serving as an antenna, and with a telephone receiver connected between line and earth. They reported that swishes were very infrequent in Ireland, except on one day when they appeared in overlapping pairs. In New Hampshire they found that the descending whistling tones did, in fact, follow distinctive static crashes, with a time delay ranging from 1.2 to 3 seconds. One night in New Hampshire, while listening to atmospherics, they observed an auroral display in which nearly every auroral flash coincided with a static crash that had a distinct frying sound. In most cases these crashes were followed by swishes, usually of the descending variety, although occasionally a short ascending whistle occurred simultaneously with the start of the descending swish (possibly a nose whistler). A positive correlation was found between swishes and magnetic disturbances.

The commonly accepted explanation of the relation between frequency and time for a whistler was first advanced by Eckersley (1935). He showed that two alternative theories of dispersion in an ionized region were possible, depending on whether the Lorentz polarization term (Ratcliffe, 1959) was or was not included. He showed that his proposed theory would be correct only if the Lorentz polarization term were neglected, and further that the frequency of the whistlers would be proportional to $1/T^2$ so long as all the waves followed the same path. Using a plot of whistler frequency as a function of time, he showed that the theoretical and observed forms were in close agreement. He concluded that the whistler is caused by the dispersion of a sudden impulse traveling through the ionosphere, and that the simple form of dispersion formula without the Lorentz polarization term is correct for transmission in an unpolarized medium like the ionosphere.

Pre-IGY period—1951 to 1957. After a lapse of almost twenty years, attributable mainly to World War II, interest in whistlers revived. The first paper of the modern period described a new technique of analysis (Potter, 1951). As is so often the case in scientific research, advances in one field are frequently made as a result of techniques and devices developed in another. Potter's paper described the application of a "sound" spectrograph, developed for studies of speech and noise, to the visual portrayal of whistlers. He showed well-defined curves of frequency versus time for various natural very-low-frequency phenomena, including whistlers, swishes, and tweeks. He suggested that renewed investigation of these effects with modern analytical tools might yield information of considerable scientific interest. His prophecy has been fulfilled, and we can attribute much of the progress in this field to the development of precise equipment for spectrum analysis. The other device that contributed greatly to the study of whistlers was the tape recorder itself, which was brought to a high level of performance after World War II.

Before the publication of Potter's paper on spectrum analyzers, L. R. O. Storey, in Cambridge, England, had begun an investigation into the nature and origin of whistlers. With the work of Barkhausen, Eckersley, and Burton and Boardman as a background, and with the aid of a homemade spectrum analyzer, Storey conducted a thorough investigation that resulted in the first interpretation of the known properties of whistlers (Storey, 1953). Using existing direction-finding facilities, he found that loud whistlers fell into two distinct classes, those that were preceded by a loud click (or atmospheric), and those that were not, and also that a whistler was never preceded by a weak click. Storey found that the properties that were observable with direction finders and waveform recorders were similar to those of the normal atmospheric clicks arising from ordinary lightning. Comparing the strength of whistlers with the distance of the causative atmospherics from Cambridge, he found that whistlers were produced by waves originating in lightning flashes located within 2000 kilometers of Cambridge.

Storey confirmed that the quantity $1/\sqrt{f}$ increased linearly with time. When the whistler followed an atmospheric click, $f^{-1/2}$ extrapolated to infinite frequency coincided with the time of the click. Comparison of these curves for the two classes of whistlers, those preceded by clicks and those not, showed that the former had dispersions about twice as great as the latter.

Storey found that the majority of multiple whistlers fell into three distinct classes: whistler trains, multiple-flash whistlers, and whistler pairs. He showed that the two members of a whistler pair could be ascribed to the same source. In studying whistler trains, he discovered that if a train followed a click, the dispersions of the successive whistlers increased in the ratios 1, 2, 3, 4, and so forth, but if there was no click, the ratios were 1, 3, 5, 7, and so forth. He found that the intensity decrement from the first whistler of the echo train to the second was usually about 10 db. He also identified the occasional very long train in which the decrement was extremely low over a narrow band of frequencies, commonly between 3 and 4 kc/s. He suggested that the low rate of intensity decrease might be explained in terms of a focusing action. Like Burton and Boardman, he noticed that occasionally a long echo train had a sharp ending.

By spectral analysis, Storey showed that the multiple-flash group of whistlers usually consisted of individual whistlers of about the same amplitude, with the same dispersion, spaced rarely more than a half second apart. He found that the dispersions of the two whistlers in a "whistler pair" were in the ratio of anywhere from 1.4 to 2.0. He found no cases of more than two components. It might seem strange that we no longer consider the whistler pair to be a primary class of whistlers. The reason Storey thought it was appears to lie in the lack of resolution of his analyzer. In his published sketches of the spectra of a whistler pair, we see that the traces of adjacent members are relatively close together. Hence if there had been one more component halfway between those shown, the result would have been a continuous spectrum and none of the components would have been defined. Storey's whistler pair thus seems to be simply a special case of what is now known as a multiple-path whistler, a whistler created by a single lightning stroke but having multiple components. Storey's classification was further confirmed by his observation that whistler pairs were rather less common than echo trains or multiple-flash whistler groups, which are multiple whistlers created by a quick succession of lightning strokes. With modern analytical equipment, the opposite result is obtained, multiple-flash groups and echo trains appearing less often than multiple-path whistlers.

Storey studied the connection between whistlers and magnetic activity and discovered a positive correlation between magnetic disturbance, as measured by K-figure, and whistler rate based on data gathered by Marconi workers over a period of seventeen months. He found that the positive correlation arose principally from periods in which there was no magnetic activity for a considerable time, and in which the incidence of whistlers was also much reduced. He found little or no association between the day-to-day fluctuations of K-figure and whistler activity during disturbed periods.

Storey's study of the diurnal variation in whistler occurrence showed that whistlers occur more frequently and are louder during the night than during the day, but on very well-defined variation was found. Sometimes the diurnal peak occurred before midnight, and sometimes after. He considered long and short whistlers separately, and found a definite opposite seasonal variation in these two types. Long whistlers were more common during the summer and short whistlers during the winter, in agreement with the thunderstorm hypothesis and the normal seasonal variation in thunderstorm activity. Dispersions for long and short whistlers were consistently in the ratio of roughly 2 to 1. Individual values ranged all the way from 20 to 120 $sec^{1/2}$ for short whistlers and from 40 to 250 $sec^{1/2}$ for long whistlers. Little variation with time of day could be detected from the data. A positive correlation was found between nightly dispersion figures and the critical frequency of the F2 layer.

Storey's original contributions to the experimental study of the properties of whistlers include the identification of long and short whistlers, the association of long whistlers with atmospherics occurring within about 2000 km from the point of observation, and the observations that long and short whistlers have dispersions in the ratio of 2 to 1, and that whistler trains have dispersions in the ratio 1, 2, 3, 4 when preceded by an atmospheric, and the ratio 1, 3, 5, 7 when not preceded by an atmospheric. Storey also showed that dispersion was virtually independent of time of day, that long whistlers occur more frequently in summer than in winter, whereas the reverse is true of short whistlers, and that a correlation exists between dispersions and critical frequency of the F2 layer.

Storey made an important contribution to whistler theory by showing that whistlers travel very nearly in the direction of the earth's magnetic field. He also showed that the group ray refractive index is practically independent of wave-normal direction when the Eckersley approximation is used. He showed that in this approximation the ray direction would be confined to an angle less than 19 deg 29 min regardless of the direction of the wave normal. He concluded that this angle, therefore, would produce a marked beaming of the rays in addition to the effects of refraction at the lower boundary of the ionosphere. He showed further that under the Eckersley approximation, the refractive index is expressible as the product of a function of frequency and a function of wave-normal direction and the local properties of the medium. This meant that the pulses of waves with different sets of frequencies would travel along the same path if they were launched into the ionosphere at the same point and in the same direction.

With these new observations and theoretical results, Storey synthesized a picture of whistler propagation in which the energy echoes back and forth approximately along the lines of force of the earth's magnetic field.

His deductions about the mechanism of propagation required an unexpectedly high electron density in the outer ionosphere. He suggested the possibility that ionization of the outer ionosphere could be increased by addition of both negative ions (electrons) and an equal number of positive ions from an outside source such as the sun. He thought that this ionization would consist principally of ionized hydrogen, which is ejected at times of solar disturbance and is presumably responsible for magnetic storms and for the aurora.

Although Storey's paper is concerned primarily with whistlers, other types of audio-frequency atmospherics are noted. These include dawn chorus, steady hiss, and isolated rising whistlers. All three types were found to be associated with magnetic activity and seemed to be related to one another. Rising whistles normally were not associated with any other kind of atmospheric, yet sometimes they were observed to follow clicks either very rapidly or with a delay of one or two seconds. Sometimes they appeared in conjunction with whistlers. If at a time of general rising-whistle activity there should be a whistler, it would usually be followed by a rising whistle, the one blending into the other so as to give the impression that the frequency variation of the whistler had changed. These blends were identified as the reversing tones described by Burton and Boardman and reproduced by Potter on his sound analyzer. Occasionally several rising whistles were observed to detach themselves from the main whistlers at different points on the downward scale. An association between whistlers and chorus was noted such that whistlers would occasionally produce a momentary enhancement of chorus. Rising whistles that were followed after a delay of a second or so by relatively slow descending whistlers were reported.

On one occasion Storey was able to relate the rising whistle to the following whistler through dispersion of the whistler. The whistler's slope corresponded to a dispersion of 150 $sec^{1/2}$ and could be extrapolated back to the instant of the fast-rising whistle. Thus he concluded that the rising whistle played the same role as the click in the production of ordinary whistlers.

The results of Storey's work were first presented by J. A. Ratcliffe to the Tenth General Assembly of the URSI held in Sydney, Australia, in 1952. This report excited considerable interest among the delegates, and greatly stimulated the work at Stanford, which was then just beginning.

At the following URSI General Assembly held in the Hague in 1954, Commission IV discussed possible tests of Storey's theory. Conjugate-point tests were discussed at length, and it was agreed that the essential features of Storey's theory should be checked as quickly as possible, so that an IGY program of observations using the best available information could be planned. At that time the knowledge that Storey and Koster had looked for whistlers on the geomagnetic equator and had found none, provided an important confirmation of a part of the theory (Koster and Storey, 1955). Specific experiments were considered, including the observation of whistlers simultaneously at conjugate points, and the observation of atmospherics in one hemisphere and associated short whistlers in the opposite hemisphere.

Short whistlers observed at Stanford were correlated with impulsive atmospherics observed on the U.S.S. *Atka* in December 1954, when the ship was near Stanford's conjugate point (Helliwell, 1956).

Echo trains of long and short whistlers with the theoretically predicted conjugate relationship were observed at Unalaska and Wellington in August 1955 (Morgan and Allcock, 1956). This observation provided the most important new evidence in support of the basic features of Storey's theory.

Morgan and Dinger (1956) reported observing whistlers simultaneously at Washington, D.C., and Hanover, New Hampshire. They found that the spectra from the two locations were roughly similar in shape, from which they concluded that the observed dispersion depends not necessarily upon the latitude of the observer, but rather upon the latitude of the storm's source. Recent evidence suggests that the dispersion of the whistler depends on the ionosphere, and that the location of source and observer affects mainly the intensity of the observed component.

Crary, Helliwell, and Chase (1956) compared the times of occurrence of whistlers observed in Seattle, Washington, and Stanford, California, to determine the degree of coincidence of whistler activity at spaced stations. These stations were spaced about 1100 km apart, and it was found that roughly 22 per cent of the whistlers observed at one station were heard simultaneously at the other. This result seemed to support Storey's estimate of the effective area of a whistler, which for long whistlers was an area of 1000 to 2000 km radius.

Helliwell et al. (1956) reported a new type of whistler recorded at College, Alaska, which they called the nose whistler. This whistler was explained in terms of the magneto-ionic theory by removing the restrictions imposed by Eckersley and Storey that the wave frequency must be small in comparison with the gyro-frequency. The resulting dispersion law showed that the whistler in general should exhibit both rising and falling characteristics just as the new experimental results indicated. This paper also established that nose whistlers tend to occur in trains in which the nose frequency falls systematically with nose delay. This was interpreted to mean that each nose whistler followed a discrete path whose latitude was related to the nose frequency. It was also pointed out that the observation of the nose at frequencies of about 3 kc/s showed conclusively that a substantial contribution to the total dispersion must have occurred in the regions of relatively low gyro-frequency near the top of a high-latitude path. This was new evidence that the whistlers had in fact traveled to a very great altitude in their trip from one hemisphere to the other.

Other investigators who derived the nose whistler dispersion law independently were Ellis (1956) and Gallet (see footnote in Helliwell et al., 1956, p. 140).

Middle-latitude nose whistlers were observed at Seattle, Washington, during March and April 1956 (Helliwell et al., 1956). The nose frequencies were in the range of 12 to 15 kc/s, in accord with theoretical predictions. This result showed for the first time that nose whistlers could in fact be observed at middle-latitude stations and that their observation required only the use of equipment sensitive to higher frequencies.

One of the first collections of spectra of unusual whistlers and other events was prepared by Dinger (1956). Spectrograms of sample recordings taken at Washington, D.C., were reported and briefly described. Among the excellent spectrograms shown in this report were examples of nose whistlers, multiple-path whistlers, and triggered single and multiple risers.

Allcock and Martin (1956), recording audio frequency noise at Wellington, and Dunedin, New Zealand, 600 km apart, found a high correlation in the occurrence of dawn chorus at the two places. Bursts of chorus occurred with a simultaneity of closer than 0.1 second.

Storey (1956b) suggested that the effect of ions on the propagation behavior at very low audio frequencies, might be measured with whistlers. He showed that at low audio frequencies positive hydrogen ions should cause the frequency-time relationship of a whistler to depart slightly from the Eckersley approximation, and that this departure could best be measured at low magnetic latitudes. For example, he predicted that at a magnetic latitude of 45°, the effect of hydrogen ions should be detectable at frequencies below 2 kc/s. The purpose of the calculation was to test Dungey's (1954) hypothesis that the outer atmosphere may consist chiefly of ionized hydrogen.

Hines (1957) showed that when heavy ions are included in the formulation of the magneto-ionic equations, whistler propagation is possible in all directions. The dispersion of frequencies takes place in opposite senses for longitudinal and transverse propagation. When only one type of heavy ion is considered, the transition frequency from the non-ion characteristic to that with ions takes place at a frequency near the geometric mean of the ion and the electron gyro-frequencies. Typical values of this transition frequency range up to about 20 kc/s. No guiding effect similar to that found for the longitudinal mode was apparent.

Storey (1957a,b) considered the problem of deducing electron density distributions from the dispersion curves of whistlers. The dispersion formula is represented by a power series whose coefficients are to be determined experimentally.

Morgan (1957) gave a general review of whistlers, dawn chorus, and the techniques of measurement, and included the history of atmospherics, tweeks, whistlers, and dawn chorus. He outlined the objectives of the IGY program on whistlers and dawn chorus and described suitable equipment and observing techniques. Suggestions for reading and for the presentation of data were included.

Ellis (1957) found that Čerenkov emission by auroral particles is a possible source of the atmospheric radio noise observed at frequencies of hundreds of kilocycles per second. He showed that the frequency range of the emission would extend downward to low audio frequencies. He pointed out that the calculated intensities are too low, however, to account for the noise observed during whistler observations unless some focusing effect is assumed.

Allcock (1957), reporting on dawn chorus activity observed at Wellington, New Zealand, found no general correlation with whistlers, a strong correlation with simultaneous local magnetic variations, and a pronounced diurnal variation. In a similar study of chorus at College, Alaska, Pope (1957) also found a large diurnal variation. Both authors used data from other stations to show that the time of maximum dawn chorus activity increased with geomagnetic latitude. Allcock argued that this characteristic could be related to the precipitation of positively charged solar particles that might produce the dawn chorus by exciting proton plasma oscillations in the outer ionosphere. These oscillations would then reach the earth in the whistler mode.

Rivault (1957) described the characteristics of whistlers observed during one year at Poitiers, France. In every case the impulsive atmospherics that preceded the long whistlers were tweeks.

Grierson (1957) discussed a technique for the rapid analysis of whistlers based on scanning in frequency at a fixed time rather than scanning in time at a fixed frequency. He suggested that the method would combine speed of operation with high resolution in frequency.

Watts (1957a,b) reported an observation of a band of hiss observed during a magnetic storm. The spectrum reached a peak near 3 kc/s, and the upper frequency limit varied during the period of observation. Simultaneously he found quasi-constant tones of gradually increasing frequency in the upper portion of the hiss spectrum.

These papers and reports published through 1957 form the background for the IGY synoptic study of whistlers and related phenomena. Discussions of significant papers published after 1957 are included throughout the book under the appropriate subject categories.

Chapter Three

Theory of Whistlers

3.1 *Magneto-ionic Theory*

Assumptions. Most of the known properties of whistlers can be explained with the aid of the magneto-ionic theory, which was described in detail by Ratcliffe (1959). In this theory it is assumed that electromagnetic waves propagate in a homogeneous gaseous medium permeated by a static magnetic field. The medium consists of neutral particles and equal numbers of positive and negative charges. At whistler frequencies the wave is affected mainly by electrons, because of their relatively small mass, and the effects of ions can often be neglected. The effects of the thermal motion of the charged particles on whistler propagation are usually negligible, and hence we can assume that the temperature of the medium is zero. Furthermore, we can usually assume that the response of the medium is linear, i.e., that the polarization of the medium is proportional to the amplitude of the wave.

The assumption of homogeneity is seldom realized in applications of the magneto-ionic theory. However, whistlers follow paths along which the parameters of the medium are believed to vary sufficiently slowly in the space of one wavelength to justify this approximation (except in the lower ionosphere).

Appleton's equations. The static magnetic field of the earth causes the ionosphere to be anisotropic. Hence there are in general two values for the refractive index, corresponding to the two characteristic waves that can propagate. In a homogeneous medium with the wave normal in the positive z-direction, the square of the refractive index is given by

$$n^2 = 1 - \frac{X}{1 - iZ - \dfrac{\frac{1}{2}Y_T^2}{1 - X - iZ} \pm \dfrac{1}{1 - X - iZ}[\frac{1}{4}Y_T^4 + Y_L^2(1 - X - iZ)^2]^{1/2}},$$

(3.1)

and the polarization is given by

$$R = -\frac{H_y}{H_x} = \frac{E_x}{E_y} = \frac{-i}{Y_L(1 - X - iZ)}\{\frac{1}{2}Y_T^2 \mp [\frac{1}{4}Y_T^4 + Y_L^2(1 - X - iZ)^2]^{1/2}\}$$

(3.2)

and

$$S = \frac{E_z}{E_x} = iY_T\frac{n^2 - 1}{1 - X - iZ},$$

(3.3)

where

n = complex refractive index = $\mu - i\chi$,
μ = refractive index (real part of n),
$\chi = \kappa c/\omega$ = absorption index (negative imaginary part of n),
κ = absorption coefficient (nepers/meter),
c = velocity of light,
H_x, H_y = components of magnetic field of the wave,
E_x, E_y, E_z = components of electric field of the wave,
x, y, z = coordinate axes as shown in Fig. 3.1,
$i = \sqrt{-1}$,
$\omega = 2\pi f$,
f = wave frequency,

$$X = \frac{f_0^2}{f^2},$$

$$Y = \frac{f_H}{f} = \sqrt{Y_L^2 + Y_T^2},$$

$$Y_T = \frac{f_T}{f},$$

$$Y_L = \frac{f_L}{f},$$

$$Z = \frac{\nu}{\omega},$$

$$\omega_0 = 2\pi f_0 = \sqrt{\frac{Ne^2}{\epsilon_0 m}},$$

$$\omega_L = 2\pi f_L = \omega_H \cos\theta,$$
$$\omega_T = 2\pi f_T = \omega_H \sin\theta,$$

$$\omega_H = 2\pi f_H = \frac{\mu_0 |H_0| e}{m},$$

f_H = electron gyro-frequency,
ν = frequency of collision of electrons with heavy particles,
N = number density of electrons,
e = charge on an electron,
ϵ_0 = dielectric constant of free space (rationalized units),
m = mass of electron,
μ_0 = permeability of free space (not to be confused with refractive index for the "ordinary" wave μ),
H_0 = imposed magnetic field,
θ = angle between H_0 and $0z$ (Fig. 3-1).

Equations (3.1), (3.2), and (3.3) are known as Appleton's equations. In all the calculations that follow, mks rationalized units will be used unless otherwise noted.

General behavior of refractive index. The general behavior of the refractive index given by (3.1) can be understood with the aid of Fig. 3-2. The variation of n^2 with X (Fig. 3-2a) and with Y (Fig. 3-2b) is shown for conditions of interest in whistler propagation. Losses are assumed to be zero. In each diagram the limiting curves are shown for purely longitudinal (L) propagation, for purely transverse (T) propagation, and for an intermediate case. The regions on the diagrams of Fig. 3-2 within which the ordinary waves (plus sign in (3.1)) and extraordinary waves (minus sign in (3.1)) must lie are shaded.

In both diagrams the whistler mode is given by the branch of the ordinary curve that lies to the right of the pole located at

$$X = \frac{Y^2 - 1}{Y^2 \cos^2\theta - 1}$$

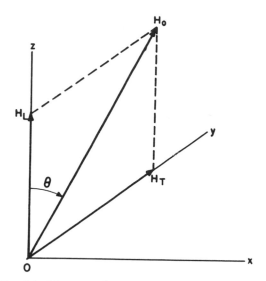

FIG. 3-1. Wave coordinates in relation to earth's magnetic field.

in Fig. 3-2*a*, or at

$$Y = \left(\frac{X-1}{X\cos^2\theta - 1}\right)^{1/2}$$

in Fig. 3-2*b*. It can be seen that the refractive index for the whistler mode is always a positive real number greater than 1, corresponding to propagation at phase velocities less than the speed of light.

If we assume a constant wave frequency, Fig. 3-2*a* shows how the square of refractive index varies with electron density when the gyro-frequency is constant ($Y = 2$). At values of X between zero and one, both ordinary and extraordinary waves can propagate, since their refractive indexes are real.

Between $X = 1$ and the pole at $X = (Y^2 - 1)/(Y^2 \cos^2\theta - 1)$, the refractive index for the ordinary wave is imaginary (since $n^2 < 0$), and therefore this wave cannot propagate. At higher values of X, the ordinary curve is again positive and propagation can take place. The extraordinary wave propagates only for values of X less than $1 + Y$. Hence only one wave, the ordinary, can propagate when X is greater than $1 + Y$.

Figure 3-2*b* shows the variation of n^2 with gyro-frequency, instead of with electron density, for $X = 3$. In contrast to the behavior shown in Fig. 3-2*a*, the ordinary refractive index is real only when

$$Y > \left(\frac{X-1}{X\cos^2\theta - 1}\right)^{1/2}.$$

It decreases as Y increases, approaching unity as Y approaches infinity. Both modes become non-propagating as Y approaches zero.

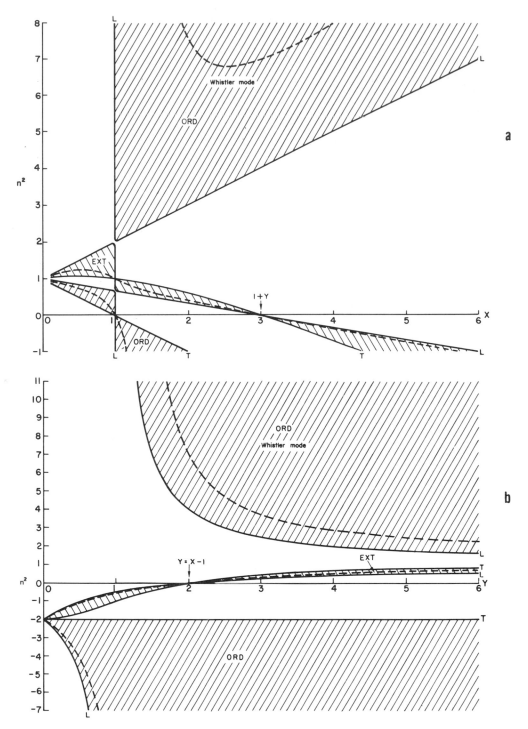

FIG. 3-2. Variation of n^2 with X (part a) and with Y (part b). Regions occupied by the ordinary and extraordinary branches are shown shaded and are bounded by the limiting curves for longitudinal (L) and transverse (T) propagation. Dashed curves represent $\theta = 30°$.

For the conditions represented by Fig. 3-2, coupling to the whistler mode from free space is difficult because the refractive index of the ordinary branch does not remain real in the transition region (between $X = 1$ and $X = (Y^2 - 1)/(Y^2 \cos^2 \theta - 1)$ in Fig. 3-2a). However, for purely longitudinal propagation the ordinary branch does join the extraordinary branch at $X = 1$, as shown in Fig. 3-2a, and coupling to free space can then occur. Another factor that promotes coupling is a steep gradient of refractive index, which reduces the thickness of the attenuating region.

If the effect of collisions is included, it is found that coupling can occur over a finite range of θ (Ratcliffe, 1959). Together with the gradient of refractive index, this coupling accounts for the excitation of the whistler mode at the lower boundary of the ionosphere. For a particular ionospheric model including losses, the real refractive index and the absorption coefficient have been computed for 18 kc/s and are shown in Fig. 3-26 as functions of height in the ionosphere.

3.2 Quasi-Longitudinal (QL) Approximation

Conditions. Because of their complexity, the complete expressions for refractive index and polarization given by Eqs. (3.1), (3.2), and (3.3) are difficult to use. For many applications of whistler theory these expressions may be simplified by using the quasi-longitudinal (QL) approximation (Ratcliffe, 1959). This approximation is valid when the direction of propagation is sufficiently close to the direction of the earth's magnetic field to permit dropping terms containing Y_T in (3.1) and (3.2). The condition necessary for the QL approximation to hold is given by

$$\frac{Y_T^4}{4 Y_L^2} \ll |(1 - X - iZ)^2| . \tag{3.4}$$

Since $Y_T = Y \sin \theta$ and $Y_L = Y \cos \theta$, condition (3.4) can be written

$$\frac{Y^2 \sin^4 \theta}{4 \cos^2 \theta} \ll |(1 - X - iZ)^2|. \tag{3.5}$$

Simplifications at very low frequencies. At very low frequencies the condition expressed by (3.5) can often be simplified. In the lower ionosphere (D and E regions) Z is important, but Y can be assumed to be large with respect to unity. In the outer ionosphere Z is small compared with $1 - X$, but Y is not always large with respect to unity. Under the conditions of interest in whistler propagation the term $X = \omega_0^2/\omega^2$ is always greater than 1 and is usually much greater than 1. Values of X from 10^2 to 10^6 are common. Hence the 1 in (3.5) can usually be neglected with respect to X and Z. With this approximation and the substitutions for X, Y, and Z given in the list following (3.3), Eq. (3.5) becomes

$$\frac{\sin^4 \theta}{\cos^2 \theta} \ll \frac{4}{\omega_H^2} \left(\frac{\omega_0^4}{\omega^2} + \nu^2 \right) . \tag{3.6}$$

The collisional term ν is important only in the lowest regions of the ionosphere, below about 80 km. Hence, except in this lowest region, we can drop the second term in the parentheses. To establish a definite criterion of validity for the QL approximation, we shall require that the right-hand member of (3.6) be at least nine times the left-hand member. Condition (3.6) then becomes

$$\frac{\sin^2 \theta}{\cos \theta} < \frac{2}{.3} \frac{f_0^2}{ff_H} . \tag{3.7}$$

The range of angles over which the QL approximation is valid under the assumed conditions is calculated from (3.7) and is plotted as a function of f_0^2/ff_H in Fig. 3-3. Since the ratio f_0^2/ff_H nearly always exceeds 1, Fig. 3-3 shows that the QL approximation is usually good up to angles of forty-five degrees or more.

We next introduce the general form of the QL approximation given by (3.4) into the general magneto-ionic formulas of Eq. (3.1) and (3.2), with the result that

$$n^2 = 1 - \frac{X}{1 - iZ \pm |Y_{\mathrm{L}}|} \tag{3.8}$$

and

$$R = \pm i \frac{|Y_{\mathrm{L}}|}{Y_{\mathrm{L}}} . \tag{3.9}$$

We must now choose the correct sign for the whistler mode. The simplest approach is to consider (3.8) at levels well above the F2 layer, where Z is negligibly small and X exceeds $1 + Y_{\mathrm{L}}$. It is then clear that propagation can take place only for the minus sign in Eq. (3.8).

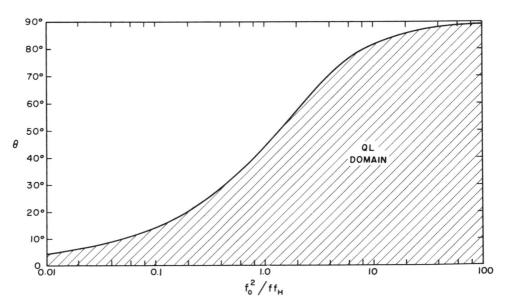

FIG. 3-3. Region of validity of QL approximation when $X \gg 1$.

Polarization. The polarization of the propagating wave is described by (3.9) with the corresponding choice of sign (minus). For downcoming waves in the Northern Hemisphere the sign of $\cos \theta$ is positive and the sign of e is negative for electrons. Hence the sign of Y_L is negative and the polarization of the downcoming ordinary wave is

$$R = +i , \tag{3.10}$$

which means that E_x, the x-component of the electric field, will lead E_y, the y-component, by ninety degrees in time, and that the two vectors are equal in magnitude. Equation (3.2) and Fig. 3-1 show that the electric and magnetic vectors for the propagating wave will rotate in a clockwise, or right-handed sense when the observer is looking in the direction of the static magnetic field.

In general, H_z, the longitudinal component of the wave's magnetic field, is zero. However, the electric field will have a longitudinal component given by (3.3). It is zero only for purely longitudinal propagation (i.e., for $Y_T = 0$).

It is interesting to note that for conditions of whistler propagation where $Z \ll 1$, $X \gg 1$, $|Y_z| \gg 1$ (the lower magnetosphere, for example), the polarization S given by (3.3) is approximately $-i(Y_T/|Y_L|)$. By comparing this result with (3.9), we find that $E_z/E_y = -Y_T/Y_L$, from which it is readily shown that the plane of polarization of the *electric* field of the wave is normal to H_0. This is physically understandable when we remember that the magnetic field H_0 greatly reduces the transverse motion of electrons relative to their longitudinal motion. The result is a relatively high value of longitudinal conductivity, which effectively short-circuits any electric field in the longitudinal direction.

At high altitudes in the magnetosphere, $|Y_L|$ is no longer large compared with 1, and therefore a significant component of electric field may appear in the direction of H_0. Using Eqs. (3.3) and (3.9) and assuming that $X \gg 1$, we can show that this component is given by $-E_y \sin \theta / Y |\cos \theta| - 1$.

3.3 Dispersion

Refractive-index approximation. Since the important dispersive effects in whistler-mode propagation take place in regions of very low collisional frequency relative to wave frequency, the quantity Z in (3.8) can be neglected, except where the magnitude of Y_L is near 1. This is an excellent approximation under most conditions of whistler propagation. With this approximation and the choice of the minus sign in (3.8), the ordinary-wave refractive index is given by

$$n^2 = \mu^2 = 1 + \frac{X}{|Y_L| - 1} . \tag{3.11}$$

In discussing the dispersion formula given by (3.11), it is convenient to replace the quantities X and Y with the appropriate expressions given in the list following (3.3), which leads to the transformation given by

$$\mu^2 = 1 + \frac{f_0^2}{f(f_H \cos \theta - f)} = 1 + \frac{B^2}{\Lambda(\cos \theta - \Lambda)} , \tag{3.12}$$

where

$$\Lambda = \frac{f}{f_H} \quad \text{and} \quad B = \frac{f_0}{f_H}.$$

If the denominator of the second term in (3.12) is negative, μ is imaginary and propagation is not possible. The condition necessary for propagation is, therefore, $\cos\theta > \Lambda$. Under conditions believed to exist in the outer ionosphere, the quantity B is appreciably greater than 1, so that the second term on the right of (3.12) is usually much larger than 1. If we drop the 1, Eq. (3.12) becomes

$$\mu^2 = \frac{B^2}{\Lambda(\cos\theta - \Lambda)}. \tag{3.13}$$

To illustrate the error in (3.13) consider the case when $B = 2$, for which the maximum difference between (3.12) and (3.13), obtained by maximizing the denominator, is only 6 per cent. The difference between (3.12) and (3.13) becomes important when B is less than 1; this case has been discussed by Garriott (1958a, b).

The approximation given by (3.13) has been widely used in the study of whistler propagation and will be adopted in the calculations that follow.

Group velocity. Since whistler data consist primarily of measurements of group delay versus frequency, it is necessary to deduce an expression for the group velocity v_g from (3.13). The dispersive characteristics of a homogeneous medium are commonly described in terms of the group refractive index $\mu' = c/v_g$, which is readily shown to be related to the refractive index by

$$\mu' = \frac{d}{df}(\mu f). \tag{3.14}$$

With the aid of (3.13) and (3.14) we find that the group velocity is given by

$$v_g = \frac{c}{\mu'} = 2c \frac{\Lambda^{1/2}(\cos\theta - \Lambda)^{3/2}}{B\cos\theta} = 2c \frac{f^{1/2}(f_H\cos\theta - f)^{3/2}}{f_0 f_H \cos\theta}. \tag{3.15}$$

Equation (3.15) describes the propagation of a beat between two infinite plane waves of slightly different frequency whose wave-normal directions are the same. Hence the direction of the group and that of the wave normal are the same and the anisotropy of the medium is not considered.

It is interesting to compare the variations of the group velocity v_g and the phase velocity v_p as functions of the normalized frequency Λ. The group velocity (3.15) is plotted in Fig. 3-4a for $B = 3$ (typical of the outer ionosphere) and $\theta = 0$ deg, with the phase velocity $v_p = c/\mu$ from (3.13). The phase velocity is maximum at $\Lambda = 0.5$ and the group velocity at $\Lambda = 0.25$. At frequencies below $\Lambda/2$, the group velocity exceeds the phase velocity, and at higher frequencies it is lower than the phase velocity. Depending on whether the frequency of the wave was less than or greater than $\Lambda/2$, the individual waves would appear to an observer moving with the wave envelope to be moving backward or forward, respectively. When $\theta = 0$, the ratio of group velocity to phase velocity is a simple linear function of Λ. From (3.13) and (3.15) it is found to be

$$\frac{v_g}{v_p} = 2(1 - \Lambda) . \tag{3.16}$$

This function is plotted in Fig. 3-4b.

The approximate group-velocity expression developed by Eckersley and used by Storey in his early work is easily obtained from (3.15) by assuming that $\Lambda \ll \cos \theta$. We get

$$v_g = 2v_p = 2c \frac{\sqrt{\Lambda} \cos \theta}{B} = 2c \frac{\sqrt{ff_H} \cos \theta}{f_0} . \tag{3.17}$$

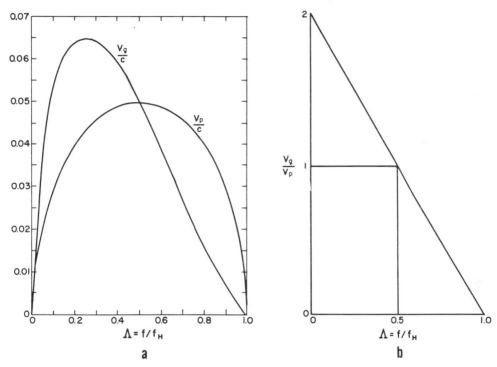

FIG. 3-4. *a*, Group velocity and phase velocity versus normalized frequency Λ. *b*, Ratio of group velocity to phase velocity versus normalized frequency Λ.

Group delay, the nose whistler, and dispersion. For purely longitudinal propagation the group delay of a whistler-mode signal traveling over a given path is simply

$$T = \int_{\text{path}} \frac{ds}{v_g} . \tag{3.18}$$

If we consider longitudinal propagation ($\theta = 0$ deg) in a homogeneous medium and over a path of length c/B, then from (3.15), the time-delay integral of (3.18) reduces to the normalized form

$$T = \frac{1}{2\Lambda^{1/2}(1 - \Lambda)^{3/2}} \text{ sec} , \tag{3.19}$$

which we shall call the high-density approximation, or, from (3.17),

$$T = \frac{1}{2\Lambda^{1/2}} \sec ,$$ (3.20)

which we shall call the low-frequency, or Eckersley-Storey, approximation.

Curves of Λ versus time from (3.19) and (3.20) are shown in Fig. 3-5 to illustrate their behavior in a form similar to that actually observed.

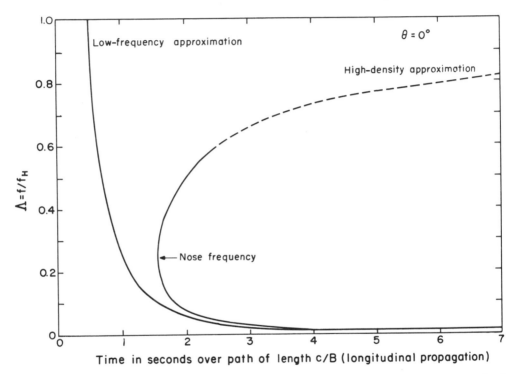

FIG. 3-5. Normalized frequency versus group delay for longitudinal propagation over a path of length c/B.

The frequency of minimum time delay, which occurs at $\Lambda = 0.25$ in a homogeneous medium, is called the nose frequency, and a whistler exhibiting this feature is called a nose whistler. It is clear that the low-frequency approximation is useful only at frequencies well below the nose frequency.

The group delay of a whistler at frequencies well below the nose is conveniently described by a quantity called the dispersion, given by

$$D = T\sqrt{f}\, \sec^{1/2} ,$$ (3.21)

which for the low-frequency approximation is a constant related to the parameters of the medium by

$$D_0 = \frac{1}{2c} \int_{\text{path}} \frac{f_0}{\sqrt{f_H}}\, ds \,\sec^{1/2} .$$ (3.22)

3.4 Ray Path

Relation between wave normal and ray.   We shall now consider the effects of anisotropy on the path of energy flow. In general the direction of energy flow, or ray direction, differs markedly from the direction of the wave normal. This difference depends on the magnitude of the refractive index and on its variation with θ, the angle between the wave normal and the static magnetic field H_0 (see Fig. 3-1). A preferred direction of energy flow from a given point

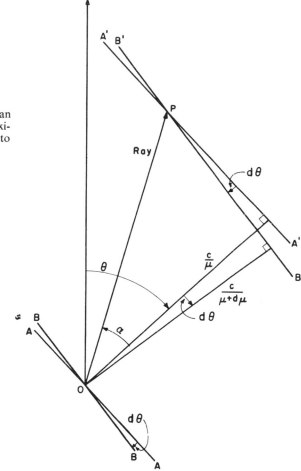

FIG. 3-6. Wave interference in an anisotropic medium. Point of maximum field intensity moves from 0 to P in unit time.

in space will exist when there is a range of wave normals involved in the electromagnetic disturbance. The ray direction with respect to the wave normal in a homogeneous medium is easily found with the aid of Fig. 3-6.

Two component waves of the same frequency and of nearly the same direction are indicated in Fig. 3-6, one labeled AA and the other BB. After unit time has elapsed, each wavefront has moved a distance equal to the velocity of light divided by the refractive index corresponding to the direction of its wave normal. These two waves then occupy the positions A′A′ and B′B′, respectively. The normal to the wavefront AA makes an angle θ with the direction of the magnetic field H_0. The normal to the wavefront BB makes a small angle $d\theta$ with the normal to AA. Initially the maximum of the sum of these two waves occurs at point 0. Unit time later the maximum arrives at point P. The locus of this maximum is the path of peak energy concentration, known as the ray path. If the wavelengths of the two component waves differ from one another, as they do in Fig. 3-6, the ray path will not coincide with the wave-normal direction. The direction of the ray path is given by the line segment 0P, which makes an angle α with the direction of the wave normal. From the geometry of Fig. 3-6 it is easily shown that

$$\tan \alpha = \frac{\left(\dfrac{c}{\mu} - \dfrac{c}{\mu + d\mu}\right)}{\dfrac{c}{\mu}} \frac{1}{d\theta} = \frac{1}{\mu}\frac{d\mu}{d\theta}. \qquad (3.23)$$

The angle between the wave normal and the ray thus depends on the magnitude of μ and the change of μ with θ. When μ is independent of θ, the medium is

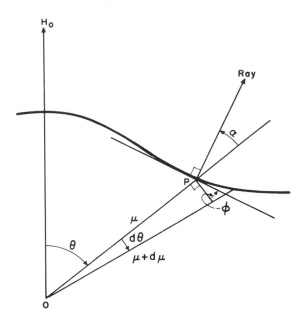

FIG. 3-7. Relation between ray and refractive-index surface in a uniaxial medium.

by definition isotropic, and as (3.23) shows, the wave-normal direction and the ray direction coincide.

Refractive-index surface and ray direction. The wave-normal direction and the ray direction can be related in a useful way by means of the refractive-index surface. Consider the refractive index to be a vector drawn from the point 0 in Fig. 3-7 and to have the same direction as the wave normal. Its length is proportional to the refractive index μ, and as θ is varied, its tip traces the curve shown. Rotation of this curve about the axis H_0 forms the refractive-index surface. It can be shown that the ray direction is always at right angles to this surface at the point of termination of the corresponding refractive-index vector (Poeverlein, 1948).

This theorem is readily proved in the two-dimensional case by using the construction shown in Fig. 3-7. The tangent to the surface at point P makes the angle ϕ with the normal to μ. From the geometry of the figure it is easily shown that $\tan \phi = d\mu/\mu \, d\theta$, which is the same as $\tan \alpha$ given by (3.23). Therefore $\phi = \alpha$, and hence, the construction indicates, the ray direction must be perpendicular to the surface. Thus the theorem is proved.

Demonstrating the theorem for two dimensions only is sufficient for our applications, since the ionosphere is uniaxial, i.e., its refractive index varies only with the angle θ between the wave-normal direction and the static magnetic field. Hence the refractive-index surface must always be a figure of revolution about H_0. By symmetry the ray direction must lie in the plane defined by H_0 and the wave-normal direction. Therefore the two-dimensional geometry shown in Fig. 3-7 will always apply. The theorem can be extended to the general case in three dimensions (Brandstatter, 1963).

Behavior of the ray direction. The ray direction is a complicated function of the wave-normal direction and the normalized frequency Λ. From (3.13) and (3.23) we find that the angle between the ray direction and the ordinary wave normal is given by

$$\tan \alpha = \frac{\sin \theta}{2(\cos \theta - \Lambda)}. \tag{3.24}$$

The total angle between the ray direction and the static magnetic field as shown by Fig. 3-6 is $\theta - \alpha$. This is readily found to be given by

$$(\theta - \alpha) = \arctan \frac{\sin \theta (\cos \theta - 2\Lambda)}{1 + \cos \theta (\cos \theta - 2\Lambda)}. \tag{3.25}$$

The behavior of the ray direction as given by (3.25) has been sketched by Smith (1960a,b) and is reproduced in Fig. 3-8. The maximum positive value of $\theta - \alpha$ is found by differentiating (3.25) with respect to θ and setting the result equal to zero. After considerable manipulation, we find that

$$(\theta - \alpha)_{\text{max pos}} = \arctan \frac{[(1 - \Lambda^2)^{1/2} - \Lambda\sqrt{3}]^{3/2}}{2^{3/2}(1 - \Lambda^2)^{3/4}}. \tag{3.26}$$

The maximum negative value is determined not from the behavior of (3.25) but from the relation $\cos \theta = \Lambda$, which defines the maximum possible value of θ for a propagating wave. By putting this relation into (3.25), we find that the maximum negative value is

$$(\theta - \alpha)_{\text{max neg}} = \theta - \frac{\pi}{2}. \tag{3.27}$$

Equation (3.27) represents only a limiting, not a guiding effect, since in fact a wave may violate (3.27) and cease to propagate. On the other hand, condition (3.26) represents an actual guiding effect upon the ray. These two equations together express the limits of ray directions for which QL propagation is possible in a homogeneous ionosphere when the collision frequency is much lower than the wave frequency. These limits are plotted in Fig. 3-9, where the higher of the two values is drawn solid to indicate the maximum possible ray direction without regard to sign. The crossing of the two curves at $\Lambda = 0.189$ marks the minimum ray cone of 11 deg. At $\Lambda = 0$, the limiting ray cone is 19 deg 29 min, as Storey (1953) found originally. As Fig. 3-9 shows clearly, all guiding is lost when the normalized frequency Λ reaches its maximum possible value of 1.0. Whistlers typically show normalized frequencies no greater than 0.6, which from Fig. 3-9 corresponds to a maximum ray cone of half-angle 37 deg. Thus in the absence of any other effect, the ionosphere acts to guide whistlers approximately along the directions of the earth's magnetic field. It is convenient to use the term magneto-ionic guiding to describe this steering, which is a result of the anisotropy of the medium. Later we shall introduce the term geomagnetic ducting to describe another property of the terrestrial ionosphere that is believed to exercise a pronounced guiding effect.

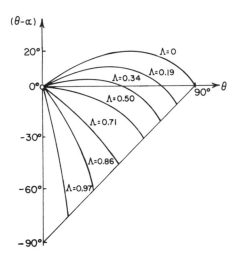

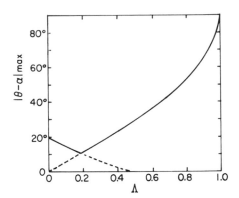

FIG. 3-8. Ray direction versus wave-normal direction, parametric in normalized frequency.   FIG. 3-9. Maximum ray angle versus normalized frequency.

The condition for which the change of ray direction $(\theta - \alpha)$ is zero and continuous with varying wave-normal angle θ is called focusing. From Fig. 3-8, this occurs for $\Lambda < 0.5$. As an example, for $\Lambda = 0$, focusing occurs at $\theta = 54$ deg, corresponding to the maximum ray direction of 19 deg 29 min.

Boundary problem—graphical solution. Boundary problems in anisotropic media can be treated graphically with the aid of refractive-index surfaces and Snell's law. For simplicity we shall take the case of two dimensions, in which the axis of symmetry (direction of H_0) lies in the plane of propagation. (Later this restriction can be removed.) Further, for convenience assume that the axis of symmetry is the same for both media.

The relationship of the ray direction to the boundary is shown in Fig. 3-10.

The given wave is assumed to be incident from medium I at an angle $\theta_1 + \beta$ to the boundary, and its associated ray is represented by R_1. The dashed line R_4 represents a possible ray that could have produced R_2 and R_3, but that would not in fact exist, since no source was assumed in medium II.

The refractive-index surface for each medium is shown in Fig. 3-11, where 0 is the origin and β is the angle between the axis of symmetry and the boundary. A line is drawn from 0 in the direction of the incident wave. It intersects the refractive-index surface at P_1. The corresponding ray direction is indicated by R_1, which is perpendicular to the surface at P_1 and makes an angle α_1 with the wave-normal direction (the same as that of the refractive index).

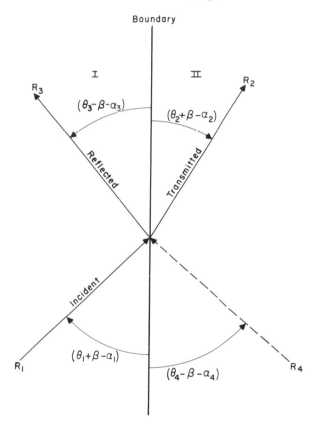

FIG. 3-10. Ray directions shown in two dimensions at boundary between two homogenous regions.

By Snell's law the incident, transmitted, and reflected waves must have refractive indexes whose projections on the boundary are equal. Therefore a line drawn normal to the boundary and passing through P_1 must also pass through all other possible refractive-index vector terminations (Poeverlein, 1948). At each of these points, P_2, P_3, and P_4, there is a corresponding possible ray R_2, R_3, and R_4.

The change in ray direction at the boundary need not have the same sign as the change in wave-normal direction. In Fig. 3-11 the wave normal rotates clockwise in crossing the boundary, but the ray rotates counterclockwise.

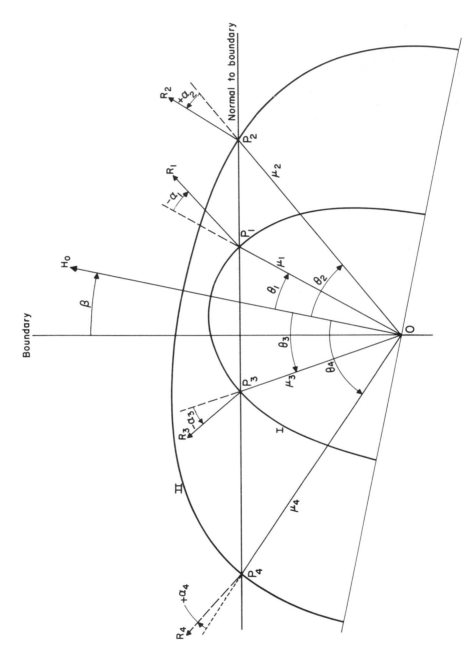

FIG. 3-11. Snell's law construction at the boundary between two media.

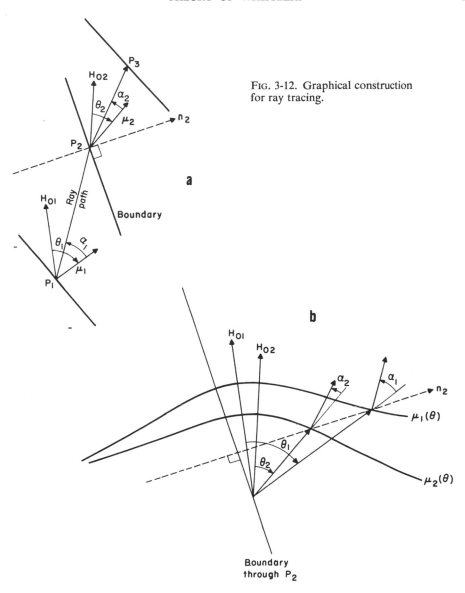

FIG. 3-12. Graphical construction for ray tracing.

Note that the angle of reflection is not in general equal to the angle of incidence. The relative magnitudes of the different waves can be determined by matching tangential components of E and H across the boundary after the relative magnitudes and directions of the refractive indexes have been found from the Snell's law construction.

If H_0 does not lie in the plane of incidence, the geometry of Figs. 3-10 and 3-11 still applies, except that the angle between wave normal and boundary is no longer $\theta + \beta$. Furthermore the curves labeled I and II represent the intersection of the plane of incidence with the refractive-index surfaces, which are figures of revolution about H_0. In general the ray direction will lie not in the plane of incidence but in the plane defined by the associated refractive-index vector μ of the ray, and the axis of symmetry H_0. This follows from the symmetry properties of the $\mu(\theta)$ surface, which is always a figure of revolution about H_0.

Graphical ray tracing. From the relation between the ray direction and the wave direction, and the Snell's law construction given in Figs. 3-10 and 3-11, we can outline a graphical ray-tracing technique for slowly varying media. We shall assume that the refractive index changes slowly in the space of a wavelength in the medium. We can then neglect the reflected components of the wave.

The ray path is assumed to start at P_1 in part a of Fig. 3-12. The required initial condition is the angle θ_1 between the wave normal and the static magnetic field. The corresponding ray angle $\theta_1 - \alpha_1$ at the starting point P_1 can then be determined either from Fig. 3-8 or from the refractive-index surface in Fig. 3-7. The ray is assumed to progress a small distance to a point P_2. The refractive index is assumed to be constant over this small element of path, and hence the wave-normal direction does not change. The surface of constant refractive index appropriate to the direction of the wave normal is then drawn through P_2 and becomes the boundary at which Snell's law is applied. At this point we must change *both* H_0 and $\mu(\theta)$. The refractive-index surfaces are drawn with H_{01} and H_{02} as axes, and are illustrated in part b of Fig. 3-12. A normal to the boundary is drawn through $\mu_1(\theta)$ at θ_1, and intersects $\mu_2(\theta)$ at θ_2. This intersection gives the magnitude and angle, with respect to H_{02}, of the new wave normal. The direction of the second segment of the ray path can now be determined from Fig. 3-8, and a suitable value for the next path increment chosen. This process is repeated at successive "boundaries" until the desired path has been sketched.

Although the ray-tracing procedure just outlined is based on a two-dimensional model, the same principles apply in three dimensions. The three-dimensional picture is, of course, more complicated, and is not readily adapted to graphical methods of solution.

3.5 Group Ray Refractive Index

Relation between phase velocity and wave-packet velocity. Since the direction of the ray and that of the corresponding wave normal are not, in general, parallel, the velocity of a wave packet traveling in the ray direction will differ from the group velocity defined for the wave-normal direction. To illustrate this situation, consider the behavior of a wave packet, which is the energy in the immediate vicinity of the point where the phase of the wave is stationary with respect to independent variations of both frequency and wave-normal direction. A representation of the propagation of a wave packet is given in Fig. 3-13. It is assumed that the packet has moved from position A to position B in unit time. If the energy were not limited in lateral extent, the velocity of the group would be given simply by (3.15). The distance moved in unit time would then be c/μ', as shown in Fig. 3-13. However in the case where the ray direction differs from the direction of the wave normal, the wave packet will move a greater distance c/μ_r', where μ_r' is the group ray refractive index. It is easily seen from Fig. 3-13 that the group ray refractive index is given by

$$\mu_r' = \mu' \cos \alpha = \frac{B \cos \theta \cos \alpha}{2\Lambda^{1/2}(\cos \theta - \Lambda)^{3/2}}, \tag{3.28}$$

where α is the angle between the wave normal and the ray.

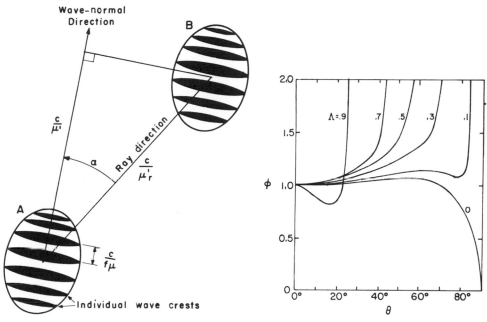

FIG. 3-13. Geometry of wave packet in aniso-tropic medium.

FIG. 3-14. Correction factor ϕ multiplying the longitudinal group ray refractive index.

We must now determine the relation between the group ray refractive index and θ, the angle between the wave normal and the static magnetic field. By substituting (3.13) into (3.23) and performing a few manipulations, we find that

$$\cos \alpha = \frac{1 - \dfrac{\Lambda}{\cos \theta}}{\left[\dfrac{\tan^2 \theta}{4} + \left(1 - \dfrac{\Lambda}{\cos \theta}\right)^2\right]^{1/2}}. \tag{3.29}$$

By substituting (3.15) and (3.29) into (3.28), we find after more manipulation that

$$\mu_r' = \frac{B}{2\Lambda^{1/2}(1 - \Lambda)^{3/2}} \phi(\theta, \Lambda) = \mu_L' \phi(\theta, \Lambda), \tag{3.30}$$

where

$$\phi(\theta, \Lambda) = \frac{(1 - \Lambda)^{3/2}}{\left[\frac{1}{4}\tan^2 \theta(\cos \theta - \Lambda) + \dfrac{(\cos \theta - \Lambda)^3}{\cos^2 \theta}\right]^{1/2}} \tag{3.31}$$

and μ'_L is the group ray refractive index for purely longitudinal propagation. The factor ϕ given by (3.31) shows how much the group ray refractive index differs from that for the purely longitudinal case. This factor is plotted in Fig. 3-14 as a function of wave-normal direction, with Λ as a parameter. As the figure shows, the longitudinal group refractive index μ'_L is an excellent approximation for low values of the normalized frequency Λ and small wave-normal angles θ. For Λ near zero, the longitudinal value is within 8 per cent of the true value up to a wave-normal angle of about 75 deg. Since the major portions of most whistlers have normalized frequencies of 0.1 or less, the correction is small for nearly all wave-normal angles. However, appreciable errors may exist for nose whistlers, since their normalized frequencies may reach 0.6.

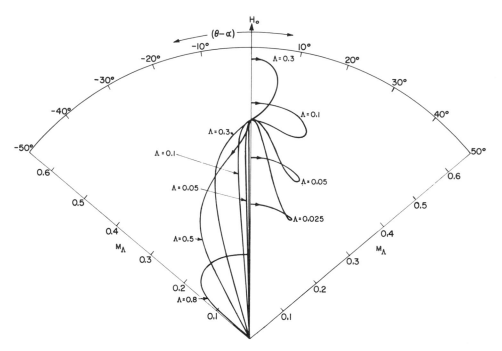

Fig. 3-15. Normalized group ray velocity M_Λ versus ray direction. Small arrows show direction of change of wave-normal angle θ, beginning at $\theta = 0$ deg.

The group ray velocity $v_{gr} = c/\mu'_r$ can be computed from (3.30). The corresponding ray direction is obtained from (3.25) or Fig. 3-8. To illustrate the general character of the group ray velocity, a normalized quantity $M_\Lambda = v_{gr}B/c$ is plotted in Fig. 3-15 as a function of $\theta - \alpha$ in polar coordinates, after Gendrin (1960a, 1961). The curves are parametric in Λ, and their rotation about the axis H_0 forms a figure of revolution that is the "group ray velocity" surface. These surfaces are in general multivalued for $\Lambda < 0.5$. For any ray angle whose magnitude is less than the magnitude of the maximum "negative" value of $\theta - \alpha$, and for any $\Lambda < 0.5$, there are three distinct values of group ray velocity, and for larger ray angles there are two. For $\Lambda \geq 0.5$, the surfaces are single-valued and the ray and wave-normal directions lie on opposite sides of H_0. For $\Lambda \leq 0.5$, the M_Λ surfaces coincide at $\theta - \alpha = 0$ and $M_\Lambda = 0.5$. This condition gives rise to what has been called the "constant-velocity" mode.

Constant-velocity mode. If we put $\cos \theta = 2\Lambda$ in (3.25), the ray angle $\theta - \alpha$ is zero, and $\cos \alpha = 2\Lambda$. Making the same substitution in (3.30), we find that the group ray velocity is given by

$$v_{\text{gr}} = \frac{c}{\mu_{\text{r}}'} = \frac{c}{2B}, \tag{3.32}$$

which corresponds to $M_\Lambda = 0.5$ in Fig. 3-15.

The corresponding behavior of the phase velocity is found by substituting $\cos \theta = 2\Lambda$ in (3.13), which gives

$$v_{\text{p}} = \frac{c}{\mu_0} = \frac{c\Lambda}{B}. \tag{3.33}$$

The longitudinal component of phase velocity is $v_{\text{pl}} = v_{\text{p}}/\cos \theta$. Since $\cos \theta = 2\Lambda$, the longitudinal component is independent of frequency and is given by

$$v_{\text{pl}} = \frac{c}{2B}. \tag{3.34}$$

Hence when $\cos \theta = 2\Lambda$, the wave packet moves in the direction of H_0 at a speed that is independent of frequency, and the corresponding wave velocity is such that its component in the direction of H_0 is equal to that of the wave packet. This constant-velocity mode was first described by Gendrin (1960a, 1961). The mode would be difficult to excite from the ground because the available range of wave-normal angles for whistler-mode transmission is restricted by the high refractive index of the lower ionosphere.

3.6 Theory of Trapping in Ducts

The need for ducts. We have seen how the anisotropy of the homogeneous ionosphere at very low frequencies can act to guide the path of propagation *approximately* in the direction of the static magnetic field. Originally it was thought that this effect was sufficient to account for whistlers. However recent evidence (see Sec. 4.8) has shown that some kind of ducting is involved in the propagation of whistlers. Furthermore the detailed ray-path calculations of Yabroff (1961) show that the wave-normal angle θ is likely to become very large for a non-ducted signal, and hence would lie outside the critical angle for total internal reflection. In that case only a weak evanescent wave would be present at the ground. To meet the need for a duct it has been suggested that there are numerous field-aligned irregularities of ionization that extend between the hemispheres and trap whistler energy somewhat in the manner of a metallic waveguide. We shall outline below the ray theory of trapping in such irregularities, following the treatment of Smith (1960b, 1961a) and Smith *et al.* (1960). The use of ray theory is justified by the internal consistency of the experimental results (see Chap. 6) over a wide range of frequencies and hence wavelengths.

Duct model. For simplicity we shall assume first that the static field is constant in magnitude and direction (the same as the x-axis) and that the electron

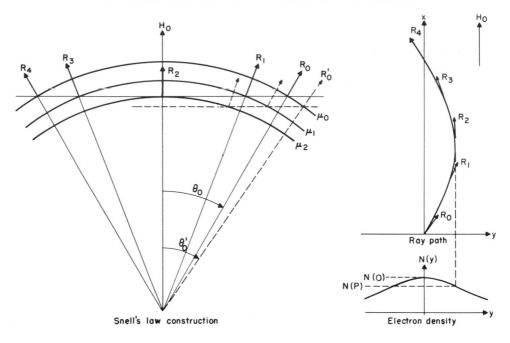

FIG. 3-16a. Ray tracing in field-aligned irregularity. Crest trapping, $\Lambda = 0$ (Region I).

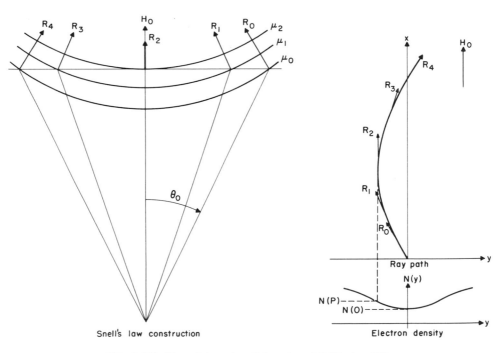

FIG. 3-16b. Trough trapping, $0.5 < \Lambda < 1.0$ (Region VI).

density $N(y)$ varies only in the y-direction, normal to H_0, as shown in the sketches on the right-hand sides of Fig. 3-16a and b. The irregularities are of two types: crests (increased density) and troughs (decreased density). The magnitude of the irregularity is given by an enhancement factor defined for crests as

$$E_C = \frac{N(0)}{N(P)} - 1 , \qquad (3.35)$$

and for troughs as

$$E_T = \frac{N(P)}{N(0)} - 1 , \qquad (3.36)$$

where $N(0)$ is the electron density on the axis of the irregularity, and $N(P)$ is the electron density at the outermost excursion of the ray path from the axis.

   Trapping when $\Lambda \approx 0$ *and* $0.5 \leq \Lambda < 1.0$. The general nature of a ray trapped in a field-aligned irregularity is illustrated in Fig. 3-16a for a crest, with $\Lambda \approx 0$, and in Fig. 3-16b for a trough, with $0.5 < \Lambda < 1.0$. In each case the initial wave normal is assumed to lie in the $(x - y)$-plane and to make an angle θ_0 with the x-axis. From the given electron density, a family of refractive-index surfaces $\mu(\theta)$ is constructed by using (3.13). The Snell's law construction then defines the wave direction and the ray direction for each value of the y-displacement. In both a and b of Fig. 3-16 the wave normal always rotates in the direction of increasing electron density. However the behavior of the ray in the two cases is different. In the crest, with $\Lambda \approx 0$, the ray angle has the same sign and rotates in the same sense as the wave normal, and the ray path therefore lies on the same side as the wave normal. In the trough, with $0.5 \leq \Lambda < 1.0$, the ray moves to the left when the initial wave normal is on the right. The ray rotates in the opposite sense to that of the wave normal, and therefore rotates *away* from regions of increasing refractive index. Because of this effect, trapping at frequencies above $0.5 f_H$ ($\Lambda > 0.5$) is possible only in troughs.

   When the ray is parallel to H_0, the path has reached its maximum lateral excursion in both cases, and as the refractive-index diagrams show, the wave normal is also parallel to H_0. From the symmetry of the Snell's law construction, it is seen that the upper half of the ray path is the mirror image of the lower half about a horizontal line through the maximum lateral excursion. Again by symmetry it is seen that the ray-path pattern from R_0 through R_3 is repeated on the opposite side of the axis of the irregularity and is similar in shape to type A of Fig. 3-18.

   An enhancement will trap only those waves that have wave-normal angles less than a certain critical value. In Fig. 3-16a, where μ_0 and μ_2 represent the refractive-index surfaces for the axis and for the outside perimeter of the duct, respectively, the angle θ_0 is the largest initial wave-normal angle that any trapped wave may have. As shown in Fig. 3-16a, the wave-normal angle θ_0', which is greater than θ_0, corresponds to a wave that will bend toward the axis but will not be trapped. The relation between the initial wave-normal angle θ_0 and the density ratio $N(P)/N(0)$ required for trapping is obtained simply by noting that the wave-normal direction, as given by the direction of the refractive-index vector, is parallel to H_0 at the maximum ray-path excursion. Then applying

Snell's law, we have for both cases

$$\mu[(N(0),\,\theta_0]\cos\theta_0 = \mu[N(P),\,0]. \tag{3.37}$$

By substituting (3.13) into (3.37), we get

$$\left[\frac{N(0)}{\Lambda(\cos\theta_0 - \Lambda)}\right]^{1/2}\frac{\cos\theta_0}{f_H} = \left[\frac{N(P)}{\Lambda(1-\Lambda)}\right]^{1/2}\frac{1}{f_H}, \tag{3.38}$$

from which we obtain

$$\frac{N(P)}{N(0)} = \frac{1-\Lambda}{\cos\theta_0 - \Lambda}\cos^2\theta_0, \tag{3.39}$$

which is valid for crests and troughs.

For the case of $\Lambda \approx 0$, illustrated in Fig. 3-16a, Eq. (3.39) reduces simply to

$$\frac{N(P)}{N(0)} = \cos\theta_0. \tag{3.40}$$

Although Eq. (3.39) was developed for a slowly varying medium, it applies also to a step discontinuity for the cases shown in Fig. 3-16. This can be seen from the Snell's law construction, which shows that for any reduction to an electron density less than $N(P)$ in Fig. 3-16a, or for any increase to an electron density greater than $N(P)$ in Fig. 3-16b, there can be no transmitted wave. Hence if $N(P)$ represents the density on the outside of the step, θ_0 becomes the critical angle for total internal reflection. Within the limitations of ray theory our analysis shows that it is only the fractional change, not the gradient of electron density, that controls trapping.

Trapping when $0 < \Lambda < 0.5$. The ray-path behavior for other conditions can be derived with the aid of the appropriate refractive-index surfaces. In general there are two principal regions of interest, $0 < \Lambda < 0.5$ and $0.5 \leqq \Lambda < 1.0$, the latter of which has already been discussed. The general case of $0 < \Lambda < 0.5$ is complicated and requires a separate discussion. The general form of the refractive index for this case is illustrated in Fig. 3-17a, which shows that $\mu\cos\theta$, the projection of the refractive-index vector on the H_0 axis, has not only a maximum at $\theta = 0$ deg, as in Fig. 3-16a, but a minimum at $\theta = \theta_2$. At θ_2 the ray is parallel to H_0. The angle θ_2 is readily found by setting the differential of $\mu\cos\theta$ with respect to θ equal to zero and solving for θ_2, which gives the result

$$\cos\theta_2 = 2\Lambda. \tag{3.41}$$

For a crest irregularity it is clear by comparing Fig. 3-17a with Fig. 3-16a that trapping will occur only when $0 \leqq \theta_0 < \theta_2$, and that the required electron density ratio is given by (3.39). It should be noted that in the case of $0 < \Lambda < 0.5$, Eq. (3.39) may give two values of θ_0 for a given enhancement. One of these values requires that θ_0 be greater than θ_2, and must be rejected, since no trapping will occur for such wave angles. Unlike the cases illustrated in Fig. 3-16, Eq. (3.39) does not apply strictly to a sharp boundary. The reason is simply that there is always a solution from the Snell's law construction that gives a ray traveling into the second medium.

For a trough irregularity, two types of behavior can be deduced from Fig. 3-17a. When $0 \leqq \theta_0 < \theta_3$, where θ_3 is defined by the refractive-index vector μ_3 whose projection upon H_0 is equal to that of $\mu(0)$, it is seen that the wave normal must be confined to the right-hand side of the diagram, and that the ray is parallel to H_0 only at $\theta = \theta_2$.

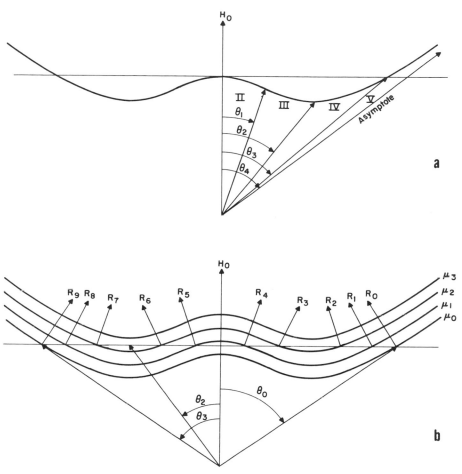

Fig. 3-17. *a*, Ray-path regions for $0 < \Lambda < 0.5$. *b*, Sequence of ray directions for trough trapping with $0 < \Lambda < 0.5$.

The value of θ_3 is readily determined by setting $\mu(\theta_3) \cos \theta_3 = \mu(0)$, which gives the result

$$\cos \theta_3 = \frac{\Lambda}{1 - \Lambda}. \qquad (3.42)$$

For $\theta_3 < \theta_0 < \theta_4$ it is seen from Fig. 3-17b that $\mu \cos \theta_0 > \mu(0)$, and therefore the ray will cross the axis of the depression in electron density. Before crossing the axis, the ray becomes parallel to H_0 at θ_2. It must then move away from the axis until it again becomes parallel to H_0 at $\theta = \theta_2$ on the left side of the diagram in Fig. 3-17b. It crosses the axis finally when $\theta = \theta_3$ on the left side of Fig. 3-17b, and then the ray path repeats on the right side of the axis of the irregularity. The form of the ray path is illustrated in case B of Fig. 3-18. The path has the same symmetry properties as case A of Fig. 3-18.

For both cases of trough trapping associated with Fig. 3-17a, the maximum lateral excursion of the ray path occurs when $\theta = \theta_2 = \cos^{-1} 2\Lambda$. The condition necessary for trapping is therefore

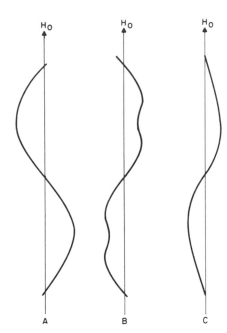

FIG. 3-18. Types of paths of trapped energy.

$$\left[\frac{N(0)}{\Lambda(\cos \theta_0 - \Lambda)}\right]^{1/2} \frac{\cos \theta_0}{f_H}$$
$$= \left[\frac{N(P)}{\Lambda^2}\right]^{1/2} \frac{2\Lambda}{f_H}, \qquad (3.43)$$

from which we obtain

$$\frac{N(P)}{N(0)} = \frac{\cos^2 \theta_0}{4\Lambda(\cos \theta_0 - \Lambda)}. \qquad (3.44)$$

Examination of (3.39) and (3.44) or of Fig. 3-17a shows that in the range $0 \le \theta_0 < \theta_2$, the required enhancement factor E_C or E_T will depend on θ_0. For values of θ_0 close to 0, the crest enhancement E_C is smaller than the trough enhancement E_T, while for values of θ_0 close to θ_2, the reverse is true. The angle θ_1, where these enhancement factors are equal, can be found by equating (3.39) to the reciprocal of (3.44), which gives

$$\cos \theta_1 = \left(\frac{\Lambda}{1 - \Lambda}\right)^{1/2} + \left[\frac{\Lambda}{1 - \Lambda} - 2\Lambda\left(\frac{\Lambda}{1 - \Lambda}\right)^{1/2}\right]^{1/2}. \qquad (3.45)$$

Ray-path regions. The ray-path regions defined by the initial wave-normal angles θ_1 through θ_4 and illustrated in Fig. 3-16 and Fig. 3-17a can be represented conveniently on the $(\cos \theta_0, \Lambda)$-plane as shown in Fig. 3-19. The region outside the large triangle corresponds to $\theta_0 > \theta_4$, for which the refractive index is imaginary and hence propagation is not possible. The boundary line is given by $\cos \theta_0 = \Lambda$.

The classification and properties of the ray-path regions are summarized in Table 3-1.

For purposes of calculation it is convenient to plot contours of the constant enhancement factors E_C and E_T on the ray-path-region diagram, as in Fig. 3-20. Of particular interest is the line $\cos \theta_2 = 2\Lambda$, along which zero enhancement is required for trapping in a trough. This results simply from the fact that at that particular initial wave-normal angle, the ray is parallel to H_0.

Limitations of the trapping theory. When the trapping theory is applied to the actual ionosphere, account should be taken of the changes in magnitude and direction of H_0. However, this factor probably will not be important unless the average radius of curvature of the ray path becomes equal to or less than the radius of curvature of the axis of the irregularity itself. Perhaps a more important error is the assumption that the refractive index is symmetrically distributed on both sides of the axis of the irregularity. However, it is believed that the electron density may be approximately proportional to f_H (see Chap. 6). Hence at low frequencies, where $\Lambda \approx 0$, the refractive index is approximately constant and the assumption of symmetry would be justified. Actual ray tracing in model enhancements by Yabroff (1961) has shown consistency with the predictions of Fig. 3-20.

Bundles of ducts within larger ducts could produce a broad swishy whistler with a well-defined width determined by the size of the large duct and a fine structure defined by the small ducts. Coupling between ducts might be important, particularly if the diameters of the small ducts were equal to or less than a wavelength. In that case considerable leakage from one duct to another could be expected.

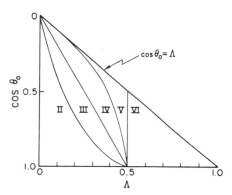

FIG. 3-19. Ray-path regions for trapped waves.

Average group ray velocity. It is important to consider the effect of a duct on the average group ray velocity. Following Smith *et al.* (1960), and Smith

TABLE 3-1

RAY-PATH REGIONS

Region	Type of Irregularity	Defining Conditions		Enhancement Equations	Typical Ray Path in Fig. 3–18	Apply to Sharp Boundary
		Λ	θ			
I	Crest	$\Lambda \approx 0$		3.41	A	Yes
II[a]	Crest Trough	$0 < \Lambda < 0.5$	$0 \leqq \theta_0 < \theta_1$	3.40 3.45	A	No Yes
III[b]	Crest Trough	$0 < \Lambda < 0.5$	$\theta_1 < \theta_0 < \theta_2$	3.40 3.45	A	No Yes
IV	Trough	$0 < \Lambda < 0.5$	$\theta_2 < \theta_0 < \theta_3$	3.45	C	Yes
V	Trough	$0 < \Lambda < 0.5$	$\theta_3 < \theta_0 < \theta_4$	3.45	B	Yes
VI	Trough	$0.5 < \Lambda < 1$	$\theta_0 < \theta_4$	3.40	A	Yes

[a] Minimum required $E_C < E_T$
[b] Minimum required $E_T < E_C$

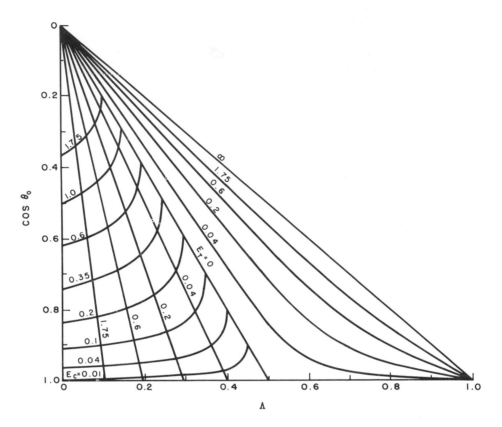

FIG. 3-20. Minimum enhancement factors required for ducting versus wave-normal direction and normalized frequency.

(1961a), we shall consider only enhancements of ionization. The wave normal of a ducted signal changes direction periodically as the ray path executes snakelike excursions back and forth across the duct, as illustrated by Fig. 3-16a. On the axis of the duct the wave normal makes its maximum angle with the earth's magnetic field, and the corresponding longitudinal component of group ray velocity is reduced by the cosine of the angle between the ray and the direction of the earth's field. There is a further reduction in the longitudinal component of group ray velocity with respect to the longitudinal value for the smaller wave-normal angles, as shown in Fig. 3-15. At the maximum lateral excursion of the ray, the wave-normal angle is zero but the electron density is reduced, causing the group ray velocity to exceed the longitudinal value on the axis. The combined result of these two compensating factors is that the average group ray velocity of the ducted wave is very nearly the same as the group ray velocity of a strictly longitudinal wave traveling along the axis of the duct. Calculations by Smith (1960b) for representative duct models show that the error in assuming that the wave travels along the axis in the purely longitudinal mode is usually less than 1 per cent.

Gradient trapping at low and high frequencies. There is a special case of trapping in which the theory outlined above is clearly inadequate. Imagine that a deep depression (trough) in electron density is created along a particular tube of force by the removal of electrons. A steep negative gradient of electron density is thus created on the inner edge of the irregularity. Waves whose normals lie within an appropriate cone of angles will then follow a path similar to that of Fig. 3-16a. However since the ray is moving inward, it will eventually encounter markedly reduced gradients. Then the curvature of the earth's field will act to deflect the ray outward. Upon entering the region of high gradient, the ray will again be refracted inward and the process will be repeated. Thus the ray is trapped by the gradient of μ and its path oscillates about the direction of the earth's field. This mechanism we shall call gradient trapping.

Gradient trapping may be important at high frequencies, where the effects of the earth's field on propagation can be neglected to a first approximation. Unlike the low-frequency wave, the high-frequency wave bends *away* from regions of increased electron density, and hence trapping must occur on the outer side of a trough or the inner side of a crest. This suggests that trapping on the outer part of a field-aligned *depression* in density may be the most stable form of trapping at high frequencies, since lateral deviations would tend to be restricted by the gradients. The possibility of HF ducting on field-aligned irregularities was suggested years ago (Pedersen, 1929) in an attempt to explain the so-called long-delay echoes at high frequencies (Størmer, 1928). The idea has recently been revived as a possible means of studying the magnetosphere (Obayashi, 1959; Gallet and Utlaut, 1961, Booker 1962).

As we have mentioned, we shall call the kind of guiding that depends primarily on the distribution of electron density "geomagnetic" ducting, and that which depends primarily on the anisotropy of the medium we shall call "magneto-ionic" guiding.

3.7 *Coupling Between Ionosphere and Earth–Ionosphere Waveguide*

Sharp-boundary model. The amount of energy entering the ionosphere in the whistler mode will depend on the boundary conditions at the lower edge of the ionosphere and on the location of the transmitter with respect to the point of entrance. Because of the long wavelengths encountered at whistler frequencies, the lower boundary of the ionosphere may be assumed to have a sharp discontinuity in refractive index. On the other hand, because of the high values of refractive index inside the ionosphere, the wavelength is greatly reduced, and we can assume that conditions are slowly varying over most of the path. The whistler mode will be excited if the incident wave (in free space) contains some energy of the appropriate polarization. The first step in the problem of calculating the transmission and reflection coefficients is to determine the relation between the angle of incidence and the angle of refraction.

Snell's law. The angles of reflection and refraction of the two characteristic waves are readily determined by matching the horizontal components of the propagation constants of the incident, reflected, and transmitted waves. The result is Snell's law:

$$\sin \theta_w = n_1 \sin \theta_1 = n_2 \sin \theta_2 , \tag{3.46}$$

where n_1 and n_2 are the refractive indexes of the two characteristic waves given by (3.8), θ_1 and θ_2 are the corresponding angles of refraction, and θ_w is the angle of incidence in the earth–ionosphere waveguide.

Since the refractive indexes can be complex, as shown by (3.8), the angles θ_1 and θ_2 can be complex (Budden, 1961). Note that the real and imaginary parts of the refractive index may have different directions. Thus the real part of n is normal to the planes of constant phase, and the imaginary part is normal to the planes of constant amplitude. Such a wave is called an inhomogeneous plane wave (Budden, 1961). In our case the peak amplitude of the incident wave is assumed to be constant over the boundary. Hence by Snell's law (3.46), the planes of constant amplitude must be parallel to the boundary.

Graphical solution of Snell's law; critical angle and cone of transmission. With the aid of the Snell's law construction, we can easily solve the refraction problem for the case of zero losses. Consider first the case of transmission across the boundary between the ionosphere and free space. The refractive-index diagrams of the boundary are derived from those for the general case illustrated in Figs. 3-10 and 3-11 and are shown in meridional cross section in Figs. 3-21 and 3-22. Each refractive-index surface is a figure of revolution about the axis H_0. In free space the surface is simply the unit sphere, labeled I. The surfaces labeled II are drawn for a typical nighttime E layer, with

$$f_0 = 0.5 \times 10^6 \text{ cps,} \qquad f_H = 10^6 \text{ cps,}$$
$$\nu = 2\pi \times 10^5 \text{ cps,} \qquad f = 16.6 \times 10^3 \text{ cps.}$$

The corresponding magneto-ionic theory parameters are

$$X = \frac{f_0^2}{f^2} = 907 , \qquad Y_H = \frac{f_H}{f} = 60.2 , \qquad Z = \frac{\nu}{2\pi f} = 6.02 .$$

In calculating the refraction over a moderate range of θ, we can neglect Z compared with Y_L in (3.8) and use (3.13) to describe the $\mu(\theta)$ surface. For the values of X and Y_H assumed above, we have $\mu(0) = 4$.

Input conditions are shown in Fig. 3-21, which is drawn for a magnetic dip angle of 60 deg. Output conditions at the conjugate point are shown in the separate drawing of Fig. 3-22 in order to clarify the relations. In Fig. 3-21, the input case, all possible wave normals on the free-space side are located within the upper half of the refractive-index surface for region I. The area in the meridional plane through this region is shown shaded. The region occupied by the corresponding wave normals in the ionosphere is found by drawing tangents (shown dashed) to the region I surface perpendicular to the boundary between regions I and II. These form a cylinder whose intersection

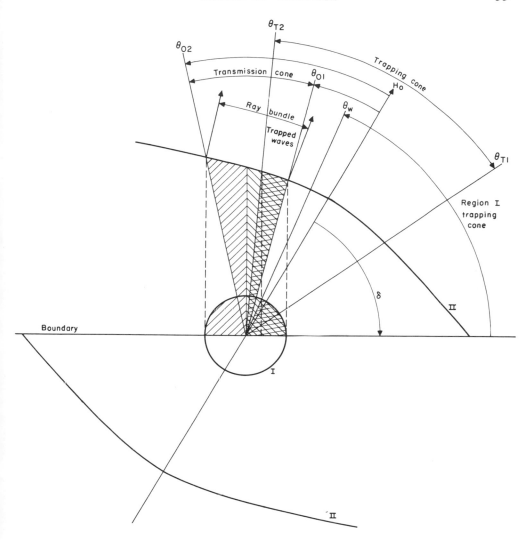

FIG. 3-21. Graphical solution for the directions of wave normals and rays at lower boundary of ionosphere, for waves incident from below. All angles except θ_w are measured with respect to H_0.

with the refractive-index surface of region II defines the cone of limiting wave normals in region II. The angle of refraction of the limiting wave normal is called the critical angle. The angles θ_{01} and θ_{02} are the limits of this cone (and therefore the critical angles) in the meridional plane. We shall call this cone the cone of transmission, since all transmitted wave normals must lie within it. A corresponding ray bundle is defined by the limiting ray directions given by the perpendiculars to the refractive-index surface at the locus of intersection of the cone of transmission with the refractive-index surface. For any given incident-wave normal, the corresponding transmitted-wave normal and associated ray direction can be found from a diagram like that in

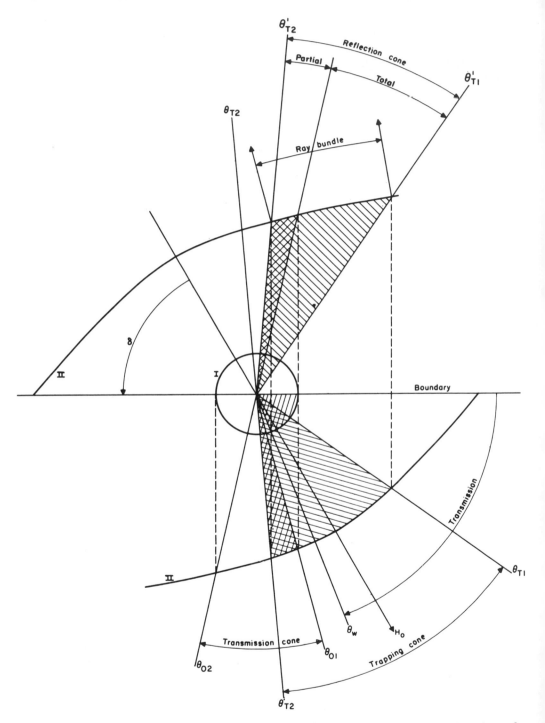

FIG. 3-22. Graphical solution for the directions of wave normals and rays at lower boundary of ionosphere, for waves incident from above. All angles except θ_w are measured with respect to H_0.

Fig. 3-21. It is clear from Snell's law that the incident-wave normal and the transmitted-wave normal must lie in the same plane (the plane of incidence). If that plane contains H_0, then the ray direction lies in the same plane and the diagram of Fig. 3-21 applies. On the other hand, if the incident wave does not lie in the magnetic meridional (north-south) plane, the ray is not in the plane of incidence; however, because of the axial symmetry of the refractive index diagram, the ray will lie in the plane defined by the wave normal and H_0. Details of the three-dimensional analysis are given in a later section.

When the direction of the wave normal (and of the associated ray) is known with respect to H_0, it is possible to trace the ray through a model ionosphere. The principles of ray tracing are outlined in Sec. 3.4. Examples of ray tracing through selected models are given by Maeda and Kimura (1959) and by Yabroff (1961).

Conditions for trapping in a duct. If we confine our attention to the wave components that are trapped in field-aligned irregularities, then we are interested only in the wave normals that make angles with H_0 less than the trapping angle θ_T and that lie within the transmission cone. Such wave normals are included in the solid angle bounded by the overlapping portions of the transmission cone and the trapping cone. The relative positions of these cones in the meridional plane are shown in Fig. 3-21, where the limits of the transmission cone are denoted by the critical angles θ_{01} and θ_{02}, and the limits of the trapping cone by θ_{T1} and θ_{T2}. In this illustration the special case of trapping, where $\theta_{T1} = \theta_{T2}$, is assumed, but this assumption could be removed if necessary. The wave normals of the trapped waves lie between θ_{01} and θ_{T2}. The corresponding input-wave normals occupy the region I trapping cone of angular width θ_w, which, the diagram shows, has a much larger angular spread than the sector of trapped wave normals in region II. A source on the ground sufficiently far to the left of the input point in the ionosphere as represented in Fig. 3-21 would create input waves with wave normals within the region I trapping cone. Since the lowest-order input rays (highest angles of incidence) are generally the most intense, it is clear that much of the whistler-mode energy in this case would be trapped even though only a small fraction, $(\theta_{T2} - \theta_{01})/(\theta_{T2} + \theta_{T1})$, of the trapping cone could be occupied by wave normals in the meridional plane. For sources to the right of the input point, it is clear that none of the energy would be trapped, and therefore there would be no discrete whistlers. This prediction assumes, of course, that scattering by ionospheric irregularities can be neglected.

Scattering assumption. After being trapped in the sector between θ_{01} and θ_{T2}, the energy is assumed to follow a snakelike ray path like the one sketched in Fig. 3-17. Since the path is many (of the order of 10^4) wavelengths long, it is reasonable to suppose that as the whistler travels to the conjugate point, small irregularities in refractive index will tend to scatter some energy out of the duct and to distribute the directions of the trapped waves evenly throughout the trapping cone. Hence we can assume that at the conjugate point the power density of the ducted energy is roughly independent of wave-normal direction within the trapping cone, and that it is virtually zero outside.

Coupling at duct output and echoing. Under the scattering assumption just described, the distribution of the wave normals at the duct output is not the same as it is at the input. This situation is illustrated in Fig. 3-22, which differs basically from Fig. 3-21 only in that the incident waves arrive from within the ionosphere and their normals are assumed to be distributed continuously throughout the trapping cone. Since the transmission sector is the same as that for the input case shown in Fig. 3-21, the output polar diagram will be identical to the input polar diagram (angular width θ_w). Within this sector there will be partial reflections whose magnitudes will depend on the nature of the discontinuity in refractive index across the boundary. However, throughout the rest of the trapping cone the angle of incidence exceeds the critical angle, and hence reflection is total (assuming that losses can be neglected). The directions of the normals of the reflected waves lie within the "reflection cone" and are obtained from the Snell's law construction shown in Fig. 3-22. The limiting angles of the reflection cone are θ'_{T1} and θ'_{T2}. If θ'_{T2} is greater than θ_{T2}, then the reflected wave normals that lie between θ'_{T2} and θ_{T2} will be trapped and an "echo" will result. In the case shown in Fig. 3-22, θ'_{T2} is less than θ_{T2}, and hence no trapping of reflected components can occur. It is clear from the diagram that reflection trapping, or echoing ($\theta'_{T2} > \theta_{T2}$), occurs only if θ_{T2} is less than $90 + \delta$. Note that the gradients of refractive index in the F2 layer have been neglected. They may be significant and can be accounted for in terms of an apparent change in the dip angle δ.

Ground coverage in meridional plane. The relation between illuminated regions on the ground and the sector of trapped wave normals in the meridional plane is shown in Fig. 3-23 for $\mu(0) = 4$. The different possible conditions are illustrated by assuming appropriate values of the parameters. In parts *a* through *d*, the trapping angle θ_T is held constant at 25 deg, while the dip angle δ is varied. Conditions for part *e* are the same as those for *d*, except that the trapping angle has been reduced to 10 deg. The equivalent geomagnetic latitude Φ (dipole approximation) can be obtained from the relation $\tan \Phi = \frac{1}{2} \tan \delta$.

On the basis of the theory outlined above we can readily calculate curves showing the conditions necessary for trapping and for echoing. The condition necessary for trapping is $\theta_{01} < \theta_{T2}$. The condition necessary for echoing and for coupling to the earth–ionosphere waveguide from directions both north and south of the zenith (two-sided coupling) is the same as the condition for echoing given previously. These conditions are plotted in Fig. 3-24 as functions of latitude and trapping cone angle for different values of wave frequency. The model ionosphere used for Fig. 3-23 was assumed. As frequency is lowered, $\mu(0)$ increases, the transmission cone shrinks, and the region of one-sided coupling (and no echoing) diminishes. Hence the probability of the existence of one-sided coupling should decrease with decreasing frequency. We can then predict that if the low-frequency components of whistlers are trapped at all, there is a good chance that the conditions necessary for two-sided coupling and echoing will exist. At the same time, waves of higher frequency are more easily trapped for properly located sources, and hence we can expect a

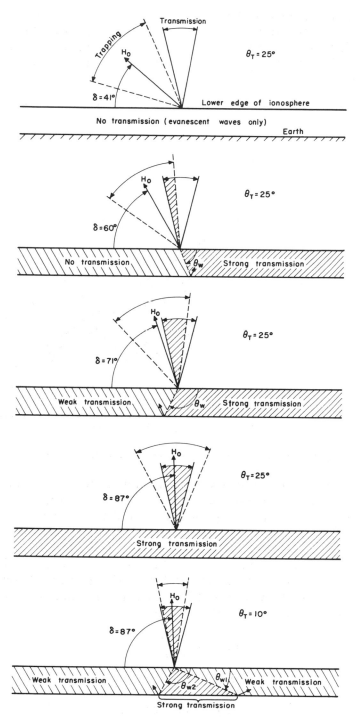

FIG. 3-23. Waveguide excitation by source within ionosphere, for different boundary conditions $\mu(0) = 4$.

low-frequency cutoff effect to be associated with trapping. At the frequencies (15 to 20 kc/s) of VLF transmitters we expect on the basis of this theory that whistler-mode activity will be higher if the transmitters and receivers are located on the high-latitude side of the ducts than it would be if they were on the low-latitude side.

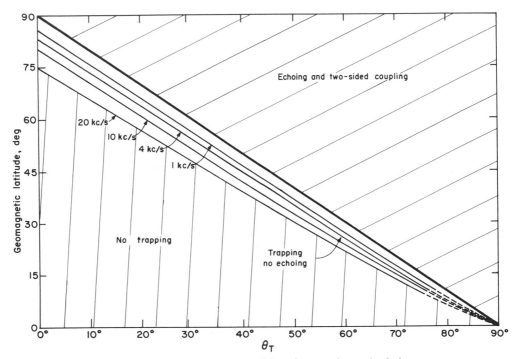

FIG. 3-24. Diagram showing conditions for trapping and echoing.

Coverage diagrams in three dimensions. Although the diagrams of Figs. 3-21 and 3-22 always describe the relation between the wave normal and its associated ray direction, they cannot be used to solve the refraction problem if the wave normal lies outside the meridional plane. In this case it is necessary to plot the intersection of the refractive-index surface with the plane that contains the wave normal and is perpendicular to the boundary between regions I and II. This, of course, is the plane of incidence. From spherical trigonometry it may be shown that this case is described by a figure similar to Figs. 3-21 and 3-22 if we replace δ by δ' and θ by θ', where

$$\tan \delta' = \frac{\tan \delta}{\cos \phi} ,$$

$$\cos \theta = \cos \theta' \cos \beta , \tag{3.47}$$

and

$$\sin \beta = \sin \phi \cos \delta ,$$

ϕ being the angle between the plane of incidence and the plane containing H_0.

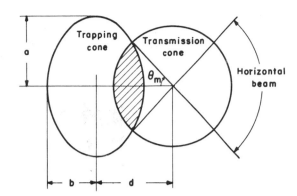

FIG. 3-25. Projections on boundary plane of the bases of the right circular trapping and transmission cones. Cones have equal slant heights.

In the general case the trapping conditions are described by the intersection of the critical-angle cone and the trapping cone. If we assume a constant value of the angle θ_T, the intersection of the trapping cone with the refractive-index surface of medium II will be a circle. The intersection of the critical-angle cone with the refractive-index surface is non-circular, but fortunately its projection on the boundary is a circle. Since the intersection of the trapping cone and refractive-index surface is a circle, its projection of the boundary plane is an ellipse whose minor axis is sin δ times the major axis

The projections on the boundary plane of the intersections of the refractive-index surface with the transmission cone and the trapping cone are shown in Fig. 3 25. Clearly,

$$a = \mu(\theta_T) \sin \theta_T, \qquad b = a \sin \delta, \qquad d = \mu(0) \cos \delta.$$

The possible configurations shown in parts a through e of Fig. 3-26 correspond to those shown in parts a through e of Fig. 3-23 for the two-dimensional case. Trapped waves are transmitted across the boundary only when the wave normal lies within the shaded area representing the solid angle common to both the trapping cone and the transmission cone. The horizontal beam width is $2\phi_m$, the angle subtended by the shaded area of Fig. 3-25. The shapes of the illuminated area on the ground may be determined from Fig. 3-22 and Fig. 3-25.

Effect of horizontal gradients. Horizontal gradients of ionization in the F2 layer will cause changes in the wave-normal direction. Significant gradients

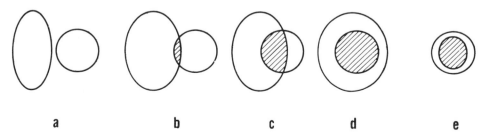

| a | b | c | d | e |

FIG. 3-26a–e. Configurations of projections on boundary plane of trapping and transmission cones corresponding to cases shown in Fig. 3-23.

are associated with sunrise and sunset and tend to lie in the east–west direction. Horizontal gradients of similar magnitude but directed toward the equator can be found at other times, especially at middle latitudes. Gradients directed toward the equator tend to bend the nearly vertical wave normal in the direction of the earth's magnetic field, and hence increase the possibility of trapping. This effect can be accounted for by changing the effective dip angle δ of the field-aligned duct. The numerical calculation requires information on the distribution of electron density, horizontally as well as vertically, and a ray-tracing technique like the one outlined in Sec. 3.4.

Effect of frequency on trapping.   We see from (3.13) that at low frequencies the refractive index is approximately inversely proportional to the square root of the frequency. Hence the size of the transmission cone will increase with frequency. Two significant effects can be expected, and they can be understood with the aid of Fig. 3-25.

First consider what happens when frequency is lowered for the initial conditions pictured in Fig. 3-25. The transmission cone shrinks while the trapping cone remains unchanged. Trapping will no longer be possible when the frequency is less than that for which the transmission and trapping cones are just tangent to one another. Hence we may expect a low-frequency cutoff in the propagation of ducted whistlers whenever $d \geq b + 1$ in Fig. 3-25. The probability of this condition increases as latitude is lowered and d is increased.

Next consider the behavior when frequency is increased to a value at which $b + d < 1$. Then wave normals entering the ionosphere from the high-latitude side in the meridional plane and at angles of transmission near the critical value will not be trapped. Thus a high-frequency cutoff is produced.

The second effect to be expected is a change in directivity with frequency. At low frequencies (or high electron densities) the transmission cone is small compared with the trapping cone, and hence the probability that the conditions pictured in Fig. 3-25 will be realized is low. The transmission cone will tend to lie either wholly within the trapping cone, giving omnidirectional coverage, or wholly outside, giving no trapping. On the other hand, at high frequencies (or low electron densities) the transmission cone is relatively large and the statistical probability of limited coverage, such as that shown in Fig. 3-25, is increased.

Coupling loss.   Whistler-mode waves passing across the lower boundary of the ionosphere encounter rapid changes in dielectric constant that cause a loss of intensity by producing reflections. For the homogeneous sharply bounded model of the lower ionosphere, this loss can be estimated by simply calculating the reflection coefficient for the wave of appropriate polarization. The power in the transmitted wave will be simply the difference between the power in the incident wave and that in the reflected wave.

As an example of the reflection loss, consider a circularly polarized wave in free space incident vertically on the lower boundary of a model ionosphere for which $\mu(0) = 4$. The magnitude of the voltage-reflection coefficient is then $(4 - 1)/(4 + 1) = 3/5$. The corresponding power-reflection coefficient is 9/25;

the power-transmission coefficient must then be 16/25, a loss of about 2 db. This loss will, of course, vary with refractive index and angle of incidence. If the gradients of refractive index are low, most of the energy will be transmitted across the boundary, and the reflection loss will be reduced. Exact analysis of this problem requires a full-wave solution, which has not yet been carried out. Detailed calculations using the sharp-boundary model are given in Sec. 3.10.

Another source of loss during coupling into the ionosphere is a mismatch between the polarization of the transmitted whistler-mode wave and the polarization of the incident wave in the earth–ionosphere waveguide. This loss is zero if the tangential components of both waves have the same polarization. On the other hand, when the incident wave is linearly polarized it does not match the whistler-mode (ordinary) wave, which must be circularly polarized. To satisfy the boundary conditions in this case, an extraordinary wave of opposite polarization is generated, but it is rapidly absorbed as it travels away from the boundary. The result is that half the energy of the incident wave is transferred to the attenuating wave, corresponding to a 3-db loss in intensity.

3.8 Absorption in the Ionosphere

Because of collisions between electrons and other particles, the whistler-mode wave loses some energy as it propagates through the ionosphere. Some of this lost energy appears as heat in the medium and some as disordered electromagnetic radiation. Much of this absorption occurs in the lower regions between 70 and 120 km as the result of collisions between electrons and neutral particles. In the F region, so-called coulomb collisions between electrons and charged particles are the chief cause of absorption. In the following sections the absorption expressions are derived and integrated for selected models of the ionosphere. Models are defined for magnetically quiet conditions during day and night, and for polar blackout conditions. The calculation is divided into two parts—one for the lower ionosphere (60 to 200 km in height), and the other for the upper ionosphere or F region (200 to 1500 km). Although the contribution from the lower ionosphere is usually dominant, that from the F region can be significant.

The effect of ions is neglected, since their interaction with the wave is small at frequencies well above the ion gyro-frequency. Reflection effects occur mainly in the lower part of the absorption region (Altman and Cory, 1962a, b) and are approximately accounted for by assuming a single sharp boundary.

Absorption coefficient for the homogeneous wave. The absorption coefficient in a slowly varying* medium is related to the imaginary part (χ) of the refractive index by

---

* A medium is said to be slowly varying if the change in n is small in the space of a wavelength (Ratcliffe, 1959).

$$\alpha = \chi \frac{\omega}{c} \text{ nepers/km} , \qquad (3.48)$$

where $c = 3 \times 10^5$ km/sec. The full expression (3.1) for n must be employed unless the criterion (3.6) for the QL approximation is satisfied. Fortunately, under most conditions at VLF, the QL approximation for the refractive index, given by (3.8), is valid. Equating real and imaginary parts of (3.8) and assuming that $|Y_L| \gg 1$, we obtain

$$\alpha = \frac{\omega}{\sqrt{2}c} [\sqrt{(1 + G |Y_L|)^2 + (GZ)^2} - (1 + G |Y_L|)]^{1/2} , \qquad (3.49)$$

where

$$G = \frac{X}{Y_L^2 + Z^2} = \frac{\omega_0^2}{\omega_L^2 + \nu^2} .$$

This expression permits few simplifications of practical value. It is necessary, however, to employ the relation

$$\alpha \simeq \frac{\omega G Z}{2c\sqrt{1 + G |Y_L|}} \qquad (3.50)$$

if

$$(1 + G |Y_L|)^2 \gg (GZ)^2 . \qquad (3.51)$$

Otherwise, the difference of the terms in the brackets in (3.49) becomes so small that, even in a digital computer, errors result. Equation (3.50) is also valid if $\omega_L^2 \gg \nu^2$, but it is more general than this last inequality suggests.

Another useful simplification results from the assumptions

$$G |Y_L| \gg 1 \qquad \text{and} \qquad |\omega_L| \gg \nu ,$$

which are valid at heights greater than 100 km. Equation (3.49) then reduces to

$$\alpha = \frac{\omega_0 \nu}{2c |\omega_L|^{3/2}} \omega^{1/2} . \qquad (3.52)$$

For a wave propagating normal to the planes of stratification of the medium, the total absorption may be obtained by integrating α in the direction of the wave normal. For vertical incidence on a horizontally stratified ionosphere, the total absorption in decibels is given by

$$A = 8.69 \times 10^3 \int_{h_0}^{h_1} \alpha \, dh , \qquad (3.53)$$

where h_0 and h_1 are the heights in km over which the absorption is significant.

Since α is an irregular function of height, this expression must be integrated numerically. Because of the complexity of the functions for α, these calculations are performed most economically on a computer.

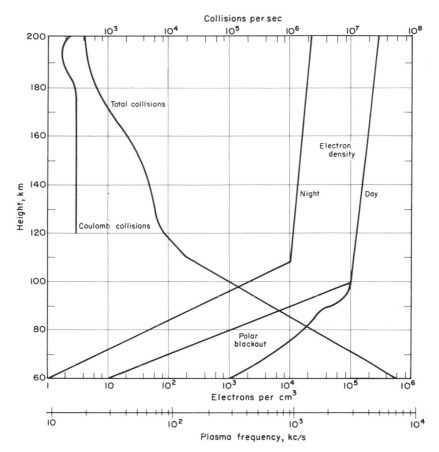

Fig. 3-27. Derived models of the lower ionosphere.

Models of the ionosphere. Since the absorption coefficient α depends on ω_0 and ν, it is necessary to know how these parameters vary with height.* For the lower ionosphere (60 to 200 km), three electron-density models were used, representing normal daytime, normal nighttime, and polar blackout conditions, as shown in Fig. 3-27. In the upper ionosphere (200 to 1500 km), only one electron-density model is shown in Fig. 3-28, but this may be scaled to correspond to any value of f_0F2 by multiplying the density at each height by the factor $(f_0F2/9)^2$, where f_0F2 is in megacycles.

The collision-frequency model represents the sum of electron-ion (coulomb) collisions, which predominate above 200 km, and electron-neutral collisions,

---

* Models of N and ν as functions of height were derived from the following sources: for electron density, Nertney (1953), Mitra (1957), Fejer and Vice (1959), Friedman (1959), Piggott quoted by Bandyopadhyay (1957), Nicolet and Aikin (1960), Ichimiya *et al.* (1961), Ramanathan *et al.* (1961), Barrington and Thrane (1962); and for collision frequency, Briggs (1951), Ataev (1959), Fejer and Vice (1959), Kane (1959), Nicolet (1959), Martyn (1959), Piggott quoted by Bandyopadhyay (1957), Schlapp (1959, 1960), Jackson and Seddon quoted by Ratcliffe (1960).

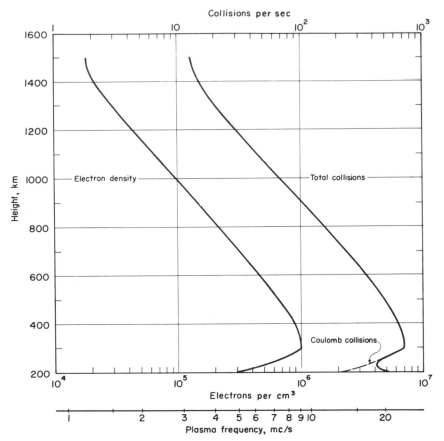

FIG. 3-28. Derived models of the upper ionosphere for normal daytime.

which predominate below 200 km. Since the ion density in the F2 region can be taken equal to the electron density, the coulomb collision rate is approximately proportional to electron density for constant temperature. For a daytime temperature of 1750°K, we have $\nu \simeq 7 \times 10^{-4}N$, and for a nighttime temperature of 1055°K, we have $\nu \simeq 15 \times 10^{-4}N$. Thus Eqs. (3.52) and (3.53) can be combined, so that the absorption integrated between heights h_0 and h_1 above 200 km (in decibels) is given by

$$A = b \int_{h_0}^{h_1} \frac{\omega_0^3 \omega^{1/2}}{|\omega_{\rm L}|^{3/2}} \, dh , \qquad (3.54)$$

where

$$b = \begin{cases} 3.2 \times 10^{-18} & \text{daytime,} \\ 6.8 \times 10^{-18} & \text{nighttime.} \end{cases}$$

Since the shape of the model for the electron density above 200 km is fixed, the absorption is simply proportional to ω_0^3. By contrast, the absorption in the lower ionosphere varies directly with ω_0^m, where $1 \leq m \leq 2$.

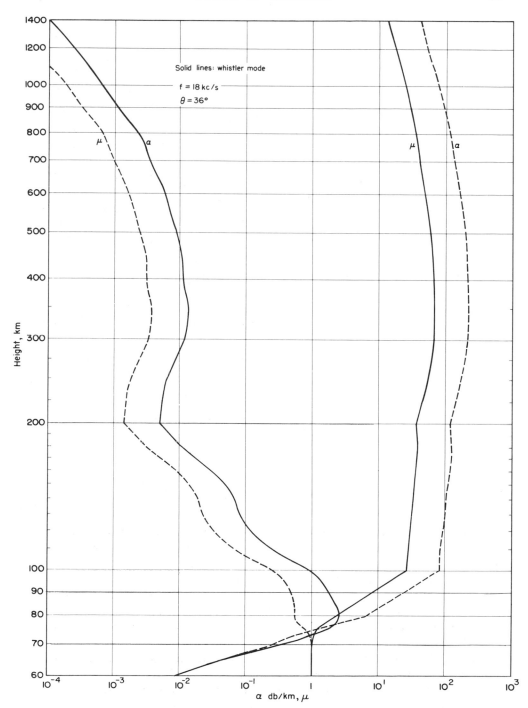

FIG. 3-29. The absorption rate and refractive index as functions of height for a vertically incident wave in the normal daytime ionosphere; $f_0F2 = 9$ mc/s. The solid and dashed lines represent, respectively, the choice of the minus and the plus sign in (3.55).

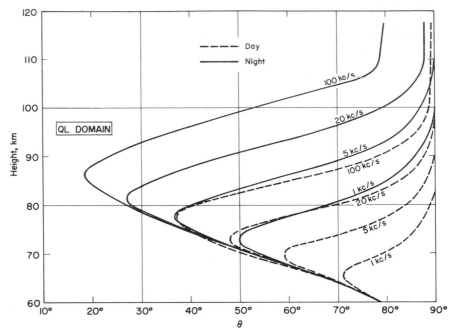

FIG. 3-30. The QL criterion as a function of wave frequency using ionospheric models of Fig. 3-27. The QL approximation is suitable for all values of θ lying to the left of each curve.

Results. The daytime model of the ionosphere has been used to determine the complex refractive index as a function of height in the ionosphere. Values were calculated from a modified form of (3.1), given by

$$n^2 = 1 - \cfrac{X}{1 - iZ - \cfrac{\frac{1}{2}Y_T^2}{1 - X - iZ} \pm \left[\cfrac{\frac{1}{4}Y_T^4}{(1 - X - iZ)^2} + Y_L^2\right]^{1/2}}.$$

(3.55)

In order that a particular value of n be associated with a particular choice of the sign, the indicated root was taken so that its real part was positive. The roots of this equation are plotted in Fig. 3-29 in terms of the refractive index and the absorption rate as functions of height in the normal daytime ionosphere. In this graph the decrease in gyro-frequency with increasing altitude above 300 km was estimated by assuming a dipole model of the earth's magnetic field with a geomagnetic latitude of 37°. The choice of the plus sign in (3.55) indicates very heavy absorption; however, this result is not strictly accurate, since for the low values of μ associated with this mode, the medium is no longer slowly varying and (3.48) is no longer valid. The choice of the minus sign in (3.55) gives the conventional whistler mode, and for this case, the absorption rate is maximum in the D layer. However, the low rate of absorption in the upper ionosphere is partially offset by the large vertical extent of this region, so that its contribution is often significant. The absorption rate is quite easily obtained by using the QL approximation. In order to test the validity of this approximation, we shall assume that the inequality (3.6) is satisfied if the quantity on the right-hand side is equal to 4 times that on the left-hand side, so that

$$\frac{\sin^2 \theta}{\cos \theta} = \frac{1}{\omega_H} \left(\frac{\omega_0^4}{\omega^2} + \nu^2 \right)^{1/2}. \tag{3.56}$$

Figure 3-30 shows curves representing this condition in the lower ionosphere for the models of the normal daytime and normal nighttime ionosphere given in Fig. 3-27.

Values of θ lying to the left of each curve satisfy the QL condition. Hence a vertically incident wave will meet the QL condition during daytime at most latitudes to which whistlers propagate, but during nighttime only at latitudes above about 45° geomagnetic. Nevertheless, the QL approximation was used for all calculations of absorption integrated through the ionosphere, since any inaccuracy incurred through the use of this approximation is assuredly less than that produced by the uncertainty in the ionosphere models employed.

The variation of integrated absorption with wave frequency is given for several ionospheric models in Fig. 3-31, which demonstrates the wide variation in absorption resulting from different ionospheric conditions. In determining

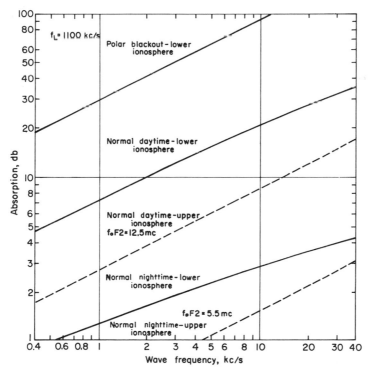

FIG. 3-31. Integrated absorption as a function of wave frequency for different models of the upper and lower ionosphere; normal daytime $f_0 F2 = 12.5$ mc/s; normal nighttime $f_0 F2 = 5.5$ mc/s.

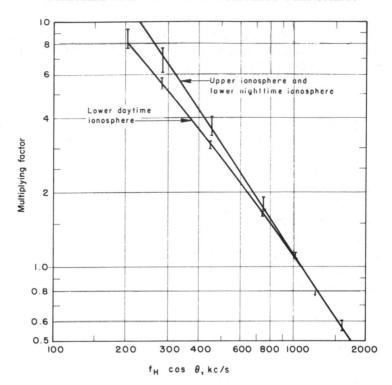

FIG. 3-32. Multiplying factors to convert absorption at $f_H \cos \theta = 1100$ kc/s to absorption at any other value of $f_H \cos \theta$.

the curves for the upper ionosphere, allowance was made for the decrease in gyro-frequency with height. From these curves it may be seen that except in the lower nighttime ionosphere, absorption at the lower frequencies is approximately proportional to the square root of the wave frequency.

This observation enables us to estimate the validity of our assumption that the effect of the motions of the ions is negligible. Absorption calculations including the effect of ions have been made at Stanford by J. Smith,* and elsewhere (Swift, 1962a). A comparison of these results with Fig. 3-31 indicates that absorption does not continue to decrease with decreasing wave frequency, but instead remains approximately constant at low frequencies. The frequency at which this deviation from the $\sqrt{f}$ proportionality becomes apparent was estimated to lie at approximately 1000 cps. Even at 400 cps, however, the assumption that the effect of ions is negligible results in an error much smaller than that produced by temporal and geographic variations in the ionosphere models, so that this assumption is justified.

The dependence of absorption upon $f_H \cos \theta$ is shown by Fig. 3-32, which gives the factor by which absorption computed for $f_H \cos \theta = 1100$ kc/s

---

* Personal communication.

must be multiplied to obtain the absorption for a new value of $f_H \cos \theta$. The curves were obtained by normalizing the results of computations performed for various values of gyro-frequency and θ. These results then fell within the limit indicated by the vertical bars. The curve for the lower nighttime ionosphere agrees very closely with that for the upper ionosphere which, as Eq. (3.54) shows, varies as $\omega_L^{-3/2}$. The factors for the lower daytime ionosphere were sufficiently different to require a separate curve. The value of $f_H \cos \theta$ appropriate to a vertically incident wave at any latitude may be determined from Fig. 3-33, which is drawn from the calculations of Mlodnosky and Helliwell (1962a,b).

As Eq. (3.54) indicates, the absorption rate in the upper ionosphere is proportional to the local value of f_0^3. This dependency, with the assumption that the electron density in the upper ionosphere varies directly with the density at the peak of the F2 layer, may be employed to adjust total absorption values for different values of f_0F2. Figure 3-34 shows the variation of f_0F2 with northern geomagnetic latitude as determined from Central Radio Propagation Laboratory F data for the representative months December 1958 and July 1953 (National Bureau of Standards 1953–1961), and on another scale the

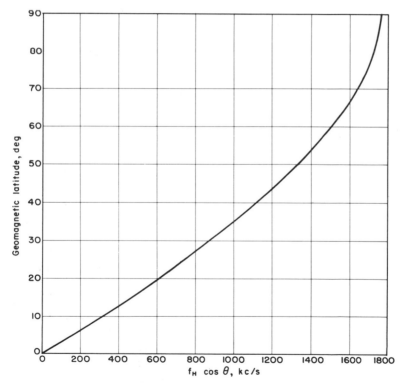

FIG. 3-33. Variation of $f_H \cos \theta$ with geomagnetic latitude for a vertically incident wave as determined from a dipole model of the terrestrial magnetic field.

values of $(f_0F2)^3$ normalized to 12.5 mc/s for noon and 5.5 mc/s for midnight. Hence the absorption in the upper ionosphere for any value of f_0F2 is obtained simply by multiplying the value given by the appropriate curve of Fig. 3-31 by the corresponding multiplying factor given in Fig. 3-34.

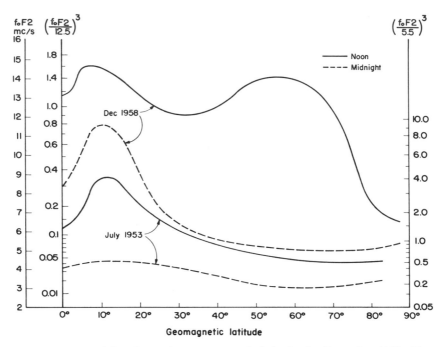

FIG. 3-34. Variation of f_0F2 in northern geomagnetic latitudes for December 1958. The scales on the left and right represent, respectively, the factors by which the absorption in the daytime and nighttime upper ionosphere should be multiplied to give the absorption for a different value of f_0F2.

Figures 3-31 through 3-34 may be employed to determine the absorption of a vertically incident wave for a variety of conditions by multiplying the value obtained from Fig. 3-31 by that indicated in Fig. 3-32. In the case of the upper ionosphere, the result should be multiplied again by the factor given in Fig. 3-34 to adjust for any desired value of f_0F2. Unfortunately, the absorption law for the lower ionosphere does not vary with electron density in any simple way, so that absorption in this region cannot readily be adjusted for different plasma frequencies.

By these methods, the absorption through the range from 60 to 1500 km at 2 and 20 kc/s has been calculated as a function of latitude, and the results are shown for normal daytime and normal nighttime models in Fig. 3-35. Values for the lower latitudes must be employed with discretion because of the marked variation in direction of the earth's field with height at low latitudes, and because of the failure of the QL approximation for large θ.

In applying these absorption calculations to whistler-mode propagation, it must be remembered that the absorption presented here represents the loss incurred in only one passage through the ionosphere, so that the absorption

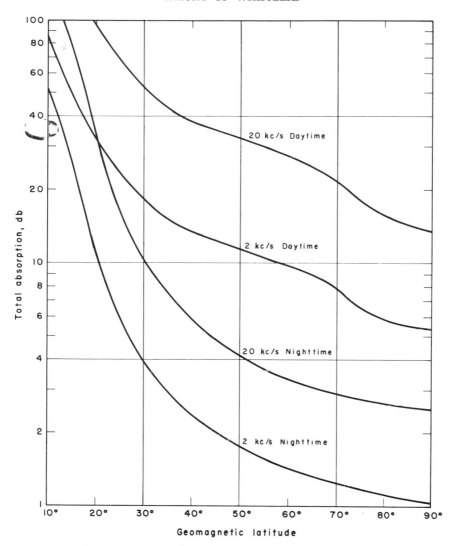

FIG. 3-35. Absorption of a vertically incident wave integrated through the lower and upper iono-sphere as a function of latitude; f_H and f_0F2 are assumed to vary with latitude as shown in Figs. 3-32 and 3-33.

of a short whistler will be twice this figure while that for a long whistler will lie between 2 and 4 times this figure, the exact value depending upon the level in the ionosphere at which the wave is reflected. This point is discussed further in a study of the annual behavior of whistler-mode signals generated by Navy transmitters (Helliwell *et al.*, 1962a).

Sources of error. In the absorption theory from which the numerical results were derived it was assumed that the waves were homogeneous. An estimate of the errors inherent in this approximation is indicated by Fig. 3-36,* which

---

* Personal communication, R. L. Smith.

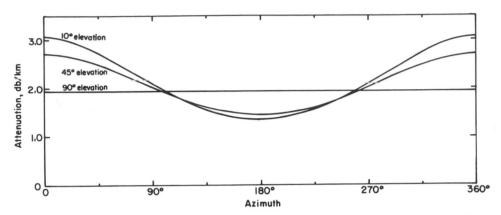

FIG. 3-36. Vertical attenuation factor of inhomogeneous wave as a function of input-wave direction; normal daytime; height = 80 km.

shows that the attentuation rate of the vertically incident homogeneous wave is within 40 per cent and 60 per cent of the absorption rate for waves with elevatic angles of 45 deg and 80 deg, respectively. For most azimuth angles, the error is considerably smaller. Although such an error is large, it is probably not larger than the errors produced by deviations from the ionosphere models employed.

Perhaps the principal source of error arises from the uncertainty in the ionosphere models to be used. Absorption depends mainly upon the electron density and collision frequency in the D layer. Collision-frequency data are consistent at this altitude, but values of electron density show wide divergence. If, for example, the results of Barrington and Thrane (1962) were to be employed in place of the logarithmic relation actually used, the absorption (in decibels) would be two to four times that obtained with the logarithmic function. Although this logarithmic function may be correct as a description of average electron density at middle latitudes, the variations in D-region ionization from the average model are likely to produce significant variations in absorption from time to time and from place to place.

3.9 Impedance Transformation

Wave impedance. Whenever the dielectric constant of the medium changes, either slowly or abruptly, there is a change in the ratio of the electric to the magnetic field of the propagating wave. The relation between electric and magnetic fields is readily obtained with the aid of the wave impedance. If the electric field E in the plane of the wavefront is given in volts/m, the corresponding magnetic field of the traveling wave is given by

$$H = \frac{E}{Z} \, \text{amp/m} , \qquad (3.57)$$

where the wave impedance Z is given by

$$Z = \frac{1}{n}\sqrt{\frac{\mu_0}{\epsilon_0}} = \frac{377}{n} \text{ ohms} .$$

In the whistler mode the refractive index n is generally greater than 1, and hence the wave impedance is less than it is in free space (377 ohms).

"*Slowly varying*" *approximation.* As the wave travels through the ionosphere, the refractive index will vary because of changes in the plasma frequency and the gyro-frequency. As we have noted, a medium is slowly varying if the change in n is small in the space of a wavelength. The medium under conditions of whistler propagation is generally slowly varying because of the substantial reduction of wavelength in it. For example, consider the lower part of the F2 layer at night and assume a plasma frequency of 0.5 Mc/s. At a wave frequency of 5 kc/s and a gyro-frequency of 1 Mc/s, the refractive index for longitudinal propagation is approximately 7. If we take the electron-density scale height to be 100 km, it is easy to show that the change of refractive index in one wavelength is less than 10 per cent. The daytime D region, however, may not appear to be slowly varying at whistler frequencies, as Fig. 3-30 shows.

Relation of power density to electric and magnetic fields. Under slowly varying conditions most of the energy is transmitted and we can neglect to a first approximation the reflections due to changes in refractive index. As the wave propagates, the ratio of E to H gradually changes, much as in the case of a wave on a tapered waveguide or a transmission line. Since no energy is absorbed or reflected, the power density P in the advancing wave must be a constant. For longitudinal propagation we can then write

$$\frac{E^2}{Z} = P = \text{constant} , \tag{3.58}$$

or

$$E = \sqrt{PZ} = \sqrt{\frac{377P}{n}} \text{ volts/m} .$$

Similarly, by substituting (3.58) into (3.57), we find that the magnetic field is given by

$$H = \sqrt{\frac{P}{Z}} = \sqrt{\frac{nP}{377}} \text{ amp/m} . \tag{3.59}$$

Hence the electric field is inversely proportional and the magnetic field directly proportional to the square root of the refractive index. Since the refractive index is proportional to the square root of electron density, the electric and magnetic fields will vary inversely and directly, respectively, with the fourth root of electron density, if we assume constant f_H.

The effect of changing parameters on the intensities of electric and magnetic fields will, of course, depend on the wave frequency. Under most conditions n is roughly proportional to $1/\sqrt{f}$, and hence the largest effects will take place at low frequencies.

Impedance transformation effects are important when either the receiver or the transmitter, or both, are situated in the ionosphere. When the transmitter and the receiver are on the ground, impedance transformations will tend to average out over the path, and hence will have little effect on the observed fields.

For a receiver with a loop antenna in a satellite, two steps are required to calculate the magnetic field at the antenna. First the magnetic field of the transmitted wave on the upper side of the boundary is calculated from (3.57). Then this value is transformed according to (3.59). By combining (3.57) and (3.59), we find that the magnetic field at a particular location in the ionosphere is

$$H_2 = \frac{E_1}{377}\sqrt{n_1 n_2}\ \text{amp/m},\qquad(3.60)$$

where E_1 is the field intensity of the transmitted wave at the boundary, n_1 is the refractive index of the ionosphere at the boundary, and n_2 is the refractive index of the ionosphere at the point of measurement.

3.10 Earth–Ionosphere Waveguide Propagation

Model. Very low frequencies travel for long distances in the space between the conducting spherical shells formed by the earth and the lower edge of the ionosphere. We shall call this space the earth–ionosphere waveguide. The field distribution within the guide for a given source can be approximated by a series of waveguide modes or by a series of rays. The ray treatment has been widely used (Budden, 1961) and we shall adopt it here for the calculation of field intensity.

For whistler calculations we shall use the ray picture that is illustrated in Fig. 3-37. Two rays are shown, one with no intermediate reflections at either earth or ionosphere and one with one reflection at each surface. Normally several such rays are required to describe the total field accurately. For the input case the signals originate on the earth at P_e and enter the ionosphere at P_i. For the output case the signals originate at P_i and are received at P_e. At each reflection from the ionosphere there is some coupling between the components of the wave that are parallel and those that are perpendicular to the plane of incidence. Hence the polarization of the wave changes as the wave

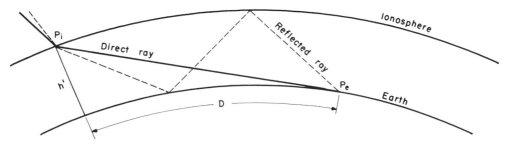

Fig. 3-37. Ray-path geometry for propagation in the earth–ionosphere waveguide.

undergoes successive reflections. The addition of multiple rays causes additional changes, and the result is that the net polarization can have virtually any value (Crary, 1961).

The lower boundary of the waveguide itself is represented by the conductivity of the ground, and the upper boundary by a double-valued expression for refractive index derived from (3.8) and written

$$n^2 = 1 - i\,\frac{\omega_r}{\omega}\,e^{\pm i\tau},\qquad (3.61)$$

where

$$\omega_r = \frac{\omega_0^2}{\sqrt{\nu^2 + \omega_L^2}} \qquad \text{and} \qquad \tan\tau = \frac{\omega_L}{\nu}.$$

In this form the transverse component of the earth's field has been neglected to simplify the calculations.

Input-field intensity. With a knowledge of the characteristics of the ground and the ionosphere, we can calculate the reflection coefficients at the ground (Fresnel coefficients) and the reflection and conversion coefficients at the ionosphere as functions of angle of incidence. We can then obtain the intensity of a particular ray by applying these coefficients to the incident field at each reflection point, taking the incident field to be the reflected field at the previous reflection point. This process is repeated until the end point of the path is reached.

To obtain an estimate of the field intensity of a wave launched into the whistler mode, we shall assume a short, vertical antenna located on the ground and radiating 1 kw of power. This is the type of antenna used in the fixed-frequency experiments described in Chap. 5. It is believed to be a good representation for the sources of whistlers. The field in the ionosphere at P_i in Fig. 3-37 is obtained by summing the significant rays from P_e. The amplitude of each ray varies inversely with the distance from the source, and the ray undergoes amplitude reduction and phase changes at the earth and ionosphere reflection points. These rays enter the ionosphere at slightly different angles of refraction, and hence their wavefronts do not coincide exactly within the ionosphere. However, this difference in angle is normally small, and the field components of the transmitted rays can be summed (taking account of their time phase) to give an effective field intensity just above the boundary. Details of this method of solution are given by Crary (1961).

Curves of input-field intensity versus distance for two different waveguide models are shown in Fig. 3-38 for $f = 15.5$ kc/s.* Models were chosen to represent normal conditions. Their parameters are given in Table 3-2, where ω_r and τ are defined in (3.61), h' is the equivalent height of the reflecting layer, and σ and κ are, respectively, the conductivity and the dielectric constant of the ground at very low frequencies.

For other frequencies in the whistler range, we obtain curves similar to those in Fig. 3-38, but with differences in the magnitudes and in the positions of the

---

* The curves were supplied by J. H. Crary.

TABLE 3-2

PARAMETERS USED IN FIELD-STRENGTH CALCULATIONS

Ionosphere		Ground (Sea Water)
Summer Night	Summer Day	
$\omega_r = 5 \times 10^5 \text{ sec}^{-1}$	$\omega_r = 1.5 \times 10^5 \text{ sec}^{-1}$	$\sigma = 4.5 \text{ mho/m}$
$\tau = 60°$	$\tau = 15°$	$\kappa = 80$
$h' = 90 \text{ km}$	$h' = 70 \text{ km}$	

minima. At distances less than 500 km, only the lowest-order ray contributes appreciably to the transmitted wave. Variations in waveguide parameters have only a small effect at distances less than 2000 km, as Fig. 3-38 shows.

Output-field intensity. For waves exiting at P_i and received at P_e (Fig. 3-37), we perform the same type of analysis as that for the input case. However, a different source must be assumed. This assumption is somewhat arbitrary in

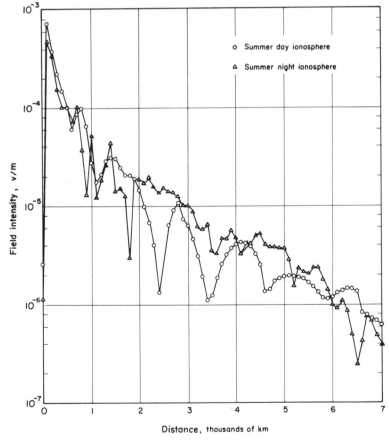

FIG. 3-38. Field intensity of transmitted ionosphere wave versus distance from short vertical antenna at ground radiating 1 kw at 15.5 kc/s.

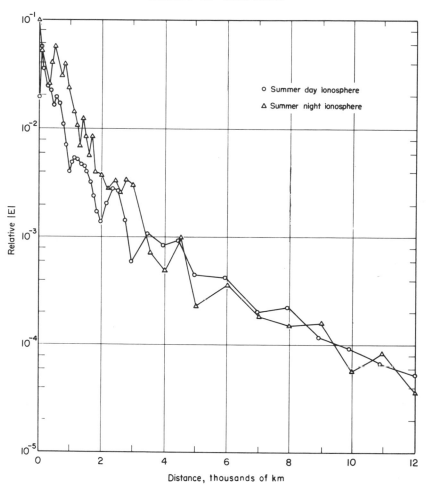

FIG. 3-39. Field intensity in volts/m at ground versus distance from sub-exit point in ionosphere for = 15.5 kc/s relative to an incident field of to volts/m at exit surface.

view of the variations possible in the range of wave normals supplied by a duct. It is convenient to assume that there is a uniform distribution of wave normals within the transmission cone and that the energy radiates from a point source at a virtual distance of 1 km from the exit point.* Crary (1961) has calculated curves of field intensity versus distance on this basis, taking the incident field at the exit surface to be circularly polarized with a magnitude of 2 volts/m.

His results are reproduced in Fig. 3-39 and are expressed in terms of the relative field intensity that would be "seen" by a loop lying in the plane of incidence of the incoming wave. The plotted field intensity is that of a horizontally traveling, vertically polarized wave that would produce the same terminal voltage as the actual wave.

---

* The actual distance depends on the refractive index and the angle of incidence.

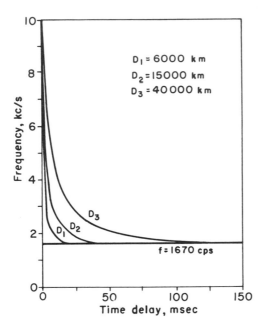

$D_1 = 6000$ km
$D_2 = 15000$ km
$D_3 = 40000$ km

FIG. 3-40. Spectrum of impulse response of earth–ionosphere waveguide for height of 90 km and zero losses. Time delay measured from time delay at infinite frequency.

Waveguide dispersion. When losses in the earth–ionosphere waveguide are small, it is possible to observe dispersive effects on frequencies near the wave-guide cutoff frequency (i.e., that frequency for which the earth–ionosphere spacing is a half wavelength). Under these conditions it is very difficult to obtain an expression by using ray theory. On the other hand, by using mode theory it is possible to obtain a useful approximate description of the dispersive behavior in the vicinity of the waveguide cutoff. For a lossless waveguide, the relation between the group velocity and the phase velocity for the dominant mode is written

$$v_g v_p = c^2 . \tag{3.62}$$

The frequency versus group time delay, obtained from (3.62), is plotted in Fig. 3-40 for different distances and for a height of 90 km. This curve explains the "hook" on atmospherics often observed at night, particularly over seawater paths. Atmospherics of this type are often called tweeks. From (3.62) it is possible to obtain the distance of the source producing the observed impulse. A convenient point of measurement is the frequency equal to 1.16 times the cutoff frequency f_c (1670 cps for a height of 90 km). The distance in kilometers to the source is then given by

$$d = c \, \Delta t , \tag{3.63}$$

where c is equal to 3×10^5 km/s and Δt is the difference, in seconds, from the leading edge of the trace to the point on the trace where $f = 1.16 f_c$.

Examples of the spectra of tweeks are given in Chap. 4.

3.11 Over-all Transmission Loss

Single duct. The field intensity of the output wave at the ground was calculated in Sec. 3.10 on the assumption that the field at the boundary of the ionosphere had an intensity of 2 volts/m and originated in a point source located a virtual distance of 1 km from the exit point. The actual altitude of this source above the boundary varies between μ km and $\sqrt{\mu^2 - 1}$ km, depending on the exit angle, and will be approximated by μ km. The total power radiated by this source is the total power trapped at the input of the duct minus the power scattered out of the duct. The total power into the duct is

$$P_{in} = \frac{E_i^2}{Z} A_d , \qquad (3.64)$$

where E_i is the field intensity of a wave transmitted into the duct, Z is the intrinsic impedance of the medium, and A_d is the effective cross-sectional area of the duct (a function of the wave-normal distribution as well as of the structure of the duct).

The total power out of the duct will be

$$P_{out} = T_d P_{in} , \qquad (3.65)$$

where T_d is the transmission efficiency of the duct.

Assuming that this power is radiated uniformly throughout the trapping cone source described above, and that the transmission cone is small and lies wholly within the trapping cone, the field intensity at the boundary (neglecting absorption) is approximately

$$E_0 = \sqrt{Z \frac{P_{out}}{A}} \text{ volts/m} , \qquad (3.66)$$

where A is the area subtended by the trapping cone at μ km from the source. Noting that $A = 2\pi \cdot 10^6 \, \mu^2 \, (1 - \cos \theta_T)$ square meters, where θ_T is the trapping angle, and substituting (3.64) and (3.65) in (3.66), we have

$$E_0 = \frac{E_i}{\mu} \sqrt{\frac{T_d A_d}{2\pi \cdot 10^6 (1 - \cos \theta_T)}} \text{ volts/m} . \qquad (3.67)$$

Multiple ducts. Multiple ducts will increase the total power entering the receiver by an amount that depends on the size and efficiency of the individual ducts and on their locations with respect to transmitter and receiver. The total power output for N ducts is given by

$$P_0 = T_{d1} P_{i1} + T_{d2} P_{i2} + \ldots \qquad (3.68)$$
$$= \sum_{n=1}^{N} T_{dn} P_{in} .$$

For the special case in which all ducts have similar characteristics and are excited equally, the total power output is

$$P_0 = N T_d P_i . \qquad (3.69)$$

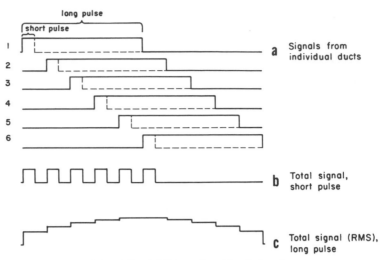

FIG. 3-41. Addition of multipath signals.

If in addition we assume that the losses between exit points and the receiver are equal, the received field intensity is

$$E_{R_N} = E_R \sqrt{N}, \tag{3.70}$$

where E_R is the received field for a single duct.

This is equivalent simply to increasing the cross-sectional area of a single duct in its effect on the rms field intensity. However, if the time delays are not approximately the same over the different ducts, multiple signals will be received. These signals will become completely separated in time if the signal duration is less than the difference in group delays between ducts. The field intensity of each such signal is then that field intensity appropriate to a single duct. If now the signal duration is increased to a value greater than the full range of time delays exhibited by the ducts, the rms field intensity will vary from the single-duct value at the leading and trailing edges to $\sqrt{N}$ times this value in the time interval when all ducts are contributing to the signal. This situation is illustrated in Fig. 3.41, in which it is assumed that ten ducts are contributing equal signals at the receiver with the same group-delay spacing between them. The rms value of the field strength at the center of the composite signal is thus $\sqrt{10}$ times the individual duct value, an increase of 10 db.

The rms envelope of a multipath signal like that illustrated in Fig. 3-39 shows a gradual rise and fall from the beginning to the end of the signal. If such a signal is immersed in noise, the apparent duration of the signal will be a function of the signal-to-noise level. Hence if the signal is strong, its apparent duration will exceed the duration of the transmitted signal. On the other hand, if the signal is barely detectable in the noise, its apparent duration will actually be *less* than that of the transmitted signal. Some evidence for the occurrence of this effect is discussed in Chap. 5.

Calculation of received field. We can now calculate the intensity of a whistler-mode signal on the ground for a given power radiated from the transmitter. The steps in the calculation may be summarized as follows:

(1) Calculate field intensity E_i of transmitted wave (Fig. 3-38).
(2) Determine effective cross section, trapping angle, and transmission efficiency of duct.
(3) Calculate field intensity at duct output from Eq. (3.67), neglecting absorption.
(4) Calculate absorption through D, E, and F regions (Figs. 3-31 and 3-34).
(5) Calculate received field intensity by reducing (3) by the absorption found in (4) and by the output waveguide *loss* obtained from Fig. 3-39.

To illustrate the calculation, consider the following example for nighttime conditions at 50° geomagnetic latitude over sea water during the summer:

Assumptions

$$f = 15.5 \text{ kc/s}, \qquad T_a = 0.5,$$
$$D_T = 1000 \text{ km}, \qquad P_T = 100 \text{ kw},$$
$$D_R = 500 \text{ km}, \qquad f_0 F_2 = 5 \text{ mc/s},$$
$$\theta_T = 25 \text{ deg}, \qquad \mu = 2.3.$$
$$A_d = 5 \times 10^7 \text{ m}^2,$$

Calculations

(1) From Fig. 3-38, we have $E_i = 5 \times 10^{-5} \times \sqrt{100} = 5 \times 10^{-4}$ volts/m.
(2) From Eq. (3.67),

$$E_0 = \frac{E_i}{\mu} \sqrt{\frac{T_d A_d}{2\pi \cdot 10^6 (1 - \cos \theta_T)}}$$

$$= 5 \times \frac{10^{-4}}{2.3} \sqrt{\frac{0.5 \times 50}{2\pi \times 0.0937}}$$

$$= 2.17 \times 10^{-4} \sqrt{42.6}$$

$$= 1.42 \times 10^{-3} \text{ volts/m} .$$

(3) From Figs. 3-31 through 3-34, we have $\alpha = 2.5 \text{ db} + 1.2 \text{ db} = 3.7 \text{ db}$ per pass, of 7.4 db total. Hence the field intensity at the boundary is

$$E_0' = \frac{E_0}{2.3} = 0.62 \times 10^{-3} \text{ volts/m} .$$

(4) From Fig. 3-39, for $D_R = 500$ km, we have relative $|E| \approx 0.04$ volts/m, giving $E_R/E_0' \approx 0.02$.
Hence $E_R = 0.02 \times 0.62 \times 10^{-3}$ volts/m $= 1.2 \times 10^{-6}$ volts/m .

3.12 Effects of Ions

In deriving the dispersion law for whistler-mode propagation, we have neglected the effect of ions. The justification for this neglect is that even the lightest ions (hydrogen) are almost 2000 times heavier than electrons. Consequently, under conditions of quasi-longitudinal propagation their contribution to the conduction current is very small, except under conditions of ion

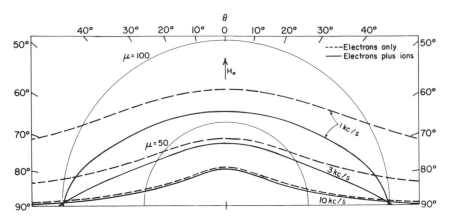

FIG. 3-42. Refractive index surfaces showing effect of ions, when electron and ion gyro-frequencies are 918 and 0.5 kc/s, respectively, and their plasma frequencies are 2143 and 50 kc/s, respectively.

resonance. However, since hydrogen ions will exhibit a gyro-frequency of approximately 500 cycles in the lower regions of the ionosphere, and since whistler propagation occasionally extends down to frequencies as low as 350 cycles, the effects of ions must be mentioned.

Work by Hines (1957), Storey (1956b), and others has shown that ions do, indeed, have an interesting effect. For waves that propagate approximately longitudinally, the principal effect of ions is to modify the dispersion relation. The result is a slight distortion of the dispersion curve at the lower frequencies. Another effect of ions is to remove the whistler-mode cutoff angle given by $\cos = \Lambda$. In the presence of ions and at sufficiently low frequencies propagation is possible in all wave-normal directions. For purely transverse propagation, the effects of ions are maximized at a frequency that is somewhat less than the geometric mean of the ion and electron gyro-frequencies. However, there is no characteristic of the dispersion relation that causes guiding in any direction other than the longitudinal. This can be seen from the curves of Fig. 3-42, replotted from Hines (1957), which shows the behavior of the refractive index of the ionosphere with electrons only, and with electrons plus ions.

An expression for the longitudinal approximation of the refractive index of the whistler mode that includes the effect of ions has been given by Storey (1956b):

$$\mu^2 \approx \frac{f_0^2}{f_H(f_i + f)}, \qquad (3.71)$$

where f_i is the ion gyro-frequency.

Some details of experiments designed to verify this predicted effect are described in Chap. 4.

From the bulk of the evidence available, it appears that although the effects of ions are present, it is not necessary to consider them in order to understand and describe most of the whistler phenomena observed on the ground.

Chapter Four

Characteristics and Occurrence of Whistlers

The term "whistler" is taken to mean any wide-band electromagnetic disturbance, generated by a mechanism external to the ambient plasma, whose spectral properties depend primarily on dispersion within the ionosphere. Most phenomena that fit this definition originate in natural lightning. Much of the early work on whistlers was based on aural observations, with the result that a colorful onomatopoetic vocabulary was developed to describe different types of whistlers. With the development of whistler spectrology and theory, there has arisen a new nomenclature that reflects the spectrographic appearance of whistlers and the mechanism of whistler propagation.

In this chapter whistlers are classified and the different types are illustrated with an Atlas of spectrograms. Characteristics of whistlers, including their amplitude, polarization, direction of arrival, dispersion, and variations in their occurrence, are discussed.

4.1 Whistler Atlas

To describe whistlers quantitatively, an Atlas of whistler spectra has been prepared from the large library of tape-recorded whistlers of the Radioscience Laboratory at Stanford University. Several examples of each principal type of whistler defined in Table 4-1 are given to indicate the range of variation within the type. The average and extremes of intensity, fading, dispersion, cutoff frequencies, and diffuseness are illustrated.

The whistler stations referred to in this chapter are listed in Table 4-2 and are shown on the modified cylindrical projection of Fig. 4-1 and the polar projection of Fig. 4-2. The conjugate points shown were calculated by Vestine (1959). The curved lines on the map of Fig. 4-1 are lines of constant geomagnetic latitude and longitude for the centered dipole approximation.

Each spectrum of the Atlas shows the frequency and time scales appropriate to the original tape recording. Where the whistler source has been identified, it is marked with a small arrow or by the origin of the time axis. When the source is not marked, the time axis begins at the left edge of the record. The universal time of the origin of the time axis is given to the nearest second. Details of each illustration are given in the legend. Each of the principal types of whistler is defined and illustrated by a sketch in Table 4-1, and a list of one or more illustrative figures in the Atlas is given for each type. Alternative names appear in parentheses.

On some illustrations certain features are labeled for clarity, according to the following notation. Capital letters refer to particular sources and their associated whistler components. Subscript numbers correspond to the number

TABLE 4-1

WHISTLER TYPES

Type and Definition	Spectral Form
I. *One-hop* (*short*) A whistler that has traversed one complete path through the ionosphere. Fig. 4-3.	A_0 A_1
II. *Two-hop* (*long*) A whistler that has traversed in sequence two complete paths through the ionosphere. The two paths may or may not be the same. Fig. 4-4*b*, trace B_2.	A_0 A_2
III. *Hybrid* A combination of a one-hop and a two-hop whistler originating in the same source. Fig. 4-5*a*.	A_0 A_1 A_2
IV. *Echo train* A. Odd order: A succession of echoes of a one-hop whistler. Delays usually in ratio 1:3:5:7, etc. Components called one-hop, three-hop, five-hop, etc. Fig. 4-7*c*, *d*.	A_0 A_2 A_4 A_6
B. Even order: A succession of echoes of a two-hop whistler. Delays usually in ratio 2:4:6:8, etc. Components called two-hop, four-hop, six-hop, etc. Fig. 4-7*a*, *b*.	A_0 A_1 A_3 A_5 A_7
V. *Multiple-component* A. Multipath: A whistler with two or more components, each of which has traversed a different path through the ionosphere. Figs. 4-11, 4-12, 4-15*d*.	A_0 $A_a A_b A_c$
B. Mixed-path: A multiple whistler of two or more hops in which combinations of the basic one-hop paths occur. Fig. 4-13.	A_0 $A_a A_b$ $A_{3a} A_{2a+b} A_{3b}$
VI. *Multiple-source* (*multiflash*) Two or more whistlers closely associated in time, but having different sources. Fig. 4-16.	$A_0 B_0$ $A_1 B_1$
VII. *Nose* A whistler whose frequency–time curve exhibits both rising and falling branches. The delay is a minimum at the nose frequency f_n. Figs. 4-17, 4-19, 4-20.	f_n
VIII. *Fractional-hop* A whistler that has completed only a fraction of a one-hop path (often observed from a probe or satellite). Fig. 4-22.	

TABLE 4-2

SYMBOLS FOR AND LOCATIONS OF VLF RECEIVING STATIONS

Abbreviation	Location	Geographic		Geomagnetic
		Lat.	Long.	Lat.
AD	Adak, Alaska, U.S.A.	52°N	177°W	47°N
AL	Adelaide, Australia	35°S	139°E	45°S
BA	Point Barrow, Alaska, U.S.A.	71°N	157°W	68°N
BC	Battle Creek, Michigan, U.S.A.	42°N	85°W	53°N
BE	Bermuda	32°N	65°W	44°N
BO	Boulder, Colorado, U.S.A.	40°N	105°W	49°N
BR	Brisbane, Australia	28°S	153°E	36°S
BY	Byrd Station, Antarctica	80°S	120°W	71°S
CO	College, Alaska, U.S.A.	65°N	148°W	65°N
DU	Dunedin, New Zealand	46°S	171°W	51°S
DR	Durban, South Africa	30°S	31°E	31°S
EI	Eights Station, Antarctica	75°S	77°W	64°S
EL	Ellsworth Station, Antarctica	78°S	41°W	67°S
ELT	U.S.N.S. *Eltanin*, mobile	—	—	—
FR	Frobisher Bay, Baffin I., Canada	63°N	67°W	75°N
GA	Gainesville, Florida, U.S.A.	30°N	82°W	41°N
GO	Godhavn, Greenland	69°N	54°W	80°N
GW	Great Whale River, Quebec, Canada	55°N	80°W	65°N
GR	Greenbank, West Virginia, U.S.A.	38°N	80°W	50°N
HO	Hobart, Tasmania	43°S	147°E	52°S
HT	Hallet Station, Antarctica	72°S	170°E	75°S
KL	Knob Lake, Quebec, Canada	55°N	67°W	66°N
KO	Kotzebue, Alaska, U.S.A.	67°N	163°W	64°N
KU	Kühlungsborn, Germany	54°N	12°E	54°N
LA	Lauder, New Zealand	45°S	170°E	50°S
LO	Logan, Utah, U.S.A.	42°N	112°W	49°N
MA	Macquarie I., South Pacific Ocean	55°S	159°E	61°S
MI	Miseno, Italy	41°N	14°E	41°N
MY	Mirny, Antarctica	67°S	93°E	77°S
MJ	Mont Joli, Quebec, Canada	49°N	68°W	60°N
MO	Moisie, Quebec, Canada	50°N	66°W	62°N
MS	Moscow, U.S.S.R.	55°N	37°E	51°N
NO	Norwich, Vermont, U.S.A.	44°N	72°W	55°N
OT	Ottawa, Ontario, Canada	45°N	76°W	57°N
PO	Poitiers, France	47°N	00°E	50°N
PL	Port Lockroy, Antarctica	65°S	64°W	53°S
QC	Quebec, Quebec, Canada	47°N	72°W	58°N
SA	Santiago, Chile	33°S	71°W	22°S
SB	Scott Base, Antarctica	78°S	167°E	79°S
SE	Seattle, Washington, U.S.A.	48°N	122°W	54°N
SP	South Pole, Antarctica	90°S		79°S
ST	Stanford, California, U.S.A.	37°N	122°W	44°N
SES	Suffield, Alberta, Canada	50°N	111°W	58°N
TO	Toyokawa, Japan	35°N	137°E	25°N
UN	Unalaska, Alaska, U.S.A.	54°N	167°W	51°N
US	Ushuaia, Argentina	55°S	68°W	43°S
VA	Vandenberg AFB, California, U.S.A.	35°N	121°W	41°N
WA	Washington, D.C., U.S.A.	39°N	77°W	50°N
WK	Wakkanai, Japan	45°N	142°E	35°N
WE	Wellington, New Zealand	41°S	175°E	45°S
WT	Wetaskiwin, Alberta, Canada	53°N	113°W	61°N

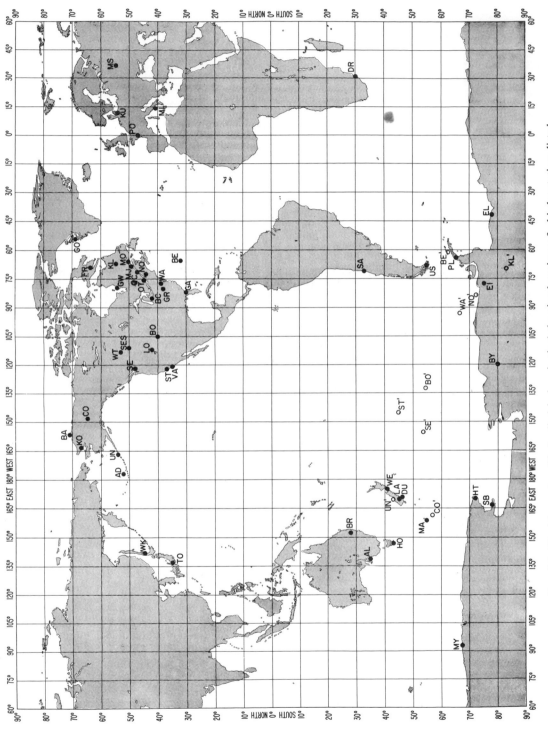

FIG. 4-1. World map (modified cylindrical projection) showing locations of whistler stations listed in Table 4-2. Station labels with primes represent the magnetic conjugate location.

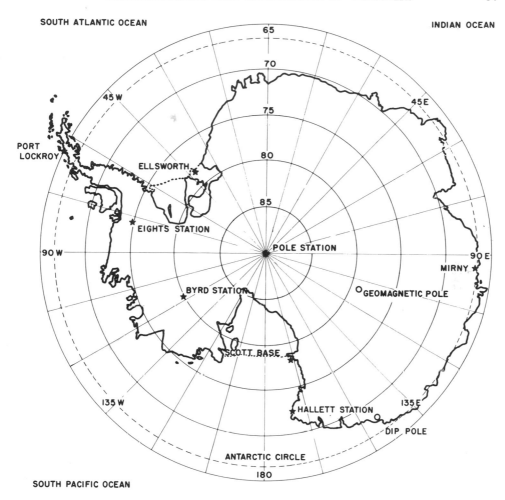

FIG. 4-2. Polar projection of Antarctica showing locations of whistler stations, south geomagnetic pole, and dip pole.

of hops over a particular path. Subscript lower-case letters identify particular paths. A mixed path is identified by a combination of subscript lower-case letters. For example, the whistler component that results from two hops over one path followed by one hop over a second path would be identified by the subscript 2a+b.

Spectrograms were prepared from the tape recordings, by using either the Kay Electric Sonograph or the Raytheon Rayspan. The Sonograph stores data for the period of interest on a magnetic drum that is scanned in time by a single bandpass filter whose center frequency sweeps slowly through the frequency range. The Rayspan employs multiple filters that are excited continously from the reproduced tape. The outputs of these filters are rapidly scanned by a

TABLE 4-3

CHARACTERISTICS OF SPECTRUM ANALYZERS

Characteristic	Sonograph	Rayspan
Number of filters	1	420
Spectrum covered	85 to 8000 cps	any 10.5 kc/s segment lying between 50 cps and 50 kc/s
Time resolution (approx.)	10 msec	10 msec
Frequency resolution (approx.)	45 cps	32 cps
Analysis time	5 min for 2.4 sec of record	equal to duration of record
Output	facsimile paper 4″ × 12½″	35-mm film or paper

commutating device to produce a record of repeated frequency scans on continuously moving film (Helliwell *et al.*, 1961). The effective range of frequencies covered by either analyzer may be changed by using a playback speed different from the recorded speed. Specifications of both analyzers are given in Table 4-3.

Pages 89–120, comprising Figs. 4-3 through 4-33, have been set up as an "Atlas" of whistler spectra.

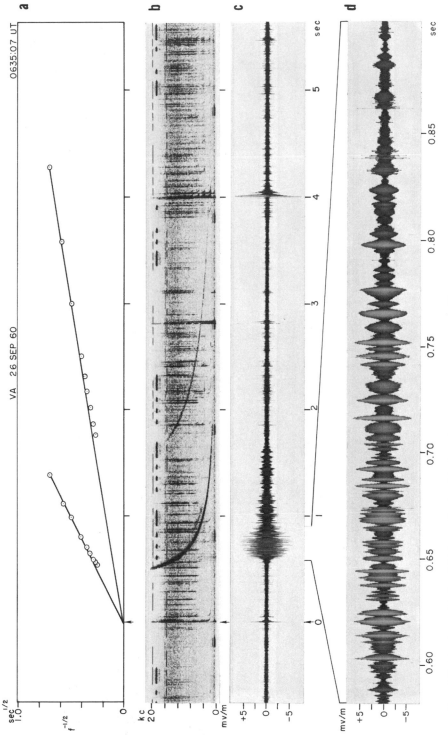

Fig. 4-3. One-hop whistler of high amplitude with three-hop echo. *a*, Curve of $1/\sqrt{f}$ versus *t*. *b*, Dynamic spectrum. *c*, Corresponding oscillogram of wide-band amplitude. *d*, A section of *c* expanded in time by a factor of 20. In parts *c* and *d*, filter passband was 600 cps to 15 kc/s.

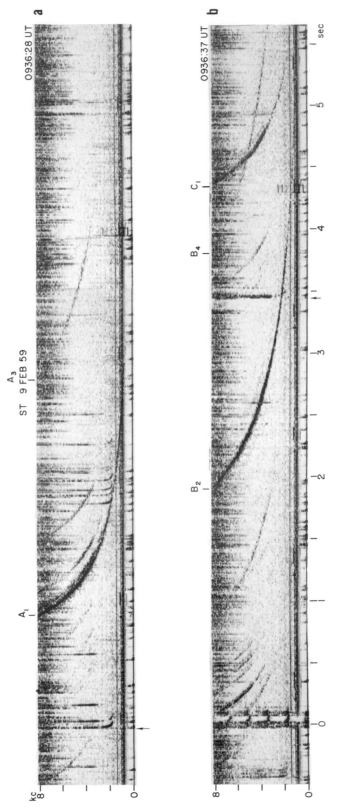

FIG. 4-4. Mixed one-hop and two-hop whistlers. *a*, One-hop whistler (A₁) with three-hop echo (A₃). *b*, Two-hop whistler (B₂) with four-hop echo (B₄) and one-hop whistler (C₁). Normalized one-hop dispersion of all whistlers at 8 kc/s, after correction for source delay, is 85.4 sec^{-1/2}.

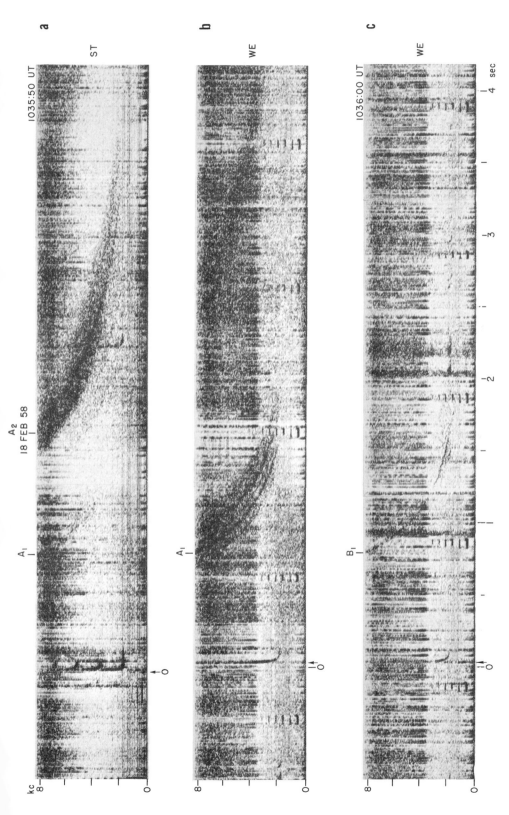

Fig. 4-5. Hybrid whistler. *a*, Strong two-hop whistler and weak one-hop whistler recorded at ST from the same source. *b, c*, Corresponding one-hop paths at WE; *c* also shows most favorable path for one-hop propagation, and it agrees with one-hop hybrid component in *a* after correction for source delay. Spectra in *b* and *c* shifted 60 ms to right with respect to the source in *a* to align the one-hop components (see text for discussion).

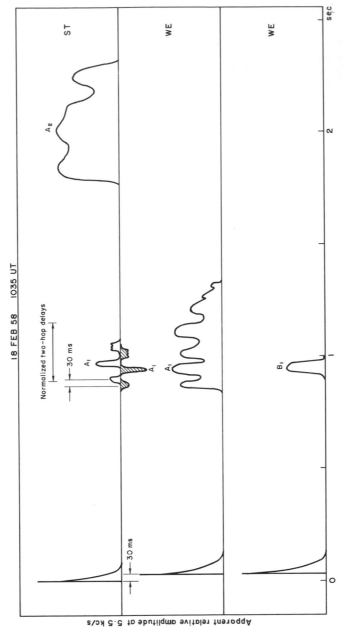

FIG. 4-6. Sketches of apparent relative amplitude versus time of hybrid and related whistlers of Fig. 4-5. Locations of hybrid traces corrected for waveguide delay are shown by shaded plots in negative direction.

92

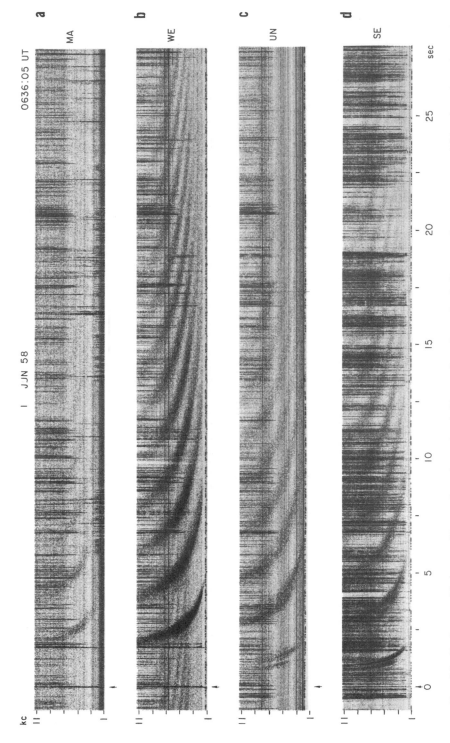

Fig. 4-7. Conjugate whistlers. *a*, Even-order echo train. *b*, Even-order echo train similar to *a*, but stronger. *c*, Odd-order echo train. *d*, Odd-order echo train similar to *c*, but stronger. One-hop dispersion of echoing trace is 88 $sec^{1/2}$ on all four records. ($K_p = 6$ during recording; $K_p = 8$ during previous three hours.) early trace believed to be of the "knee" whistler type (see Chap. 6).

93

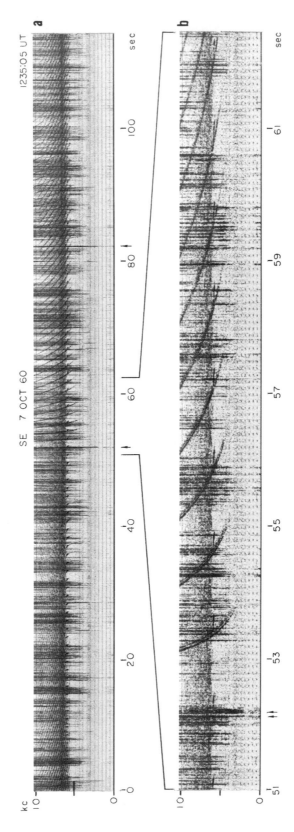

Fig. 4-8. Long-enduring whistler echo trains. *a*, Two even-order echo trains, with sources indicated, superimposed on a background of echoes from a previous whistler with associated periodic emission at a frequency of about 6 kc/s. *b*, Expanded version of *a* from 51 to 62 sec; whistler is seen to be of the multiflash type, with two main components. From the dispersion of the whistlers measured in *b* and the slope of an echo in the long train of *a*, the number of hops in the long train of *a*, the number of hops in the long train at 50 sec is approximately 210. The planetary magnetic index reached 9 during the 24 hours preceding this recording.

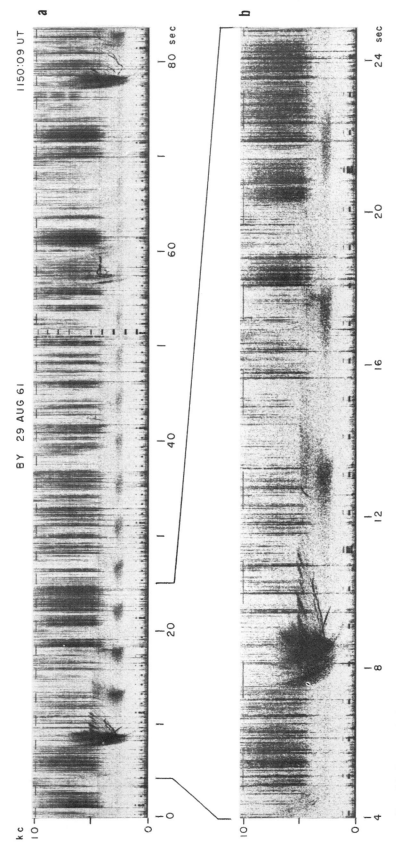

FIG. 4-9. Long-enduring whistler echo train. *a*, Echo train initiated by one-hop multipath nose whistler with numerous associated triggered emissions; echo train is limited primarily to the band from 2 kc/s to 3 kc/s; echoes resemble periodic emissions in shape, but do not exhibit the growth characteristics of emissions. *b*, Expansion of *a* showing details of whistler spectrum.

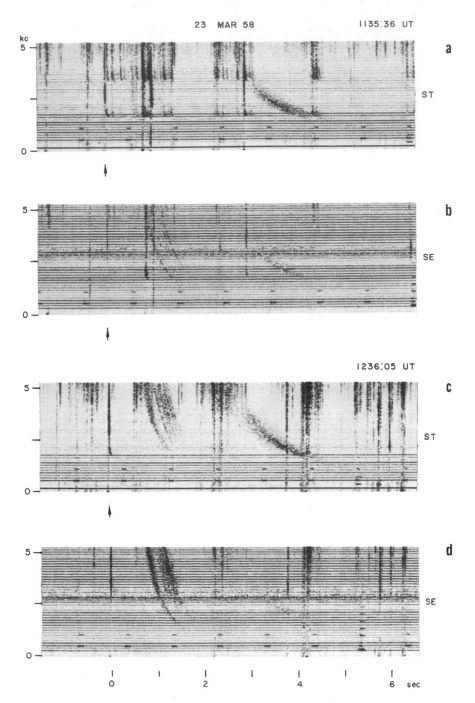

FIG. 4-10. Anomalous echoes. *a*, Three-hop echo at ST with no discernible one-hop parent. *b*, Same three-hop whistler at SE, with one-hop components well defined; dispersion of three-hop whistler is three times dispersion of first component of one-hop whistler ($D = 56.8 \ \text{sec}^{1/2}$ at 2.5 kc/s). *c*, Three-hop echo is stronger and extends to lower frequencies than one-hop parent. *d*, Same events at SE, but three-hop echo is weaker than one-hop parent, as is normally the case. Path latitudes of first-hop components are estimated to range from approximately 50° to 56°.

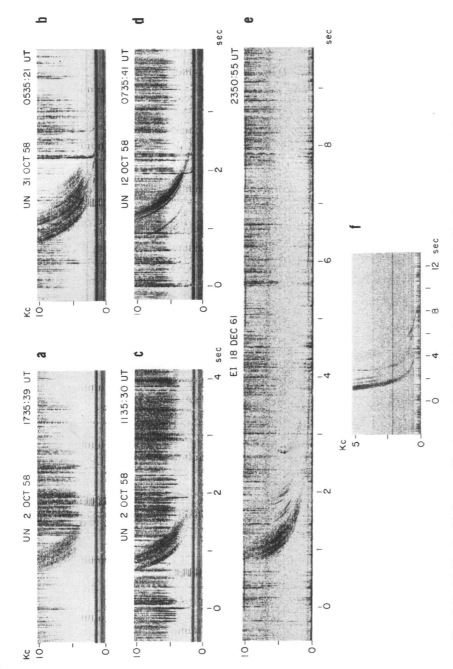

FIG. 4-11. Multipath whistlers. *a*, Closely spaced. *b*, Closely spaced components. *c*, Closely spaced, well-defined components. *c*, Closely spaced components. *d*, Group of closely spaced components preceded by an isolated component. *e*, Closely spaced components including nose components. *f*, Compression of *e* to show delayed low-frequency (500 cps to 1000 cps) component not readily seen in *e*; over-all delay ranges from the minimum of 0.8 sec at 10 kc/s to the maximum of 7.8 sec at 500 cps, an over-all range of 7 sec.

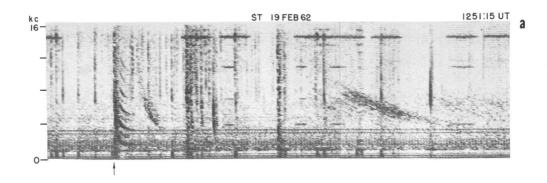

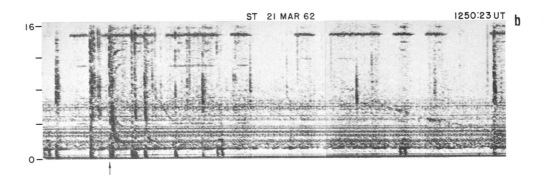

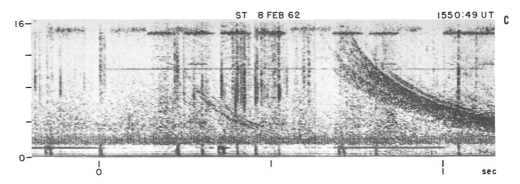

FIG. 4-12. Multipath one-hop whistlers with very short first component. The dispersions in secs^{1/2} at 5 kc/s of the main trace and the early trace are, respectively, 60 and 9 in *a*, 60 and 13 in *b*, and 75 and 27 in *c*. These measurements include a correction for an assumed source delay of 30 ms.

98

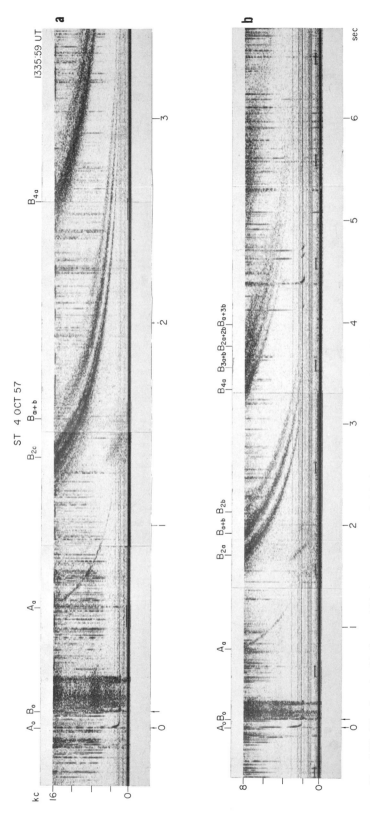

Fig. 4-13. Mixed-path whistler. *a*, 16 kc/s spectrogram. One-hop whistler, labeled A_a, excited by source A_0, travels same path as two-hop whistler, labeled B_{2a}, excited by source B_0. Two-hop whistler also shows second path, labeled B_{2b}, and combination path labeled B_{a+b}. Four-hop whistler shows further combinations labeled B_{4a}, B_{3a+b}, B_{2a+2b}, and B_{a+3b}; $D_5 = 75$ sec$^{1/2}$.

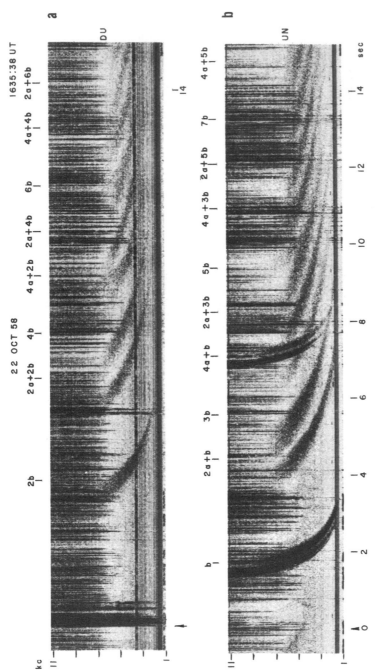

FIG. 4-14. Anomalous mixed-path whistler. a, Two-hop whistler (path 2b) followed by echoes (paths 4b and 6b); other components are interpreted as having arisen through coupling from the "b" path to a shorter "a" path; labels indicate consistent combination paths, and each is located above the corresponding trace approximately where it crosses 5 kc/s. b, One-hop whistler (path b) and echoes (paths 3b, 5b, and 7b); other components result from combinations of the same one-hop paths found in the conjugate record a. Interpretation shows combination paths include only an even number of traverses of path "a." This is interpreted to mean that coupling between path "a" and either path "b" or the earth-ionosphere waveguide can take place only at the UN end of the path. Thus the one-hop component over path "a" is not detectable because the source does not couple to path "a" at the DU end of the path. This interpretation also implies that echoes with delays $2a + 3b$ and $2a + 4b$ are each made up of combinations with the same total delay, the first consisting of bbbaa plus baabb (seen at UN) and the second of baabbb plus bbbaab (seen at DU). The traces corresponding to these paths are seen to be somewhat stronger than adjacent traces, in agreement with this interpretation. Although path "a" is not detectable on these Rayspan records, a very weak trace corresponding to the predicted position of path "a" was found on a Sonogram in the range 1.9 to 4.0 kc/s. The measured dispersion of path "b" (based on delay of trace leading edge) at 5.9 kc/s is 128 sec$^{1/2}$. Dispersion over path "a" (from overlay) at 3.0 kc/s is 85 sec$^{1/2}$.

100

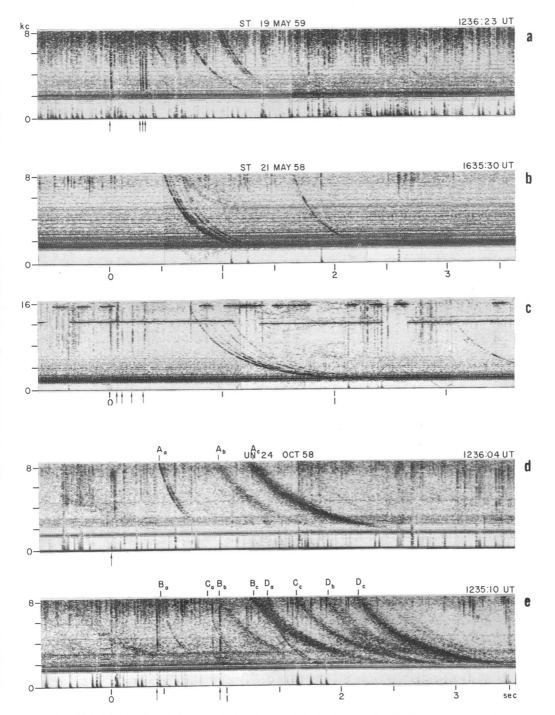

FIG. 4-15. Multiflash whistlers. *a*, *b*, One-hop multiflash single-path whistlers. *c*, Same as *b* but with double frequency range. *d*, One-hop multipath whistler with components labeled A_a, A_b, A_c. *e*, Three one-hop multipath whistlers labeled B, C, and D, each of which exhibits the same multipath components (labeled a, b, and c) shown in *d*.

101

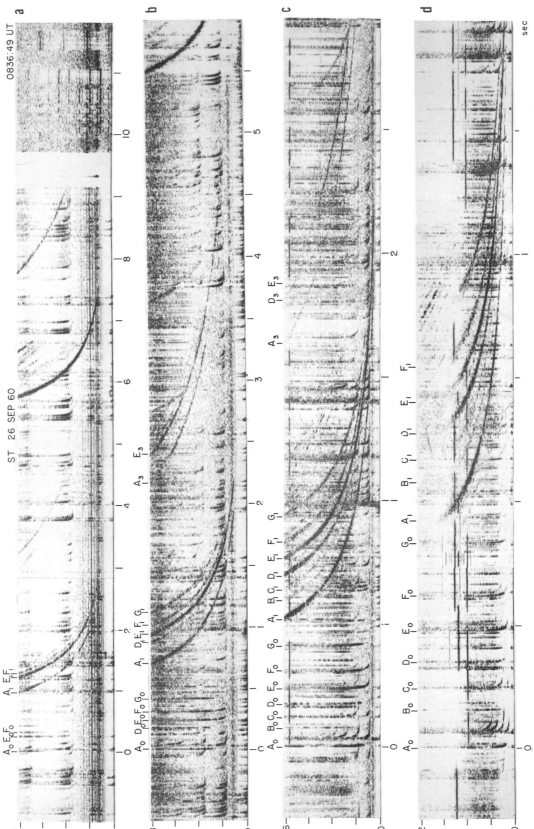

Fig. 4-16. Multiflash, single-path whistler. *a*, Zero- to 4-kc/s spectrum; three sources marked; record ends at approximately 9 sec. *b*, Zero- to 8 kc/s spectrum; five sources marked. *c*, Zero- to 16-kc/s spectrum; seven sources marked. *d*, Zero- to 32-kc/s spectrum; same sources marked as in *c*. Stronger components are followed by three-hop echoes. On the basis of the echo delays, the sources of these whistlers show an earth-ionosphere waveguide delay of approximately 20 ms, consistent with a postulated Southern Hemisphere location. Records show other one-hop whistlers that are not marked.

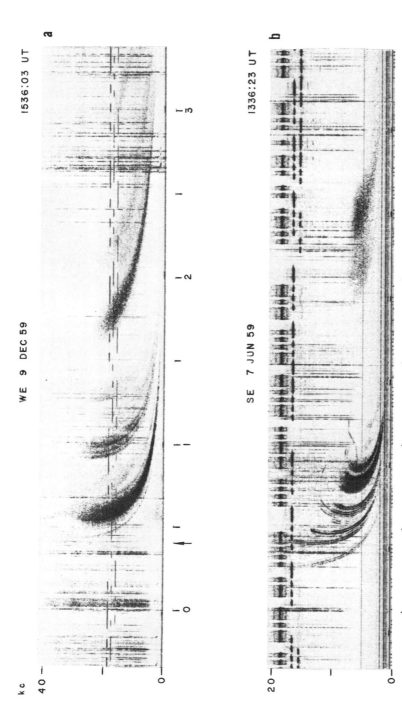

Fig. 4-17. Multipath nose whistlers, showing wide range cf nose frequency. *a*, Two one-hop whistlers at WE, spaced 0.335 sec, each with three-hop echo; nose frequencies cluster near 25 kc/s. *b*, Multiflash whistler with two sources spaced 25 ms, whose nose frequencies vary from about 6 kc/s to 32 kc/s; weak emission associated with some components above nose frequency; three-hop echo is diffuse.

103

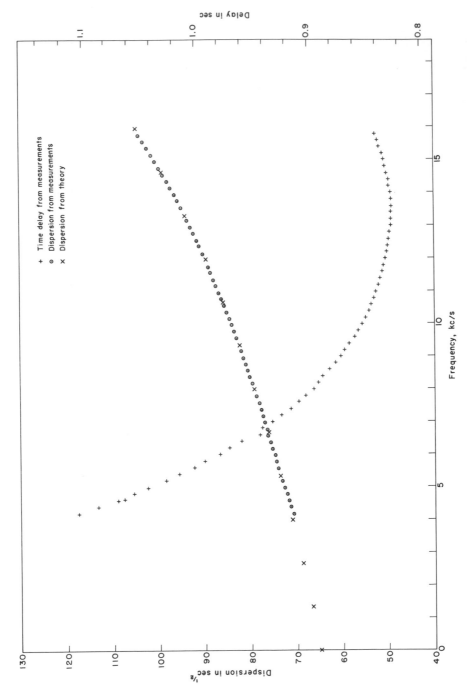

FIG. 4-18. Comparison of measured and theoretical dispersion. Crosses represent time delay measured from one of nose whistler components of Fig. 4-17b; circles represent values of dispersion calculated from delay measurements; X's represent theoretical values of dispersion calculated for a path latitude of 55° and electron density proportional to r^{-3}, where r is the geocentric earth radius. The scale factor of the model was chosen so that the curves coincide at the nose frequency (13.35 kc/s). (Data supplied by J. Angerami.)

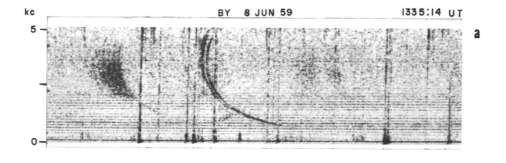

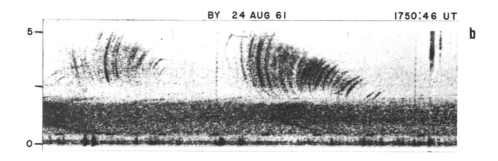

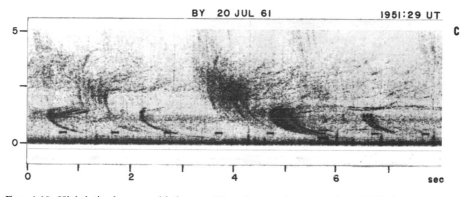

FIG. 4-19. High-latitude nose whistlers. *a*, Nose frequencies range from 3.6 kc/s to 4.4 kc/s. *b*, Multipath whistlers with decreasing upper cutoff frequency and roughly constant lower cutoff frequency (2.5 kc/s); polar chorus band below 2 kc/s. *c*, Repeated nose whistlers associated with triggered emissions; observable nose frequencies range from 1.2 kc/s to 2.5 kc/s; recording followed severe magnetic disturbance ($K_p = 8$).

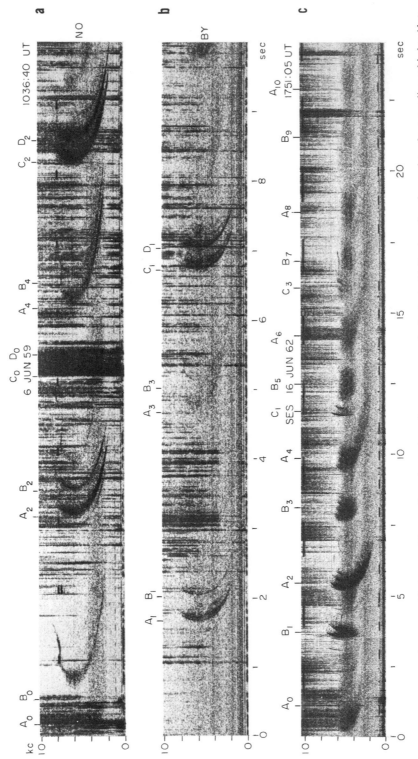

FIG. 4-20. Echoing nose whistlers. *a*, Even-order echo trains; four sources marked; first whistler is a four-hop echo of a preceding whistler (dot shown). Note emissions triggered above nose. *b*, Odd-order echoes of same whistler; $f_n = 6.0$ kc/s, $t_n = 1.52$ sec. Station NPG provides relative timing. *c*, Odd-order echo trains, marked B_1 to B_9 and C, C_1, C_3; even-order echo train, marked A_0 to A_{10}; nose frequencies range from less than 4.4 kc/s to 5.3 kc/s ($t_n = 2.0$ sec); echoes show path mixing, with average period between echo groups of 2.19 sec.

106

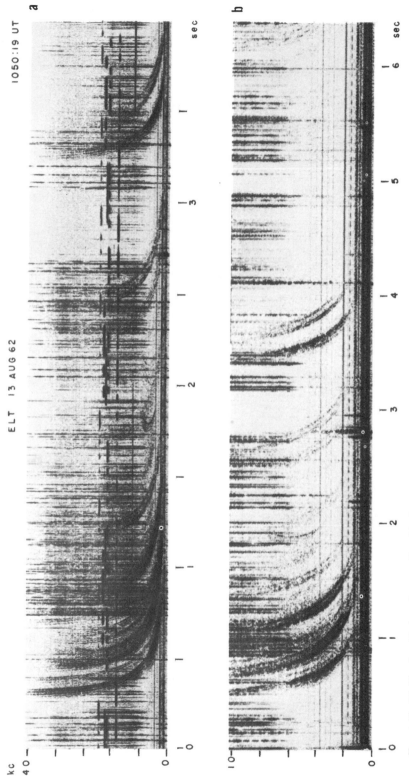

FIG. 4-21. Multipath whistler of unusually wide frequency range. *a*, Upper cutoff frequency exceeds 40 kc/s. *b*, Lower frequency portion of *a* showing lower cutoff frequency of 1.3 kc/s. Location of *Eltanin*: lat. 58° S, long. 65° W.

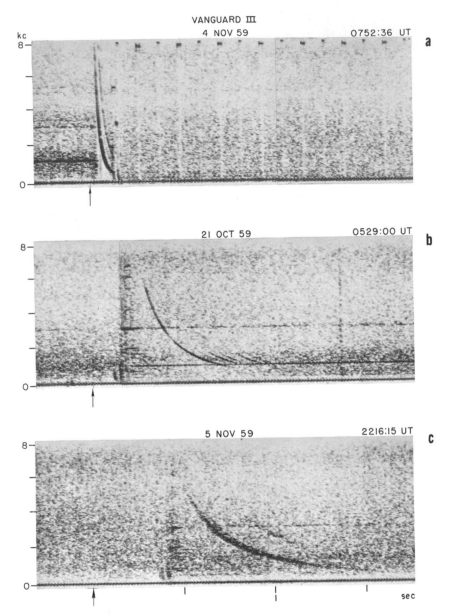

FIG. 4-22. Whistlers observed from Vanguard III. Approximate times of origins marked with arrows. *a*, Lat. 2.4° N, long. 78.2° W, altitude 512 km, $D = 2.8$ sec$^{1/2}$; low-frequency cutoff 500 cps; harmonics of whistler probably of instrumental origin. *b*, Lat. 33.5° S, long. 71.1° W, altitude 581 km, $D = 21$ sec$^{1/2}$; several multiflash whistlers of the same dispersion can be seen following the main trace in the range 1.0 kc/s to 1.6 kc/s. *c*, Lat. 29.7° S, long. 65.1° W, altitude 2888 km, $D = 35$ sec$^{1/2}$; two or three closely spaced components and a trace of the second harmonic can be identified.

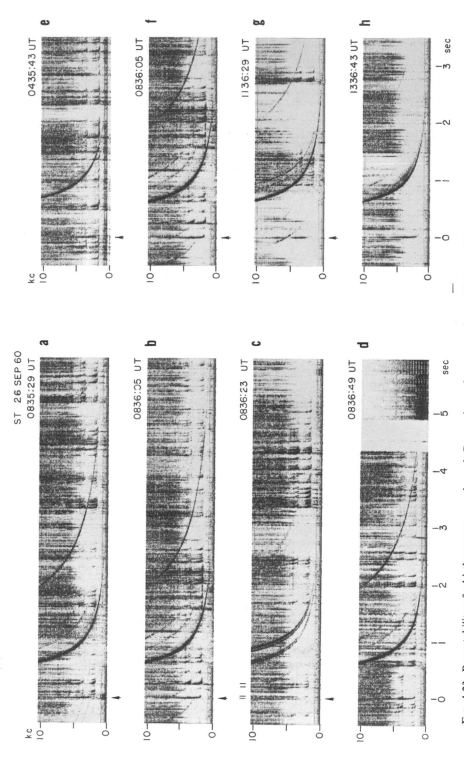

ST 26 SEP 60
0835:29 UT

0435:43 UT

0836:05 UT

0836:05 UT

0836:23 UT

1136:29 UT

0836:49 UT

1336:43 UT

FIG. 4-23. Repeatability of whistler spectra. *a, b, c, d,* Comparison of seven one-hop whistlers within a single two-minute run showing dispersions that are identical within experimental accuracy. *c,* Multiflash whistler with four components whose sources are marked by vertical lines at top of record. *e, f, g, h,* Samples from nine-hour period show dispersions that vary no more than 6 per cent from the average.

109

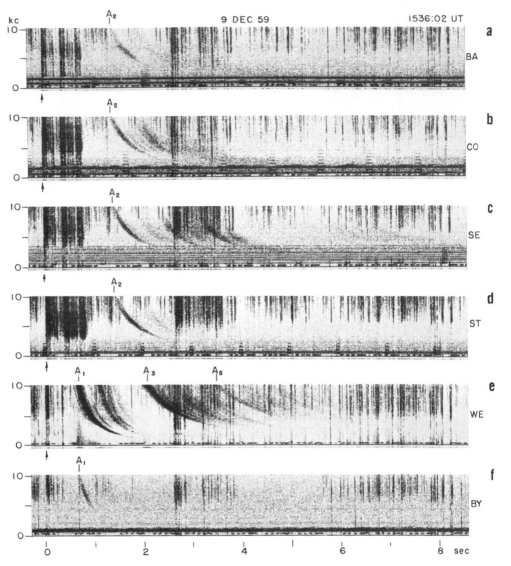

FIG. 4-24. Widespread whistler. *a, b, c, d,* Two-hop whistler with main component marked A_2. *e,* One-hop whistler, (A_1) and echoes (A_3 and A_5). *f,* One-hop whistler (A_1); $D_5 = 68 \text{ sec}^{1/2}$. Nose frequency measured from A_1 component in part *e* is about 28 kc/s. Other whistlers from different sources together with echo components are present.

110

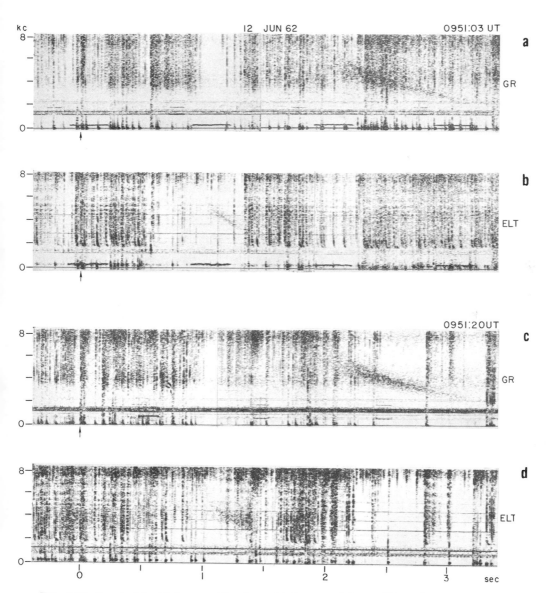

FIG. 4-25. Equatorial whistlers. *a*, Two-hop whistler recorded at middle-latitude station; D_5 (main trace) = 76 to 80 sec$^{1/2}$. *b*, One-hop component of same whistler recorded on geomagnetic equator; $D_5 = 78$ sec$^{1/2}$. *c, d*, Second example of events shown in *a* and *b*, respectively.

111

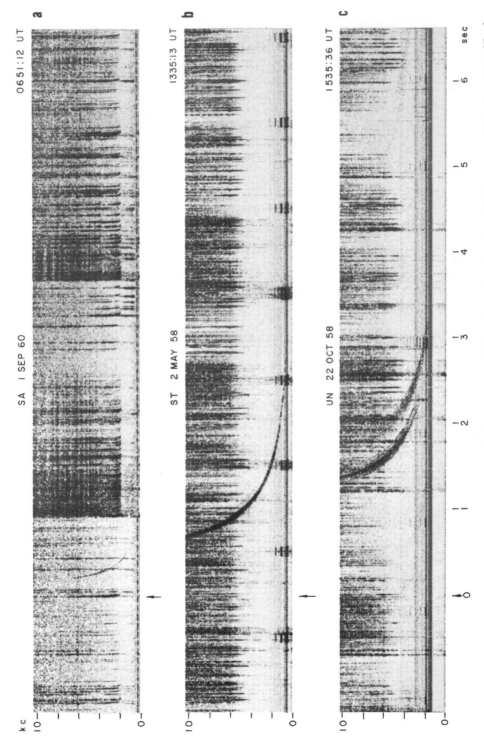

FIG. 4-26. Range of whistler dispersion. a, One-hop single-component whistler observed at Santiago (22° S geomagnetic); $D_5 = 20$ sec$^{1/2}$. b, One-hop single-component whistler observed at Stanford (44° N geomagnetic); $D = 67$ sec$^{1/2}$. c, One-hop two-component whistler observed at Unalaska (51° N geomagnetic); $D_5 = 140$ sec$^{1/2}$ (later component).

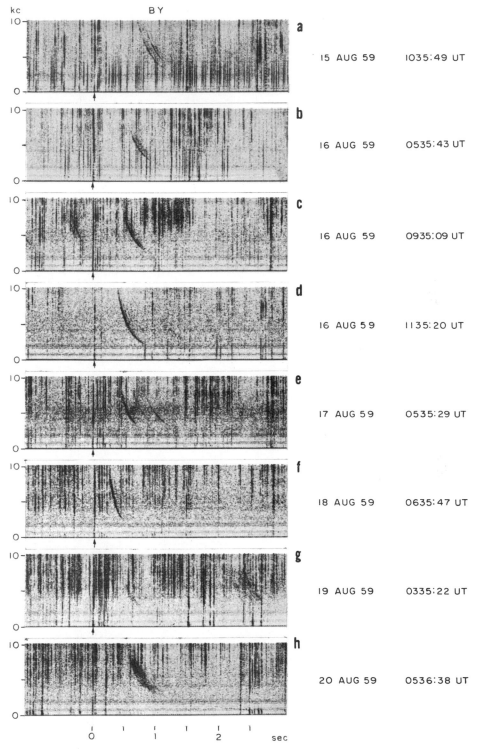

FIG. 4-27. Effect of magnetic storm on dispersion. Sequence of runs from Byrd Station illustrating a typical reduction in dispersion (based on earliest trace) during a severe magnetic storm. (Sudden commencement at 0404 UT on 16 Aug 1959.) According to nose analysis the path latitudes of these whistlers fall in the range of 45° to 50° geomagnetic. Dispersions (measured at 5 kc/s) range from a pre-storm value of approximately 65 sec$^{1/2}$ in a to a minimum value of 23 sec$^{1/2}$ in f.

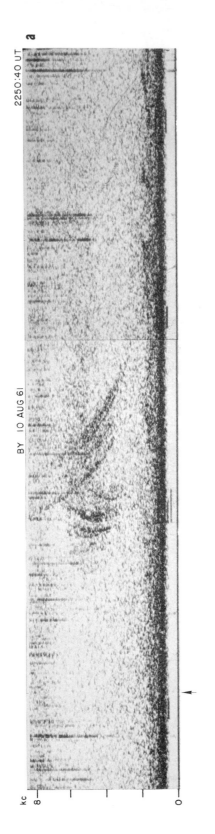
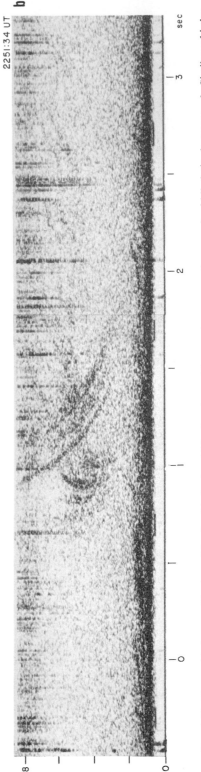

FIG. 4-28. Knee whistlers. *a*, Single multipath whistler in which the observable nose traces precede normal middle-latitude traces. *b*, Similar whistler from same run to illustrate repeatability of the phenomenon (see Chap. 6 for discussion). Faint chorus can be identified in the vicinity of 6 kc/s triggered by the nose components appearing near the beginning of each whistler.

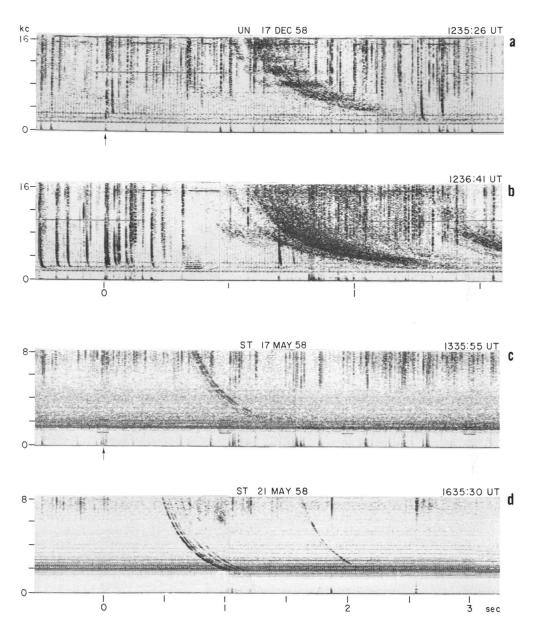

FIG. 4-29. Variation of whistler amplitude with frequency. *a*, Multipath nose whistler shows approximately the same variation in amplitude in each component. Somewhat similar variations appear in spectrum of source. *b*, Weakening of whistler traces above about 9 kc/s may be related to corresponding weakening of the source spectrum. *c*, Multiple-path components show deep minima in amplitudes at the same frequencies, i.e., at 3.4, 4.4, 4.9, and 7.0 kc/s. *d*, Six multiflash whistlers, each showing deep minima in amplitude at the same frequencies.

115

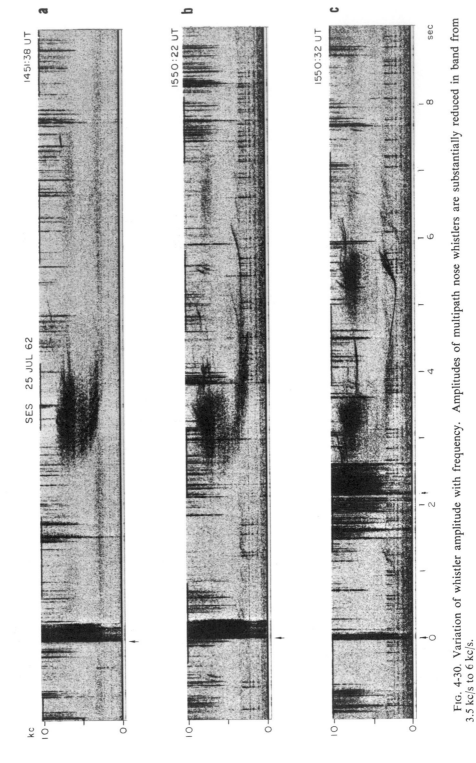

Fig. 4-30. Variation of whistler amplitude with frequency. Amplitudes of multipath nose whistlers are substantially reduced in band from 3.5 kc/s to 6 kc/s.

116

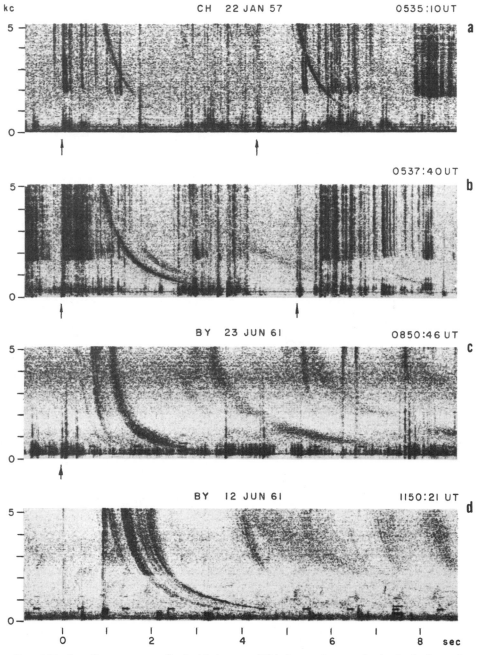

FIG. 4-31. Low-frequency cutoff of whistlers. *a*, Whistlers and atmospherics both show sharp decrease of amplitude at 1.7 kc/s, which is close to normal cutoff frequency of the earth–ionosphere waveguide. *b*, Strong whistler from same run shows no decrease in strength at 1.7 kc/s, suggesting relatively short waveguide path. *c*, Sharp drop in strength at approximately 2 kc/s. Intensity of middle-latitude components recovers at lower frequencies. Early component shows no corresponding recovery at lower frequencies. *d*, Low-frequency cutoff approximately 2.3 kc/s. Partial recovery at lower frequencies observed in very strong whistler.

117

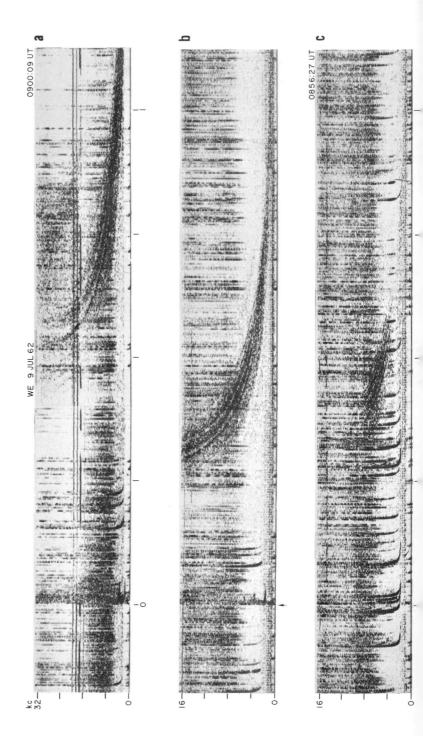

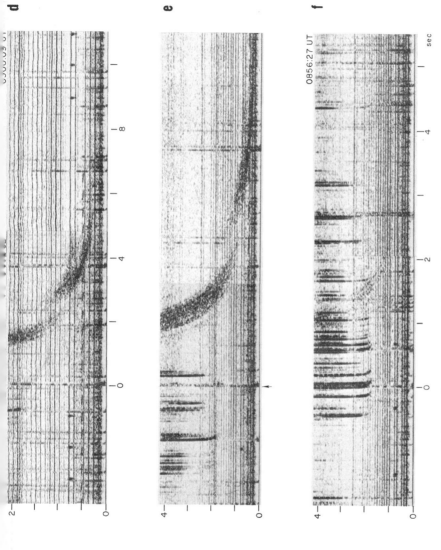

Fig. 4-32. Starfish Prime whistler. *a*, Spectrogram at 32 kc/s, showing one-hop multipath components with nose frequencies ranging from 20 kc/s to 30 kc/s. *b*, Spectrogram of same event at 16 kc/s. *c*, Natural whistler showing identical trace structure to Starfish Prime whistler. *d*, *e*, Low-frequency spectrograms showing details of delayed low-frequency components that appear mainly below 1 kc/s and cutoff at 350 cps. *f*, Natural whistler with identical multipath characteristics, except that it is much weaker and the delayed low-frequency components are absent.

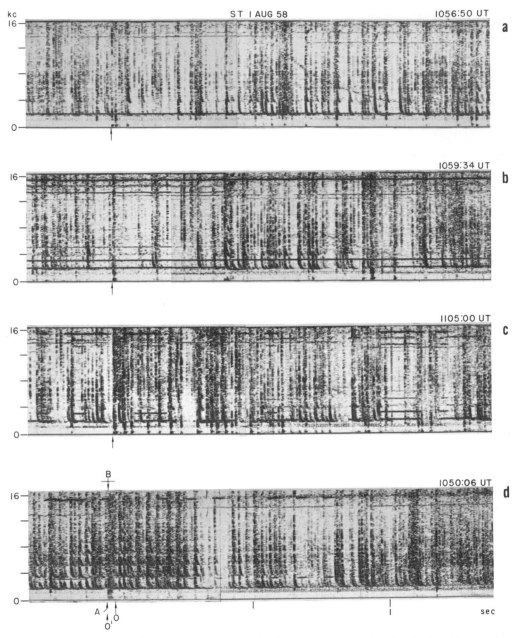

FIG. 4-33. Teak whistler. *a, b, c,* Natural whistlers observed shortly after Teak whistler. *d,* Spectrogram of Teak whistler showing structure similar to that of natural whistlers, illustrating differences in various times of origin as discussed in text.

4.2 Whistler Sources

The subject of whistler sources has received relatively little attention in the literature. There is evidence that the amplitude spectra of some whistler sources may peak at slightly lower frequencies than the average lightning discharge.

A brief study of the relation between the spectrum of the causative atmospheric and the resulting whistler was made at Boulder and at Stanford in 1956 (Helliwell et al., 1958). Recordings were made of the amplitude versus time of the atmospherics associated with whistlers, using a short, vertical monopole antenna and a broad-band amplifier. An oscilloscope with triggered sweep and a moving-film camera were used to obtain continuous records of the waveforms of successive atmospherics.

The spectrum of the source was obtained by making a Fourier transformation of the amplitude–time function. Crossed-loop direction finding at Boulder and at Stanford indicated that these particular sources were many thousand kilometers west of the Pacific Coast. With these results, suitably corrected for propagation losses, the intensity of the lightning strokes was estimated. It was found that the total electromagnetic energy in a whistler-producing stroke was approximately 200,000 coulombs, about ten times as great as that in the average lightning flash. It was also found that the spectrum of a whistler source measured at the receiver in this particular experiment peaked near 5 kc/s, whereas non-whistler sources observed about the same time showed predominant components near 10 kc/s. The combination of high total energy and a spectral peak at 5 kc/s accounts for the production of whistlers by these sources. Similar results were obtained in a study of whistlers and their sources made in Sweden (Norinder and Knudsen, 1959).

It should be emphasized that the only known characteristic of whistler sources that distinguishes them from ordinary lightning is their relatively high energy content. The conclusion that any sufficiently strong lightning stroke can produce a whistler is supported by the fixed-frequency experiments described in Chap. 5, which show that a detectable whistler-mode signal may readily be excited by a source at the ground that emits vertically polarized energy.

Further evidence that whistler sources are not very different from ordinary lightning is found in a recent study of atmospherics (Pierce, 1962). It is shown that the average amplitude spectrum for return-stroke atmospherics, at a distance of 100 km from the source, peaks at a frequency of 5 kc/s and drops 6 db at frequencies of roughly 2 kc/s and 10 kc/s. This range of frequencies is surprisingly close to that in which most whistlers are found. It is probable, therefore, that the intensity variations of most whistlers are controlled largely by the spectrum of the source.

On occasion the spectrum of the lightning source shows large variations in amplitude with frequency, which are reflected in the spectrum of the whistler itself. Each component of the whistler should show roughly the same spectral peaks in this case. An example is shown in Fig. 4-29a.

When observed aurally, most whistler sources resemble a sharp click, and this type appears as a vertical line on the spectra shown in the Atlas. At night, when the earth–ionosphere waveguide is highly conducting, the energy of an atmospheric reflects between the earth and the ionosphere with relatively little attenuation. Many different ray paths can then exist between source and receiver. The group delay increases as the number of reflections increases, giving rise to a train of pulses at the receiver. The period between pulses increases with time, approaching an asymptotic limit corresponding to the group delay for one round trip between earth and ionosphere, as we have already discussed. This train of pulses exhibits a distinctly musical sound and is often called a "tweek." The spectrum of a tweek is hook-shaped and depends on the distance from the source and the height of reflection. Examples are shown in Fig. 4-32a, b, c and Fig. 4-12a of the Atlas. Harmonics of the hook are often seen and may arise either from overloading effects in the equipment or from the excitation of higher-order modes in the waveguide. Examples of these harmonics are seen in Fig. 4-12a and Fig. 4-33d.

The source of a whistler is usually difficult to identify definitely because of the relative abundance of atmospherics. The following techniques are often useful in establishing the source time unambiguously (Carpenter, 1959).

1. Comparison of several whistlers in a run.
2. Comparison of similar whistlers in successive runs.
3. Comparison of simultaneous records from several spaced stations.
4. Study of mixed long and short whistlers.
5. Measurements of echo-train delays.
6. Use of an overlay.

Many cases require the use of more than one of these techniques. Most frequently used is 1, in which two events are compared by placing one Sonogram on top of the other, carefully aligning the trace structure by alternately raising and lowering a corner of the upper Sonogram. When two whistlers from the same run are aligned, their respective causative impulses should also be aligned within roughly 1 mm of each other (on 0- to 8-kc/s Sonogram records). High reliability is achieved with this method alone when at least three whistlers are available. A set of whistlers whose sources were identified by this method is shown in Fig. 4-23a, b, c, d. When only one or two whistlers are available, one or more of the other methods must also be used to support any findings. Figure 4-16 shows that multiflash whistlers are often very useful in establishing source time.

Methods 2 through 6 are generally useful in verifying the results obtained by method 1, and are of special importance in cases where 1 cannot be applied.

Method 2 is particularly useful when there are fewer than three whistlers available during a single run. The application of this method is illustrated by Fig. 4-23e, f, g, h.

Method 3 is of great importance, since conditions that obscure the whistler source at one station may well be absent at others. When recordings for the same period but from opposite hemispheres are available, impulses that might otherwise prove impossible to locate are often readily identified. Examples of method 3 are shown in Figs. 4-7 and 4-24.

Records from stations located in the same hemisphere often reveal that the same whistler is received at several stations. However, the structure of the whistler, the atmospherics, and the general background may exhibit considerable differences on the various Sonograms. Hopefully, an identification derived from the "best" station may be applied to the others, on whose evidence alone no source identification would have been possible.

Method 4 is illustrated in Fig. 4-4, and method 5 in Fig. 4-20. In method 4, where measurements were made at 8 kc/s between points corresponding to A_1 and A_3, the distance between A_0 and A_1, impulse to whistler, is then found to be very nearly half the distance between A_1 and A_3.

Method 6 is used as a consistency check in every impulse identification. By itself, however, it is insufficient evidence for a determination. Curves of constant $D = t\sqrt{f}$, plotted on transparent material at intervals in D of 10, are placed over the whistler and aligned with its traces over their lower range of frequencies. The vertical line representing $t = 0$ on the curves is then found to lie somewhat to the right of the true causative impulse. The error ranges most frequently between 0.0 and 0.4 seconds, although higher values are occasionally observed.

4.3   Identification of One- and Two-Hop Whistlers

The identification of one- and two-hop whistlers presents certain problems. One-hop whistlers enter the ionosphere in one hemisphere and are observed in the opposite hemisphere after once traversing the path. Two-hop whistlers, on the other hand, are one-hop whistlers that have been reflected back to the hemisphere of origin. Usually a two-hop whistler travels over the same path in both directions. However, it is occasionally possible for a whistler to travel in one direction on one path and in the opposite direction on another path. In almost all cases of practical importance a whistler can be classified as one-hop or two-hop by means of echoes. If the delay of the first echo is three times that of the whistler, then the whistler is of the one-hop type. On the other hand, if the echo delay is twice that of the first whistler, then the whistler is of the two-hop type. In the absence of echoes, positive identification is often difficult. For whistlers without detectable echoes, it is sometimes still possible to use the echo criterion by comparing the whistler in question with echo-type whistlers in the same run or in adjacent runs. If a general pattern of similarity can be established, one can establish the classification of the whistler.

A whistler can sometimes be classified as a one-hop whistler or a two-hop whistler on the basis of dispersion alone. The measured dispersion is compared with the statistical average for that station and month, with allowance for possible effects of magnetic storms (Carpenter, 1962a, 1962c). Again, examining other whistlers in the same and adjacent runs will increase the reliability of the identification considerably. It is particularly useful to attempt to obtain examples of both one- and two-hop whistlers. Usually any two-hop whistlers will show a dispersion (or dispersions) twice that of the one-hop whistlers, and the classification is then quite clear.

Although the general appearance of the source of a whistler cannot be taken to define the classification unambiguously, there are nevertheless distinct differences in the general character of the sources of long and short whistlers. At middle latitudes an extremely strong source is usually in the observer's hemisphere; the corresponding whistler is then nearly always two-hop. An exception would be the one-hop component of a hybrid, a rare occurrence. If the source is not identifiable because it is too weak, it is almost always in the opposite hemisphere. For intermediate cases, where the source is well defined but not exceptionally strong, an ambiguity arises. If the source shows a clearly defined hook like the one illustrated in Fig. 4-12a, the shape of this hook can often be used to estimate the distance of the source from the observer by the method outlined in Sec. 3.10. If this distance is within a thousand kilometers or so, one can generally conclude that the source is in the observer's hemisphere. On the other hand, hooks that suggest distances of the order of 10,000 km may be observed, in which case the source is usually in the opposite hemisphere.

Methods based on the dispersion and appearance of the source are usually quite satisfactory when a statistically large number of whistlers is being considered. However, when only a few data are available, such methods can be misleading. The use of echo trains is then necessary to ensure a correct interpretation.

4.4 Amplitude of Whistlers

The amplitude of a whistler can be determined approximately in terms of the apparent field strength received by the antenna. The relation between the apparent field intensity and the vector field intensity of the incoming wave depends on the type and orientation of the antenna used.

Methods of measurement. The apparent field strength of a whistler can be measured in a number of ways. If the whistler is very strong, it is sufficient simply to record the amplitude as a function of time. From this record the maximum, minimum, and average values can readily be obtained. A limitation of this method is the fact that a broad-band recording of amplitude versus time includes all the significant components of the whistler. For detailed study of the whistlers propagating along different paths, it is necessary to separate the spectral components. This can be accomplished by using either the Sonograph or the Rayspan to produce curves of amplitude versus frequency. Another method, less quantitative, is to match an artificially generated whistler of known amplitude aurally with the natural whistler in question (Iwai and Outsu, 1958a).

Range of intensity. Whistlers exhibit a wide range of intensities. A class 5 (on an aural intensity scale ranging from 1 to 5) whistler recorded at Vandenburg is illustrated in Fig. 4-3 of the Atlas. From the calibration of the field equipment, the peak intensity was found to be 4 mv/m. On the other hand, the weakest whistler is one that is barely detectable in the background noise. The whistler recorder attains its maximum sensitivity during a daytime period in the winter because the atmospheric noise level is then at its minimum. The effective intensity of a whistler that can be detected under these conditions is roughly 5 μv/m.

Whistler intensities were measured at Toyokawa by Iwai and Outsu (1958a), who employed a calibrated artificial whistler generator that was adjusted aurally to match the intensity of the received whistlers. They obtained minimum and maximum values of 6 and 80 μv/m, respectively. The higher absorption occurring at low latitudes accounts in part, at least, for the difference between the maximum whistler intensity recorded there and that recorded at Vandenburg.

Fading. Records of whistler amplitude versus time, such as Fig. 4-3, typically show deep fading of the total whistler that cannot readily be attributed to the source. One possible cause is the beating of discrete spectral components of the whistler. Since in general the spectral components of whistlers have different variations of frequency with time, the sum of the components will show wide fluctuations in amplitude. Another possible cause of fading is a resonance effect in the space between earth and ionosphere (Poeverlein, 1961). The field intensity at the ground varies with frequency, reaching maxima when the effective height is a multiple of a half wavelength. In this explanation it is necessary to assume that the ionosphere and the ground have fairly high reflection coefficients, so that many multiple reflections will be produced. When the receiver is located a considerable distance from the exit point of the duct, the fading will be less regular. In this case the addition and cancellation of different rays are more complicated, and the magnitudes and locations of the minima are irregular. Since fading of whistlers has several possible causes, the amplitude variations cannot be readily interpreted without complete information on the characteristics of the propagation medium. Additional examples of fading are seen in Figs. 4-29 and 4-30.

Cutoff frequencies. Whistler cutoff frequencies vary over a wide range of values. The low-frequency cutoff ranges from a minimum of about 300 cps to as high as 10 kc/s. The upper frequency cutoff may be as low as 2 kc/s and as high as 40 kc/s, or as high as the upper frequency cutoff of the equipment. Most whistlers lie between 2 kc/s and 10 kc/s as noted earlier. Spectra showing variations of cutoff frequencies are shown in Figs. 4-17, 4-19, and 4-31.

Several factors may affect the observed cutoff frequencies of whistlers. Both the upper and lower cutoffs are affected by the source spectrum, as explained earlier, and by the properties of the earth–ionosphere waveguide. In addition the lower cutoff may be affected by ion resonances,* and the upper cutoff by collisional absorption in the ionosphere, by duct properties, and by thermal (Landau) damping near the top of the path.

An important cause of whistler attenuation at low frequencies is the earth–ionosphere waveguide, through which both the whistler and source energy usually travel. In Sec. 3.10 it was shown that a cutoff can be expected in the vicinity of 1600 cps during nighttime. The low-frequency cutoff of whistlers commonly falls near this value. Although the source spectrum has some effect, the sharpness of this cutoff is caused mainly by the attenuation characteristics of the earth–ionosphere waveguide.

---

* J. Smith, personal communication.

Occasionally whistler traces pass through the waveguide cutoff frequency with no measurable decrease in intensity. Especially interesting is the occurrence of whistlers showing a marked cutoff at 1600 cps together with others in the same run that show a much lower cutoff. Two whistlers illustrating this effect are shown in Fig. 4-31a, b of the Atlas. The dispersions of these two whistlers are the same, indicating that both followed the same propagation path through the magnetosphere.

The difference in the low-frequency cutoffs of these two whistlers can be explained if we note that the cutoff effect can be produced not only between the exit point of the duct and the receiver but also between the source and the input end of the duct. We then assume that the duct in this case was so close to the receiver that the cutoff effect at the receiving end was unimportant. Then for a source close to the input end of the duct, the whistler will show no waveguide cutoff. On the other hand, for a source far (1000 km or more) from the input end of the duct, the whistler will show a cutoff associated with the waveguide path between source and duct input. The relative rarity of whistlers that pass through the waveguide cutoff frequency without appreciable attenuation can be explained by the low probability that the situation described above, in which both receiver and whistler source must be close to a duct, will occur.

Attenuation owing to collisional absorption is considerably higher during daytime than during nighttime, as Fig. 3-31 shows. This kind of attenuation, measured in decibels, increases a little more slowly than the square root of frequency. When the attenuation is low, the frequency variation is not so important as when it is high. Hence at night the change in collisional attenuation between 5 kc/s and 10 kc/s is only about 2 db (see Fig. 3-31) for one-hop whistlers and a maximum of 4 db for two-hop whistlers. Both figures are less than the corresponding 6-db decrease in source intensity that was mentioned above. Since the upper cutoff frequency of nighttime whistlers averages about 10 kc/s it would appear that collisional attenuation during normal nighttime is not a dominant factor.

During normal daytime the change in collisional attenuation between 5 kc/s and 10 kc/s is estimated from Fig. 3-31 to be about 17 db for one-hop whistlers and 34 db for two-hop whistlers that penetrate the D region at both ends of the path. These changes exceed that associated with the source spectrum, and therefore collisional attenuation is an important factor during daytime.

The upper cutoff frequency of a whistler may be limited as a result of the failure of the duct to trap the energy above a certain frequency (Smith, 1961a). Reference to the ray-path region diagram of Fig. 3-20 shows that trapping in columns of enhanced ionization (i.e., crests) is limited to normalized frequencies (f/f_H) less than $\frac{1}{2} \cos \theta_0$. Hence the highest frequency at which trapping in crests can occur is one-half the local gyro-frequency. Most whistlers are thought to be trapped in crests of ionization because at the relatively low altitude of the duct entrance, the minimum enhancement factor required for trapping in a trough is large compared with that required for trapping in a crest. As the whistler travels up the field line, the normalized frequency increases because the local gyro-frequency is decreasing. When the normalized frequency reaches

$\frac{1}{2} \cos \theta_0$, trapping in a crest is no longer possible and the energy can escape from the duct. As this critical value is approached, the enhancement factor required for trapping is reduced (see Fig. 3-20), causing a corresponding reduction in the deviations of the ray from the direction of the earth's field. It is therefore possible for the wave packets to remain within the duct over an appreciable length of path in the region where the wave frequency exceeds the critical value $(f_H/2) \cos \theta_0$. If the wave packets do not escape from the duct until the frequency is again below the critical value, the whistler will remain trapped.

If the trapping mechanism described above is applicable to whistlers, then a sharp cutoff in the vicinity of one-half the minimum gyro-frequency can be expected. The observed upper cutoff frequency of most whistlers is much less than one-half the minimum gyro-frequency, and is not very sharply defined. It is therefore probably ascribable either to source limitations or to collisional absorption in the ionosphere. However, the upper cutoff of nose whistlers (see Figs. 4-17 and 4-19b) is usually very abrupt and seldom exceeds 0.6 of the minimum gyro-frequency. It is possible, therefore, that this cutoff is in fact explained by the failure of trapping to take place, as outlined above.

Another source of attenuation of whistlers is thermal damping associated with cyclotron resonance between the whistler wave and electrons (Liemohn and Scarf, 1962a, b). In this mechanism, which is basically similar to Landau damping (Stix, 1962), the electrons spiral along field lines in a direction opposite to the wave velocity, encountering a doppler-shifted wave frequency approximately equal to their own natural gyro-frequency. For an equilibrium velocity distribution, energy is transferred from the wave to the particles. Assuming a Maxwellian form for the distribution of velocities in the ambient plasma, Liemohn and Scarf (1962a) found that the observed nose whistler cutoff frequencies required a plasma temperature of roughly 2×10^5 °K at a geocentric distance of 4 earth radii. Their analysis also showed that the thermal loss should increase very rapidly with frequency, in accordance with observations.

Similar damping effects could occur in a non-equilibrium velocity distribution in which a relatively small fraction of the electron population has the velocity distribution required to explain the observed damping, while the bulk of the plasma remains at a much lower temperature.

A comparison of the duct and the cyclotron damping explanations of the upper cutoff suggests that a definitive test might be made with a whistler receiver carried by a probe or a satellite into the region of predicted cutoff. If thermal damping is the important mechanism, then both ducted and non-ducted whistlers should exhibit roughly the same cutoff characteristics. If the duct controls the cutoff, then the receiver should observe whistlers with normalized upper cutoff frequencies well above those observed on the ground.

The low-frequency cutoff is occasionally considerably higher than 1600 cps. With some whistlers, particularly nose whistlers, the low-frequency cutoff may reach 10 kc/s. It is difficult to attribute this effect to a lack of low-frequency energy in the source, since other multipath components often show much lower values of the low-frequency cutoff. This suggests, therefore, that some property of propagation in the magnetosphere controls the low-frequency cutoff. One possibility is that the effective diameter of the duct in wavelengths becomes too small for trapping to occur. Another possibility is that the shrinking of the transmission cone (see Sec. 3.7) as frequency is reduced causes the waves to be totally reflected below a certain frequency. This implies, of course, different sets of boundary conditions at the two ends of the path. For example, horizontal gradients of ionization of the appropriate magnitude in the F region at the two ends of the path could produce trapping of the low frequencies at the input end but prevent exiting of the same frequencies at the output end.

Echo-train decrements. The net loss in the whistler mode can be estimated from the ratio of the amplitudes of successive whistler echoes. There seem to be two general classes of whistler echo trains. For those observed on magnetically quiet days, the echo intensity decreases relatively quickly with order of arrival. The first echo of the whistler is typically 10 db or more lower in field strength than the initial whistler. The other class of whistler is usually observed during magnetically disturbed periods. It is characterized by an extremely low decrement in the decay of whistler echoes. In fact, on some occasions the intensity of the echoes appears to increase with order. Because of the low decrement, the echo train continues for a considerable time. Whistler echo trains with a dozen or more echoes are common on magnetically disturbed days. In one case, illustrated in Fig. 4-8 of the Atlas, it was deduced that there were at least 210 echoes in the echo train. In this case the echo decrement was virtually zero.

Since there must be finite losses at the ends of the path in the absorbing regions, plus some leakage from the whistler duct, energy must have been added to the whistler with 210 echoes. It has been postulated, therefore, that under conditions of magnetic disturbance, long whistler echo trains are produced as a result of selective traveling-wave amplification (see Chap. 7).

For the normal quiet-day whistler, the two-hop decrement of 10 db can be used to estimate the total loss over the whistler path. If we assume that reflection of the whistler takes place at the lower boundary of the ionosphere, then each passage through the ionosphere must be accompanied by a certain amount of collisional absorption loss. From Figs. 3-31 and 3-34 it is estimated that the ionosphere absorption loss per hop for nighttime (assuming $f_0 F2 = 3$ mc/s) at 5 kc/s is approximately 5 db. This leaves 0 db to account for leakage in the duct and for reflection coupling loss, which suggests either that there is lossless ducting and lossless reflection or that reflection of the whistler does not in fact take place at the bottom of the ionosphere. Another possibility is that some traveling-wave amplification occurs on streams of charged particles that are present even on quiet days.

On rare occasions a whistler may be relatively weak or entirely absent over a range of frequencies in which an echo of the whistler is relatively strong. Examples are shown in Fig. 4-10. In this figure the relationship of whistler and echo is normal at Seattle, but the same event observed at Stanford is characterized by absence (Fig. 4-10a) or by reduction in strength (Fig. 4-10c) of the whistler in the frequency range occupied by the third-hop echo. An explanation of this effect has not been found, but may be associated with unfavorable wave-normal angles in the one-hop whistler.

Echoes of nose whistlers are relatively rare, but the few cases that have been studied indicate that the integral group-delay relationship between whistler and echo is preserved at and above the nose. An example of an echoing nose whistler is shown in Fig. 4-20 of the Atlas.

Diffuseness. Whistler traces on spectrograms exhibit varying widths along the time axis. The so-called "pure" whistlers can be extremely well defined, as Fig. 4-3 shows. Swishy whistlers, on the other hand, may spread over a considerable time, often as great as one-half second, as illustrated by Fig. 4-11. The spread in time of a whistler trace has been described by the term "diffuseness" (Crouchley and Finn, 1961). Diffuseness is measured at a given frequency by the duration of a whistler relative to its average delay. Storey (1953) commented that the spread of a whistler seemed to increase with dispersion. Crouchley and Finn (1961) showed that diffuseness increases rapidly with latitude (and therefore also with dispersion). Their curve of diffuseness shows a marked rise beginning at 35° latitude. The rate of whistler occurrence also rises rapidly in the same general region, as Fig. 4-39 indicates.

From spectral examination of whistlers it is clear that in most cases diffuse whistlers consist of a multiplicity of well-defined, closely spaced, single traces. We may conclude, therefore, that diffuse, or swishy, whistlers result simply from the presence of a large number of discrete whistler ducts whose spacing in group delay is less than the width in time of the individual whistler components.

4.5 *Polarization and Direction of Arrival*

Methods of measurement. Polarization and direction of arrival can be calculated from four independent measurements of an incoming plane wave. The required relationships have been derived and presented by Crary (1961). One practical method of measurement is to record the relative phases and amplitudes of signals received by two mutually perpendicular vertical loops and a vertical monopole antenna. These three channels provide two relative phases and two relative amplitudes from which the direction and polarization of phase may be obtained. The application of this method to whistlers is described by Crary (1961).

Another technique is based on independent measurements of polarization and direction of arrival. Direction of arrival can be obtained by a phase-comparison method in which three identical antennas are located at the corners of a triangle having legs at least $\lambda/6$ long (Crombie, 1955). From two of the three possible pairs, the relative phases are obtained, each phase serving to define a cone of revolution whose axis is oriented along the line connecting the two antennas. The upper intersection of these two cones defines the direction of arrival for antennas located at the surface of the ground. If the direction of arrival is known, the polarization can be deduced from measurements of the relative phase and amplitude obtained from one pair of crossed loops.

This technique of direction-finding has been successfully employed by

Delloue (1957, 1960a, 1960b), who made use of three receiving stations equipped with loop antennas. Signals from two of the stations were transmitted to the central station, roughly 20 km distant, by microwave radio links. With the direction of arrival thus determined, polarization information was obtained from crossed loops at the central station. Using this equipment, Delloue found that in general the wave normals of most whistler components in a 500-cps passband centered about 5.5 kc/s lay close to the direction of the magnetic field and to the vertical. The wave normals were rarely found to lie close to the horizontal.

Apparent polarization. In an attempt to test the basic theory of whistlers, which predicts circular polarization of the waves in the ionosphere, the apparent polarization of whistlers was measured at Stanford by the crossed-loop method (Crary, 1961). It was hoped that whistlers arriving from nearly overhead would produce an interpretable polarization pattern. The results showed that the polarization is usually not simple. Cases of elliptical polarization with either sense, as well as cases of linear polarization, were found.

Subsequent analysis of the effect of the earth–ionosphere waveguide on propagation between the duct exit point and the receiver showed that the polarization of the received signal is a function of the waveguide parameters. It was found, in fact, that under certain conditions the signal could be introduced into the waveguide with one sense of polarization and observed at the receiver with the opposite sense. Conversion of the polarization to virtually any value is possible as a result of the anisotropic properties of the upper boundary of the earth–ionosphere waveguide. Thus it is possible to interpret qualitatively the complicated polarization behavior of incoming whistlers.

These results differ from those reported by Delloue (1960a, 1960b), which could be explained in terms of the simple theory. Moreover, Delloue's most recent results indicate that polarization consistently varies from circular for nearly vertical wave normals to linear for horizontal wave normals.* The differences in Crary's and Delloue's observations may result simply from a difference in geomagnetic latitude. Crary's measurements were made at a geomagnetic latitude of 44° (Stanford), while Delloue's were made at 51° (Paris), which lies within the zone of maximum whistler activity. Therefore it might be expected that strong whistlers exiting close to the station would be observed rather frequently at Paris, but infrequently at Stanford. A sample of strong whistlers at Stanford should include a relatively higher percentage arriving from greater distances.

From a measurement of the azimuth of arrival of a whistler at each of two spaced stations, the exit point can be located. With this information, the interpretation of nose whistlers can be verified and details of refraction of the whistler paths in the F2 region studied. In making azimuth measurements on whistlers, the first problem is to separate multiple-path components. A device for doing this was developed by Watts (1959). It consists of a crossed-loop goniometer, which is rotated at roughly ten revolutions per second. The

---

* Personal communication.

signals at the output of the goniometer are tape recorded and later subjected to spectrum analysis. Each whistler trace shows a pattern of maxima and minima resulting from the rotation of the goniometer. It is thus possible to obtain independent measures of the direction of arrival of each of the components.

Crary (1961) developed an improved version of the Watts goniometer that incorporated a vertical antenna to provide sense information. With it, Crary measured the direction of arrival of a number of whistlers at Stanford. From a sample of ten whistler components obtained over a six-month period, fixes were obtained, ranging in geomagnetic latitude from 29.0 deg to 54.0 deg. The latitude of each fix was compared with the effective path latitude determined independently from the nose frequency (see Chap. 6). The difference between the latitude of the direction-finding fix and the effective path latitude varied from -17.8 deg to $+8.0$ deg, and averaged -3.7 deg.

Analysis of similar records taken at Seattle provided an independent set of directions from which fixes were obtained. The apparent points of origin of two such whistler components, recorded on 3 July 1960 at 1436:29UT, were found to be in the Pacific Ocean at geomagnetic latitudes of 37° and 46°. From independent measurements of the dispersion of these whistler components, the nose frequencies were estimated. From these estimates, the effective geomagnetic latitudes of the corresponding whistler paths were found to be 47° and 54°, respectively. Although the discrepancy is about 10°, the latitude spacing measured by the two methods is about the same. Crary pointed out that although the comparison supported existing theories of whistlers, one could not place much confidence in the results. His reasoning was based on an analysis of the errors in the direction of arrival as measured by the crossed-loop system. It was found that errors in azimuth as large as ± 90 deg could occur, owing mainly to the cross-polarized component in the received wave. Averaging over a wide range of frequencies minimized these errors, but in most whistlers there was an insufficient number of minima to provide a reliable average. The conclusion of these studies was that although the measurements are consistent with the current theory of whistlers, they are not sufficiently accurate to provide much useful information.

4.6 Dispersion

Methods of measurement. As we have stated, dispersion is defined by the expression $D = t\sqrt{f}$. To obtain the dispersion it is necessary to measure the time delay t from the source to the whistler at a given frequency f. The practice at Stanford has been to make the delay measurement at 5 kc/s, where whistlers tend to reach peak amplitude. Unless the frequency of measurement is much lower than the minimum gyro-frequency, the dispersion as measured by this method will be considerably larger than that obtained by measuring at relatively low frequencies.

In the absence of the source time, an estimate of the dispersion can be obtained from the slope of the whistler trace. Assuming that D is constant at the value $t\sqrt{f}$, one obtains by differentiation the relation $D = -2f^{3/2}\, dt/df$. This gives the dispersion in terms of the slope, and can be used when it is impossible to identify the time of origin. Since it is based on the assumption that D is a constant, it will give a different answer from the group-delay method whenever the frequency of measurement is not small compared with the nose frequency. As the frequency is raised, the apparent dispersion determined from the slope decreases, reaching zero at the nose frequency. At zero frequency both the delay method and the slope method yield the same result. As frequency is raised, the "delay" dispersion increases, while the "slope" dispersion decreases. The variation of dispersion with frequency is illustrated by the nose whistler analysis shown in Fig. 4-18.

Range of dispersion. The dispersion of whistlers observed at a particular station generally shows a wide range of values. At Stanford, for example, the lowest value of dispersion ever observed was 12 $sec^{1/2}$. The highest one-hop dispersion was 200 $sec^{1/2}$. Since two-hop whistlers show twice the dispersion of one-hop whistlers, the over-all range in dispersion is 12 $sec^{1/2}$ to 400 $sec^{1/2}$. As one might expect, the dispersion increases with latitude. An illustration of this variation is shown in Fig. 4-26. At high latitudes, however, the dispersion, as defined above, is of less significance because the observable frequencies are usually near the nose frequency. In such cases the nose time delay is a more significant quantity. During magnetic storms the dispersion may drop appreciably, as illustrated in Fig. 4-27.

Dispersion measurements of whistlers received at high latitudes (Ungstrup, 1959; Allcock, 1960b) support the suggestion first advanced by Martin (1958) that high-latitude stations receive whistlers that have propagated poleward after emerging from the ionosphere at lower latitudes. Whistlers at Byrd Station, for example, have nose frequencies corresponding to paths terminating near 50° geomagnetic latitude.

Multipath whistlers. Many whistlers show multiple components that are often well defined. Those that originate in a single source are called multipath whistlers. Of these there are three principal types. In the first type, which we shall call ordinary multipath, the paths are all of either the one-hop or the two-hop type, differing only in length. The ordinary multipath whistler is illustrated in Fig. 4-15d. The second type is a mixed-path whistler in which the total path is a succession of varied one-hop paths (Morgan et al., 1959). It is illustrated in Figs. 4-13 and 4-14. The third type is one in which a one-hop whistler is coincident with a two-hop whistler from the same source. This is called a hybrid and is illustrated in Fig. 4-5. Occasionally multipath whistlers are repeated with sufficiently small spacing in time to cause confusion. These are called multiflash multipath whistlers, and are illustrated in Fig. 4-15e.

The range of dispersion in multipath whistlers, exclusive of the mixed-path and hybrid types, can be quite wide. The ratio of the delay of the first trace to that of the last trace is often as low as one-third. The spacing of the corresponding path latitudes, deduced from nose frequencies, may vary from virtually 0° during some magnetic storms to as high as 15°. Rarely, a typical middle-latitude component is associated with a very short component, possibly arising from a short path near the equator. An example is shown in Fig. 4-12 of the Atlas. The range of nose frequencies at middle latitudes is illustrated in Fig. 4-17 of the Atlas.

In one unusual type of multipath whistler, called the "Knee" whistler, the spectrographic traces cross one another. An example is shown in Fig. 4-28 of the Atlas. Such crossed-trace whistlers are thought to occur when the electron density varies widely between different ducts. Hence if a high-latitude duct shows a depression in density, possibly associated with a magnetic storm, the delay of the corresponding whistler will be much less than normal, and a trace that shows a nose may actually cross a non-nose trace corresponding to a lower-latitude path (see Sec. 6.8).

The hybrid whistler was predicted on the basis of the discrete-path concept (Helliwell, 1959). It was postulated that if the whistlers traveled only along well-defined ducts in the ionosphere, it should be possible to find a one-hop and a two-hop whistler that propagated along the same duct and that originated in the same source. An extensive search of records from the Whistlers-West network did in fact produce a number of examples that fulfill these conditions. One of these is shown in Fig. 4-5a. To test the idea quantitatively, measurements were made of the delay from source to whistler component and were then corrected to account for the propagation time of the causative atmospheric in the earth–ionosphere waveguide. Graphs of these measurements for the whistlers of Fig. 4-5 are shown in Fig. 4-6. With the proper correction for waveguide delay, the one-hop and normalized two-hop delays agree within experimental error. Although the number of such cases is small, their close agreement with the prediction lends strong support to the hypothesis. The path followed by hybrid whistlers is not completely defined by these measurements. It would be possible for the one-hop whistler either to enter at the same end of the path as the two-hop whistler, returning to the observer by crossing the equator in the earth–ionosphere waveguide, or to enter the other end of the duct after having first crossed the equator in the waveguide.

Temporal variations of dispersion. Statistical studies of dispersion show diurnal, seasonal, and solar cycle variations. Since dispersion data are relevant to the study of electron density, these results are considered in detail in Chap. 6. Generally speaking, whistlers show relatively little change from one hour to the next. Often the same duct structure can be identified in adjacent hours and the values of dispersion are usually quite similar. This is not always the case, however, especially during magnetically disturbed periods, when large changes in dispersion may occur between hourly runs. Marked changes in dispersion are also observed at high-latitude stations under quiet as well as disturbed conditions.

Studies of multiflash whistlers from the Whistlers-West network show that the dispersion is constant for the corresponding members of a multiflash group. Examples are shown in Fig. 4-16 in which the sources of the multiflash whistlers are marked with arrows. Following the suggestion of Hoffman (1960a), Clarence and O'Brien (1961) have reported evidence for a slight increase in the dispersion of successive multiflash whistlers, which they suggest might be caused by an increase of ionization along the whistler path produced by the discharges themselves.

Observations of whistlers from satellites. The first direct observation of whistler-mode propagation within the ionosphere was made in the Vanguard III satellite. Whistlers were received on a magnetometer that could record frequencies of the magnetic field up to about 6 kc/s (Cain *et al.*, 1961, 1962). Examples of these whistlers are shown in Fig. 4-22 of the Atlas.* Of particular interest is the fact that many of them are very short, with dispersions as low as 1.0 sec$^{1/2}$, which indicates fractional-hop propagation. Analysis showed that the observed values of dispersion are consistent with propagation along the magnetic line of force through the satellite, if an electron distribution characteristic of a quiet nighttime ionosphere is assumed. However, discrepancies of as much as two to one were obtained between the measured values and the predicted values. Although the explanation for this is not yet available, it is possible that the reason lies in the normal, but unpredictable day-to-day variation in electron content of the F2 layer.

The occasional observation of much longer whistlers in Vanguard III indicates the possibility of an echoing process. From the theory of whistlers it is expected that satellites should observe whistlers propagating along a ray path that terminates at the satellite. Because of the infrequent occurrence of ducts, it is unlikely that any of the whistlers observed in Vanguard III were in fact ducted. Ducts are not required to explain the observation of whistlers in a satellite. In the non-ducted case the ray path is defined by the gradients of refractive index in the ionosphere. It is likely that whistlers observed in satellites would usually follow paths substantially different from those followed by whistlers observed on the ground.

Whistler ducts. The spacing of whistler ducts can be estimated by counting the number of whistler components over a given range of latitude and assuming a spread in longitude. On days when the components are closely spaced (e.g., see Fig. 4-17*b*), a duct spacing of about 100 km at the lower edge of the ionosphere is estimated. No straightforward method of measuring the duct cross section has yet been found. However, from the width of a single trace we can derive an upper limit on the range of effective latitudes of the ray paths within a single duct. This approach leads to an upper limit for the effective diameter of the duct of about 10 km. However, the applicability of ray theory to ducts of such small diameter has not yet been established.

The minimum diameter of a duct may be estimated by assuming that when the diameter of the duct becomes as small as a wavelength in the medium, it will no longer be an effective trap. The maximum wavelength corresponds to the lowest frequency, which we will take to be typically 2 kc/s. For this wave frequency and for a local plasma frequency of 1 mc/s (upper F region at night), the refractive index is approximately 20, corresponding to a wavelength of 7.5 km. Since this is less than the maximum diameter obtained, it is at least not unreasonable. It is possible that field-aligned irregularities with diameters

---

* Some whistlers received in the Alouette satellite are shown in Fig. 7-67.

much less than a wavelength may function as guiding centers, or ducts, for the waves. However, a quantitative analysis of this case has not yet been carried out.

The presence of field-aligned ducts up to at least 1000 km has been confirmed by sounding apparatus carried in rockets (Calvert *et al.*, 1963). Measurements showed a variation of apparent duct diameter from 0.3 km to 6 km, with a median of 1.4 km, and a spatial separation from 1 km to 30 km. These results are not inconsistent with the larger separations and diameters of ducts that appear to be associated with whistlers.

4.7 Explosion-Excited Whistlers

It is well known that nuclear explosions produce strong, impulsive VLF signals that show a spectral peak in the vicinity of 10 to 15 kc/s (Glasstone, 1962). Frequently these impulsive signals excite detectable whistlers (Allcock *et al.*, 1963; Helliwell and Carpenter, 1963; Dinger and Garner, 1963). The spectral shapes of explosion-excited whistlers are like those of natural whistlers observed both before and immediately after detonation.

Observations of explosion-excited whistlers were begun at Stanford in 1953, with the aid of conventional recording equipment. The particulars of these observations are summarized in Table 4-4, which shows the universal time of each explosion, the location, yield, and altitude of the shot, and the recorder location and its approximate distance from the shot location in kilometers. In the last column are listed the types of whistlers observed in each case. It will be seen from the table that whistlers were produced by nuclear devices ranging in yield from a few kilotons to over a megaton. Altitudes ranged from

TABLE 4-4
WHISTLERS RESULTING FROM NUCLEAR EXPLOSIONS

Date, Time (UT)	Shot, Location	Yield	Altitude, km	Recorder Location	Approximate Distance from Shot, km	Type
Mar. 24, 1953 1310:00.01	Nancy (Operation Upshot Knothole), Nevada	24 kt	0.09	Stanford	600	two-hop
Aug. 1, 1958 1050:05.6	Teak (Operation Hardtack, Phase I), Johnston I.	Megaton range	77	1. Stanford 2. Boulder 3. Kauai	5100 6700 1200	one-hop one-hop none
Aug. 12, 1958 1030:08.6	Orange (Operation Hardtack, Phase I), Johnston I.	Megaton range	43	1. Stanford 2. Unalaska 3. Kauai	5100 3900 1200	one-hop none
Oct. 13, 1958 1320:00.1	Lea (Operation Hardtack, Phase II), Nevada	1.4 kt	0.45	Stanford	600	two-hop
July 9, 1962 0900:09	Starfish Prime (Operation Dominic), Johnston I.	1400 kt	400	1. Wellington 2. Stanford 3. Byrd 4. U.S.N.S. *Eltanin*	6800 5100 11,000 11,500	one-hop none none none

less than 100 meters to over 400 kilometers. Explosion-excited whistlers were received at locations covering a very wide range of distances from the source. Thus for shot Nancy on March 24, 1953, the receiver was located only 600 km from the shot. The greatest distance of the receiver from the shot or the shot's conjugate point occurred when a Teak whistler was received at Boulder, 6700 km from the source.

The most intense explosion-excited whistler observed in this study was produced by the high-altitude shot known as Starfish Prime. The yield was 1400 kilotons, and detonation occurred at an altitude of 400 km over Johnston Island (geomagnetic latitude 14°). This whistler was very strong at Wellington but was not observed at Stanford or Byrd, or on the *Eltanin*. This was interpreted to mean that a good path of propagation was present in the vicinity of Wellington but not at the other stations. Spectra of the Starfish Prime whistler are shown in Fig. 4-32*a*, *b*, *d*, *e* of the Atlas. These figures show that the explosion-excited whistler extended over a much wider frequency range than did the strongest natural whistler observed in the same period. From the observed nose frequency of the Starfish whistler, the path latitudes were found to cluster around 49°, typical of whistlers observed at Wellington.

An anomalous feature of the explosion-excited whistler can be seen on the spectrograms shown in Fig. 4-32*d*, *e*. The early components, which are strong at the higher frequencies, disappear below approximately 1 kc/s. A set of delayed components beginning at 1 kc/s and continuing down to about 400 cycles is seen on the Starfish Prime whistler but not on the weaker natural whistler. It is tempting to suggest that the later, low-frequency components are a unique feature of explosion-excited whistlers. However, the examination of whistlers from Byrd and Eights, as illustrated in Figs. 4-11*f* and 4-19*c* of the Atlas, shows that a delayed trace or group of traces occupying the lower portion of the frequency range is a common occurrence, at least at Byrd. It can be concluded, therefore, that the Starfish Prime whistler does not in fact exhibit any features not found in natural whistlers.

On the Starfish Prime whistler the energy extends at least to 32 kc/s, whereas the natural whistler recorded at 0856:27 UT disappears above 10 kc/s. Such a wide range of upper cutoff frequency has not been reported for natural whistlers observed over a comparable interval of time. This striking difference in upper cutoff frequencies is tentatively attributed to a relatively greater energy content in the spectrum of the explosion impulse in the range above 10 kc/s.

The Starfish Prime whistler can be explained in terms of a model much like that used for natural whistlers. In this model the impulse is produced in the earth–ionosphere waveguide by radiation from the bomb. Then it travels in the earth–ionosphere waveguide to the input end of an already existing magnetospheric duct along which the whistler is propagated. The whistler exits in the normal way and travels to the receiver in the earth–ionosphere waveguide.

Examination of the dynamic spectrum of the causative impulse of the Starfish Prime whistler shows that it does not differ significantly from the spectra of natural whistler sources. If the impulse had been formed at the altitude of the bomb, then dispersion through the F layer would have lengthened the impulse noticeably. Since there is no evidence of whistler-mode dispersion, it is concluded that the impulse was in fact produced within the earth–ionosphere waveguide and not in the vicinity of the detonation.

From shot Teak, a one-hop whistler was observed at Stanford. Its spectrum is shown in Fig. 4-33d of the Atlas together with the spectra of three natural whistlers recorded within a few minutes of shot time. The leading edge of the causative impulse for each of the natural whistlers is marked with an arrow in the lower margin. The records are aligned with respect to the whistler traces at 8 kc/s. The 0 on the bottom record is aligned with the arrows on the upper three records. The causative impulse from shot Teak is identified by the arrow labeled A on the bottom record. The observed travel times at a given frequency are within about 1 per cent of one another for the three natural events. The average travel time from causative impulse to trace leading edge at 8 kc/s for the five natural whistlers examined during this period was 0.719 seconds.

With the aid of nose frequency extrapolation techniques, the geomagnetic latitude of the path for the natural whistlers was found to be approximately 50 degrees, a value normally observed at Stanford. As a check on the time of origin of the Teak whistler, the dispersion of the natural whistlers was used to estimate the expected time of origin as shown by the dash and arrow labeled B. The closeness of B to 0′, the true time of origin of the natural whistlers, is a verification that the dispersion characteristics of the shot-time events are similar to those of the natural whistlers.

From an analysis of the possible locations of the magnetospheric path and consideration of the sub-ionospheric path delays, it was concluded that the observed position of the causative impulse marked A could be interpreted relative to the natural sources only if it were assumed that the one-hop whistler was excited at the southern end of the path. This interpretation required that the causative impulse propagate from Johnston Island across the equator into the Southern Hemisphere. The alternative interpretation, in which the impulse enters the northern end of the path and returns to the receiver after exiting from the southern end of the magnetospheric path, gave a time of origin that was not compatible with the observed times. In addition, the latter hypothesis requires a much longer sub-ionospheric path, and hence would have resulted in more attenuation.

The first interpretation is consistent with the data and supports the favored interpretation for the excitation of hybrid whistlers discussed in the previous section. Other observations made on shots Lea, Nancy, and Orange confirm the more detailed interpretation of the results described for Starfish Prime and Teak. The observations during the Johnston Island tests of 1958 at Kauai in the Hawaiian Islands showed no whistlers at any time. No observations were made in the Hawaiian Islands during the Johnston Island tests of 1962.

From the results obtained so far on the properties of explosion-excited whistlers, there is little evidence to indicate that these events could be used to detect the occurrence of nuclear explosions.

4.8   Occurrence of Whistlers

Indexes of activity.   Most of the synoptic whistler data available in the IGY World Data Centers were derived from two-minute tape recordings repeated once each hour.   One measure of whistler activity is obtained by counting the number of whistlers in each two-minute interval and dividing by two, which gives the whistler rate in number of whistlers per minute.   Another measure is obtained simply by noting the presence or absence of whistlers in each schedule. On this basis, a curve of diurnal activity is obtained by dividing the number of runs during which whistlers were observed by the total number of runs in the day.   This method has the disadvantage that if the whistler activity is high, nearly all runs contain some whistlers.   Hence under conditions of high whistler activity no information about the variation can be obtained.   The disadvantage of the whistler-rate method is that it may be relatively more sensitive to thunderstorm activity.   Hence, of the days in which the propagation characteristics are identical, those with higher thunderstorm activity near the ducts should show more whistlers.

An attempt was made to determine which index would be more indicative of propagation activity.   Both indexes were computed for the same period of time and were compared with the echo index obtained from fixed-frequency measurements.   Neither method appeared to be clearly superior to the other at the middle-latitude station (Stanford) for which the study was made.   Because of the saturation effect inherent in the schedule index, it was concluded that the whistler rate would be more useful.   Henceforth all whistler occurrence statistics will be given in terms of the number of whistlers per minute observed aurally from the magnetic tapes.

Influence of background noise level.   During magnetically quiet periods at middle- and low-latitude stations, the background noise level is determined primarily by atmospherics from thunderstorms and, at some stations, by power-line interference.   During magnetically disturbed periods at stations like Seattle, the background noise level is determined primarily by hiss and chorus.   At high-latitude stations, such as Byrd, hiss and chorus are at all times the main source of noise near 3 kc/s.   When the total background noise level is high, the detectability of whistlers is naturally reduced.   Since the whistler rate varies with the noise-level conditions, a station located in a thunderstorm area during the height of the thunderstorm season will report relatively fewer whistlers than stations at high latitudes in the quiet season of the year.

At middle latitudes the seasonal variation in atmospheric noise level is usually large.   For purposes of estimating the minimum field intensity of a detectable whistler, the intensity of the background noise between 1 and 10 kc/s has been measured for two days corresponding to midsummer and midwinter. During midwinter the atmospherics were isolated enough that the relatively steady noise occurring between them could be measured, while during summer this was no longer true.   The approximate field intensities of noise thus obtained were 20 μv/m for winter noon, and 200 to 700 μv/m for summer noon.   Owing to this large variation in background noise intensity, it is difficult to use the observed whistler rate in a quantitative way.   Various presentations that take

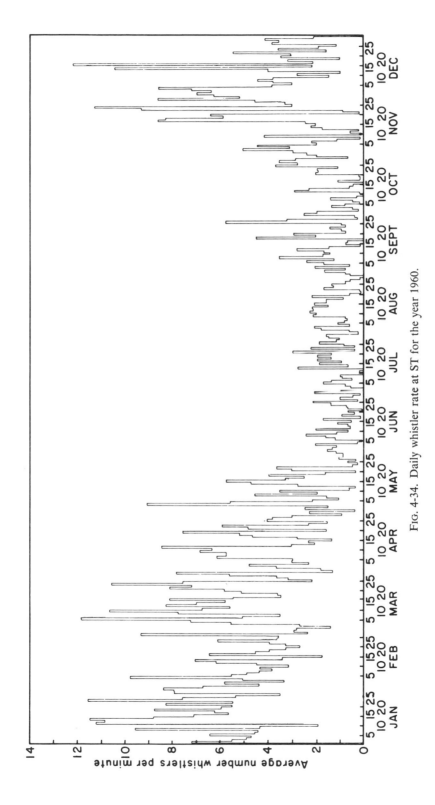

Fig. 4-34. Daily whistler rate at ST for the year 1960.

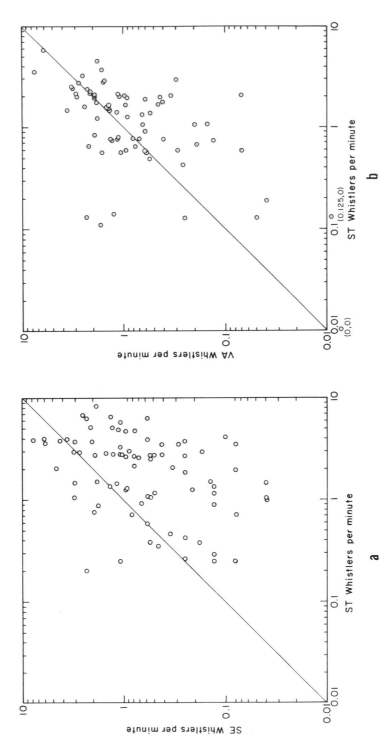

FIG. 4-35. Scatter diagram of daily whistler rate at spaced stations for August, September, and October; the diagonal lines represent the locus of equal whistler rate. *a*, At ST and SE (1100-km spacing); represents 12 hours of data from 04 to 15 UT; *b*, At ST and VA (300-km spacing); each point represents the 24-hour UT day. A few days are excluded because of equipment failure.

this limitation into account have been devised to illustrate the different types of variation in occurrence.

Hour-to-hour variation. Periods of whistler activity show considerable variation in length, often lasting as long as several hours. A statistical distribution of the occurrence of whistler periods of different lengths, obtained by counting the number of successive runs in which one or more whistlers were observed at Stanford, Wellington, and Byrd, showed that the most frequently occurring unbroken minimum period of whistler reception is the period of one hour. On one occasion at Byrd, whistlers were observed every hour for a period of 79 hours.

In a study of whistler activity near Uppsala, Sweden (Norinder and Knudsen, 1959), it was found that whistlers occur in groups, called "whistler situations," with periods of roughly $\frac{1}{2}$ to $2\frac{1}{2}$ hours. This result is consistent with that mentioned above.

Day-to-day variation. Activity also shows great variations from day to day. Sometimes many days will pass without the observation of a single whistler, whereas on other days the rate may be as high as two per second. To illustrate the day-to-day variation, the daily average whistler rate for Stanford is plotted in Fig. 4-34 for the year 1960. The marked day-to-day variation is readily apparent, as is the tendency for periods of whistler activity to last several days.

The correlation between the daily average whistler rate at spaced stations is illustrated by the scatter plots of Fig. 4-35. A definite positive correlation is seen between Vandenburg and Stanford, separated by 300 km. Between

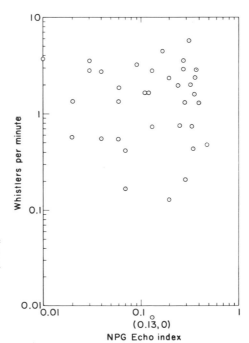

FIG. 4-36. Scatter diagram of daily whistler rate and NPG echo index at ST during the period 25 Aug. to 31 Oct. 1960. Each point represents a 24-hour UT day.

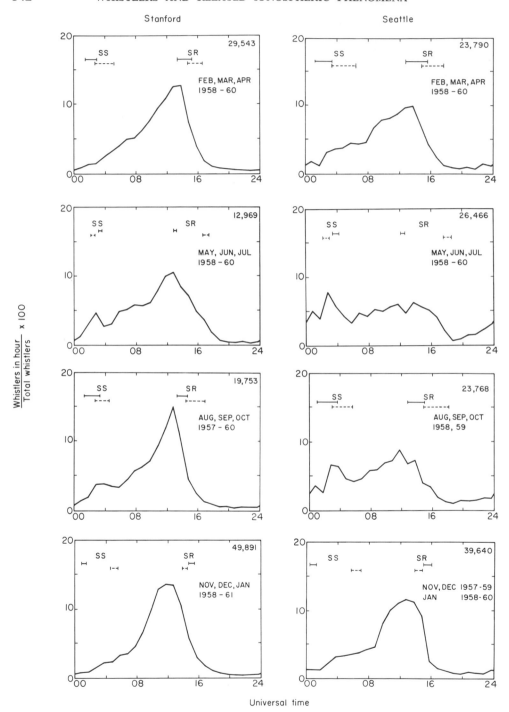

Fig. 4-37. Diurnal variations in whistler occurrence for different seasons of the year. The letters SR and SS represent times of sunrise and sunset, respectively, at the receiver (solid line) and at the Vestine conjugate to the receiver (broken line). *a*, At Stanford and Seattle. *b*, At Wellington and

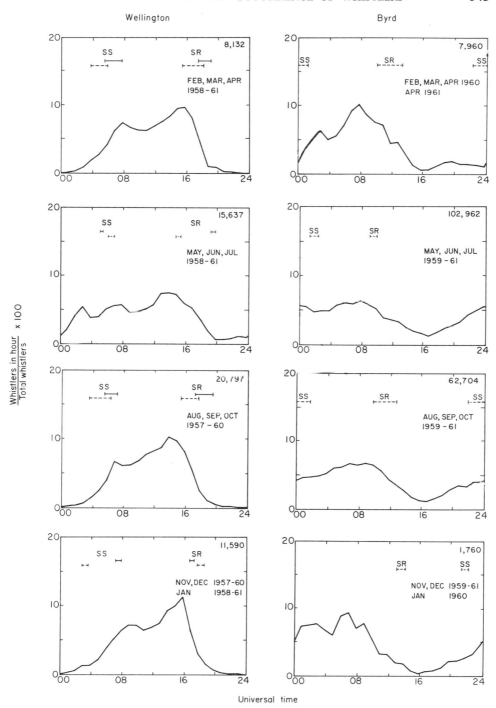

Byrd. Note that the sum of the 24 ordinates of each curve equals 100 per cent. The total number of whistlers represented by each group is shown in the upper right-hand corner. At Byrd, sunlight is continuous from Nov. to Jan. and darkness is continuous from May to July.

Stanford and Seattle the correlation is less evident, as might be expected, since their spacing is about 1100 km. Shown in Fig. 4-36 is a scatter plot of Stanford whistler rate versus the NPG-Stanford echo index (see Chap. 5).

The low correlation shown by this plot may result from the facts that NPG echoes do not depend upon thunderstorm activity as do whistlers, and that while NPG echoes are observed at 18.6 kc/s, whistlers are concentrated near 5 kc/s and show a variable high-frequency cutoff. In addition, the whistler data consist mainly of one-hop whistlers, whereas the NPG echoes are entirely two-hop, and the correlation between one- and two-hop propagation has not been investigated. When both whistlers and NPG echoes are recorded, the group delays are usually the same, indicating that the same paths are being excited.

Diurnal variation. It has long been known that whistlers are more common during the hours of darkness than during daylight hours. To demonstrate the diurnal behavior, each of several years was divided into quarters, based on calendar months and centered approximately on the solstice and equinox periods. Curves of average whistler occurrence in each hour, given in per cent of the total for the quarter, are shown in Fig. 4-37. They include the range in times of ground sunrise and sunset both at the receiving station and at the Vestine conjugate (Vestine, 1959) to the receiving station.

In general there seems to be a relation between the times of sunrise and the principal changes in the activity curves. This is explained in terms of absorption of the wave as it passes through the D region in the daylight hemisphere. Attenuation in the earth–ionosphere waveguide, generally greater during daytime than during nighttime, also affects propagation. Support for the D-region absorption explanation is obtained from the calculated values of absorption in the lower ionosphere at 5 kc/s, shown in Fig. 3-31. From these curves the difference between nighttime and daytime whistler intensity for a one-hop path is predicted to be about 25 db. The difference in waveguide attenuation rates between day and night is less than about 3 db/1000 km at 5 kc/s (Wait, 1962), and so is not thought to be a dominant factor in the diurnal variation.

A prominent feature of many of the diurnal curves is the peak in whistler rate between midnight and dawn. The cause is unknown, but it is unlikely that absorption can account for the variation through the night hours. It is almost certain that propagation factors are responsible for the difference, since the diurnal curves of the man-made echoes discussed in Chap. 5 show the same behavior. Two possible explanations are suggested. First, there may be more field-aligned ducts after midnight than before. Observations of spread F indicate that this phenomenon occurs more frequently after midnight at middle-latitude stations (Shimazaki, 1959). It has been postulated that spread F is caused by field-aligned enhancements of ionization, and these may be related to whistler ducts. Another possibility is that the horizontal gradient of ionization is more favorable to the launching of whistlers into ducts after midnight than before.

Seasonal variation. Marked seasonal variations in whistler occurrence are seen at most stations. Storey (1953) was the first to report this effect, and deduced that it was closely related to the occurrence of thunderstorms and to local noise at the receiver. Thunderstorm activity is highest in local winter.

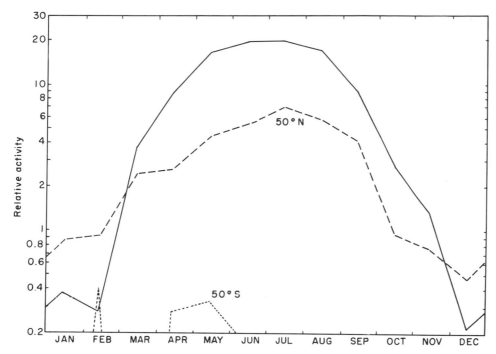

FIG. 4-38. Whistlers and thunderstorms. Solid line represents the ratio between the number of whistlers in each month × 100 and the number of whistlers in year at Byrd; dashed and dotted lines represent, respectively, the number of thunderstorm days per month on the Byrd magnetic meridian at geomagnetic latitudes 50° N and at 50° S. Thunderstorm data from *World Distribution of Thunderstorm Days, 1956.*

This means that many sources are available for the excitation of one-hop whistlers and also that atmospheric noise at the station is minimal. Hence the whistler rate would normally be at its highest in local winter.

An especially marked seasonal variation in whistler occurrence is shown by the normalized data from Byrd for the years 1959, 1960, and 1961 (Fig. 4-38). Also shown is the frequency of occurrence of thunderstorms in the area conjugate to the exit region (average 50° geomagnetic latitude) of Byrd whistlers. The two curves have virtually the same shape, reaching their peaks in southern winter. It is concluded, therefore, that the seasonal variation in whistler activity at Byrd is controlled in part at least by thunderstorm activity in the conjugate area. However, data from Byrd on the occurrence of fixed-frequency echoes (Chap. 5) also show a peak in wintertime, indicating a seasonal variation in propagation conditions that has the same phase as the Byrd whistler occurrence. This has been explained by the fact that the field-line paths of many of the Byrd whistlers terminate in a region of continuous daylight during local summer (Helliwell *et al.*, 1962). Thus the D-region absorption at the exit end of the path is high at all hours, which accounts for the reduced level of activity in local summer.

The whistler rate at Byrd in local winter is one of the highest ever recorded.

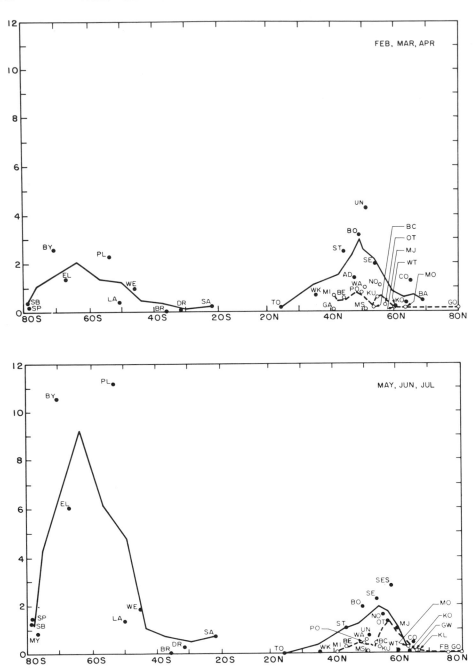

FIG. 4-39. Average whistler rates versus latitude for different seasons of the year. Solid line and solid dots in Northern Hemisphere represent stations grouped in the Pacific area. Dashed line and open dots represent Northern Hemisphere stations grouped in the Atlantic area.

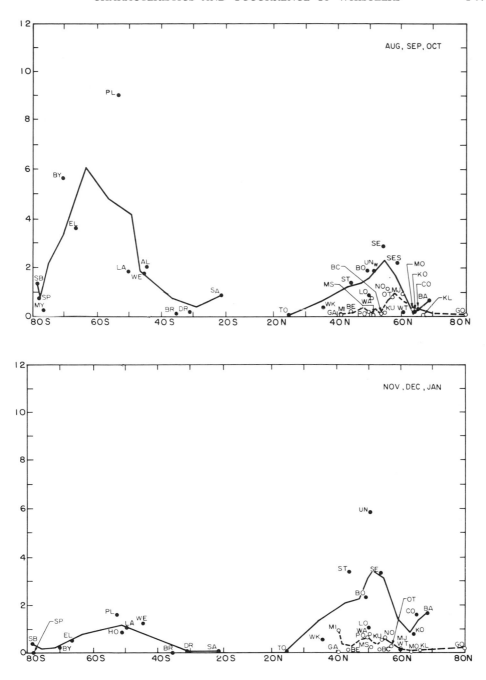

FIG. 4-39 (continued).

This circumstance can be explained qualitatively by two factors. First, the local noise level at Byrd is very low because of the remoteness of thunderstorm centers. Second, the geomagnetic equator reaches its most southerly position on the meridian passing through Byrd. At this meridian, the whistler belt is closest to the Northern Hemisphere thunderstorm belt. Hence the supply of lightning discharges near the duct inputs is increased.

Latitude variation. The whistler rate varies markedly with the location of the receiving station. Some of this variation probably results from the use of different station equipment, different monitoring techniques, and different levels of natural and man-made interference. On the other hand, some of this variation may be interpreted in terms of whistler-mode propagation characteristics, which depend on geomagnetic latitude.

To obtain an indication of the latitude variation of whistler rate, whistler data from many stations were plotted for each season of the year as shown in Fig. 4-39. This figure represents approximately 16 station-years of data in the years 1957 to 1962. The points on the smoothed curves represent the average rate for three adjacent stations and are plotted at the average latitude of the three stations. Because Northern Hemisphere stations in the Pacific area appeared to have higher whistler activity than those in the Atlantic area, the data from these two groups were plotted separately.

Figure 4-39 indicates that there exists a broad range of latitudes centered near 50° geomagnetic at which the whistler rate is high. In general, there is higher whistler activity in the Southern Hemisphere, probably as a result of the high thunderstorm activity in the Northern Hemisphere for the same season. In general, the highest whistler activity for either hemisphere occurs during the winter and spring of the year for that hemisphere. The high thunderstorm activity along the east coast of the United States causes the stations lying along this magnetic meridian in the Southern Hemisphere to have the highest whistler rates of any of the world's stations.

Whistler data from a station that moved over a wide range of latitudes are available from the National Science Foundation research ship, the U.S.N.S. *Eltanin*. The latitude variation of the whistler rate recorded on this ship is shown in Fig. 4-40. When allowance is made for the difference of vertical scales in the two figures, it may be seen that the *Eltanin* data support the latitude variation of whistler rate shown in Fig. 4-39.

An important feature of the latitude-variation curves is the high whistler rate observed at high latitudes compared with that at low latitudes. This can be explained primarily on the basis of two factors. One is the tendency for whistlers to propagate away from the equator after exiting from the duct, as explained in Sec. 3.7. The other is the reduced level of atmospheric noise at high latitudes, which permits the detection of weaker whistlers.

The data of Fig. 4-39 imply that at least for some season of the year, even the low-latitude stations receive a few whistlers a day. An early test made on the equator showed no whistlers (Koster and Storey, 1955). However, our explanation of hybrid whistlers suggests that whistlers should be heard occasionally on the equator. The whistler station on board the *Eltanin* recently recorded

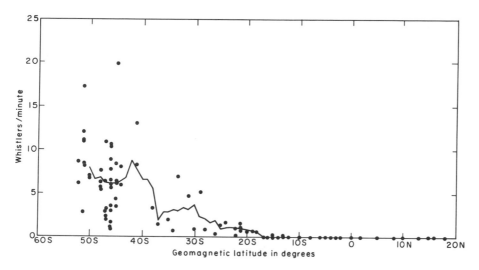

FIG. 4-40. Whistler rate observed on the U.S.N.S. *Eltanin* as a function of geomagnetic latitude. Each point represents 24 hours of data, and curve shows running mean over 7° of latitude. Data obtained during periods 1 Jun to 26 Jun and 6 Jul to 31 Aug 1962.

several weak one-hop whistlers while lying within one degree of the geomagnetic equator. Two-hop whistlers from the same source were recorded simultaneously at Greenbank, indicating that the one-hop whistlers reached the *Eltanin* via the earth–ionosphere waveguide from an exit point in the Southern Hemisphere. Spectra of these events are shown in Fig. 4-25 of the Atlas.

Correlation of whistler rate and multipath occurrence. Among the propagation factors that control the whistler rate, the area density of discrete paths, or ducts, would appear to be important. Hence if other factors are the same, an increase in the number of ducts per unit area of the earth's surface should result in an increase in the number of detectable whistlers at a particular station. To test this hypothesis, the whistler rate was compared with the rate of occurrence of the so-called multipath whistler. Data from Dunedin for 25 months between January 1958 and October 1960 were used. On days when there were no multipath occurrences, the average whistler rate was 2.2 per minute. On days with multipath whistlers, the whistler rate was 4.8 per minute, giving support to the hypothesis.

On the basis of this result the whistler rate would seem to be controlled, in part at least, by the density of whistler ducts. However, before a conclusion is reached on this point, it is important that a careful study be made based on the actual spectral properties of the whistlers. In such a study the actual spacing of discrete-whistler components might be used as a measure of the density of multiple paths.

Effect of magnetic disturbance on whistler occurrence. Attempts have been made to associate the occurrence of whistlers with magnetic activity. Storey (1953) reported a positive correlation, but concluded that it resulted from the absence of whistlers during periods of exceptionally low magnetic activity.

Allcock and Morgan (1958) found that the correlation was high when magnetic activity was compared with whistler rate measured about one and one half months later.

Kimpara (1960a) has presented data correlating whistler occurrence at Wakkanai with K-index. He found that whistlers observed in winter occurred most commonly two days after the beginning of a magnetic disturbance as measured by a K-index greater than 6. In the summer no such correlation was found, possibly because of the effect of atmospheric noise on whistler rate.

A study of the effect of magnetic disturbances on the whistler rates at stations covering a wide range of latitudes has been carried out by Yoshida and Hatanaka (1962a, b). They found that whistler rates at high-latitude stations decrease with increasing K_p, while the rates at middle- and lower-latitude stations reach a peak at middle and high K_p values, respectively. Their work supports and extends a study of whistlers at Scott Base (Allcock and Rodgers, 1961), in which a marked inverse correlation was found between the occurrence of whistlers and geomagnetic activity. These results may be interpreted as indicating that the most favorable latitude for whistler propagation moves southward during times of magnetic disturbance. Whistler-rate data collected by Laaspere et al. (1963) support these findings and further show that at certain stations there is some seasonal variation in the dependence upon K_p.

Another quantity that may affect whistler rate is the horizontal gradient of electron density. W. R. Piggott* has suggested that the horizontal gradient of ionization in the F2 layer increases markedly during magnetic disturbance.

An increase in gradient toward the equator could reduce the angle between the wave normal and the earth's magnetic field, thereby reducing the enhancement of electron density required for trapping. Hence the number of effective whistler ducts could be increased during a magnetically disturbed period.

Echo activity.   From the theory outlined in Chap. 3, whistler echo activity would be expected to increase with latitude because of the correspondingly more favorable conditions for retrapping the reflected whistler. An index of echo activity was determined by counting the number of whistler schedules during each day in which echoes were observed and dividing this number by the total number of whistler schedules in which whistlers of any kind were observed. The echo index, therefore, ranges from 0 to 1.

An example of the diurnal variation of whistler echo index is shown in Fig. 4.41. It is clear that the echo index is high at night and low during daytime. One of the ways in which this can be explained is in terms of D-region absorption, which reduces the intensity of echoes with respect to the first whistler by a much larger factor during day than during night. The variation of echo index with geomagnetic latitude is shown in Fig. 4-42. Very few echoes are reported from stations below about 40° geomagnetic latitude. Echo activity is low also at relatively high latitudes. The former circumstance can be explained by the unfavorable dip angle, which causes the required enhancement factors to be very large indeed if echoes are to be produced. The reduction in echo activity

---

* Personal communication.

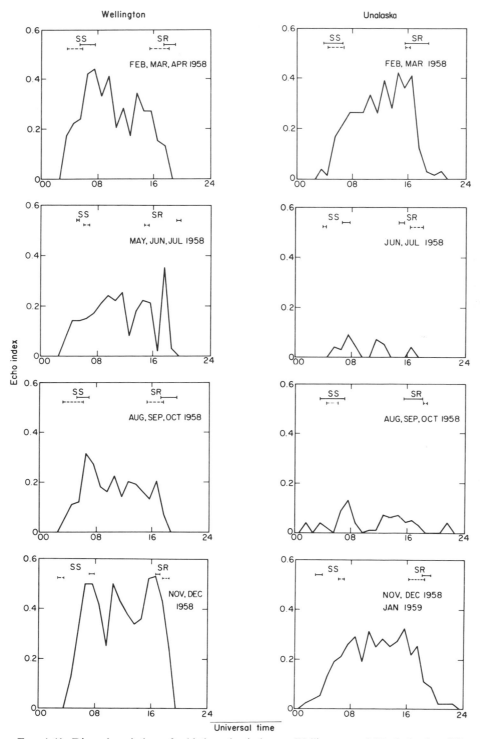

FIG. 4-41. Diurnal variation of whistler-echo index at Wellington and Unalaska for different seasons of the year. (Some curves are limited to two months by lack of data.) The letters SR and SS represent times of sunrise and sunset, respectively, at the receiver (solid line) and at the Vestine conjugate to the receiver (broken line).

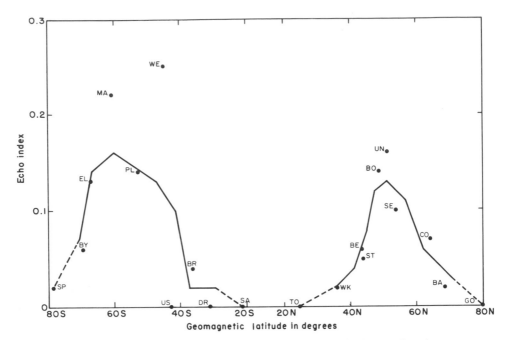

FIG. 4-42. Whistler-echo index as a function of geomagnetic latitude. Each point represents roughly one year of data at one station. The solid curve is the average of the indexes of three adjacent stations, and each point of the curve is plotted at the average latitude of those three stations.

at high latitudes is less easily explained, but probably results from the fact that the path lengths are extremely great and more loss of whistler energy is likely to occur over such long paths. The curve of echo activity versus latitude provides qualitative support for the trapping and transmission theory outlined in Chap. 3.

Echo activity, as well as the whistler rate itself, often becomes surprisingly high during daytime, suggesting that the discussion above may be over-simplified. One important factor that has not yet been considered in studies of whistler activity is sporadic E ionization. Intense sporadic E layers often form at levels above the absorbing D region and, because of their steep gradients of refractive index, are capable of efficient reflection of whistler-mode signals arriving from above or below. Thus a two-hop whistler reflected from a patch of sporadic E at the end of its first hop would experience half as much D-region absorption as one reflected from the lower boundary of the ionosphere. At the same time the intensity of one-hop whistlers at either end of the path would be reduced, giving a possible explanation for the observation that two-hop whistlers sometimes occur at one end of a path when no one-hop whistlers are observed at the other. Sporadic E at both ends of a path could conceivably reduce the decrement between echoes to a relatively low value in daytime.

Sporadic E at the DU end of path "a" of the anomalous mixed-path whistler of Fig. 4-14 could account for the postulated poor coupling to the earth–ionosphere waveguide.

Chapter Five

Fixed-Frequency Whistler-Mode Experiments

The study of whistler-mode propagation has been based mainly on the dispersion characteristics of whistlers. The measurement of other properties, such as occurrence of whistler-mode propagation and attenuation loss along whistler paths, requires a regularly available source with known characteristics. Since natural lightning does not meet all these requirements, it is desirable to employ a controllable man-made source, such as a high-power VLF transmitter. The use of man-made signals was introduced in 1957, when whistler-mode signals broadcast on a frequency of 15.5 kc/s from the U.S. Navy station NSS at Annapolis, Maryland, were received at Cape Horn, Chile (Helliwell and Gehrels, 1958).

In this experiment pulses of roughly one-quarter-second duration were transmitted every two seconds for the purpose of measuring the transmission loss and group delay of the whistler mode. Results of these early experiments showed that the technique was a profitable one, and it has since been extended to cover several transmitting stations and several receiving stations.

This chapter describes some of the results obtained in a program of measurements using fixed-frequency transmissions (Helliwell, Katsufrakis, and Carpenter, 1962) from stations listed in Table 5-1. Topics included are methods of measurement, types of echoes, occurrence of echoes, fading, group delay, transmission loss (ground-to-ground), and reception of whistler-mode signals in a satellite. It is shown that certain questions about occurrence of whistler-mode transmission can be answered only by using fixed-frequency transmissions. The results reported in this chapter will be particularly useful to communications engineers and others interested in the quantitative behavior of this mode of propagation.

5.1 Methods of Measurement

Pulse method. Perhaps the simplest method for studying whistler-mode propagation is based on the use of a pulse whose length is less than the expected group delay. The amplitude of the echo and its delay with respect to the transmitted pulse are measured to provide information on transmission loss and group delay. A simple receiving apparatus with which these measurements can be made is illustrated in Fig. 5-1. A mechanical or electrical keyer turns the transmitter on for periods of about 200 milliseconds. In practice, the pulses are usually repeated every 2 or 3 seconds for 4 minutes every hour (see Table 5-1). The first signal to reach the receiver travels through the earth–ionosphere waveguide and serves as a time reference. Signals are usually stored on magnetic tape for analysis later. Two displays are convenient: the first,

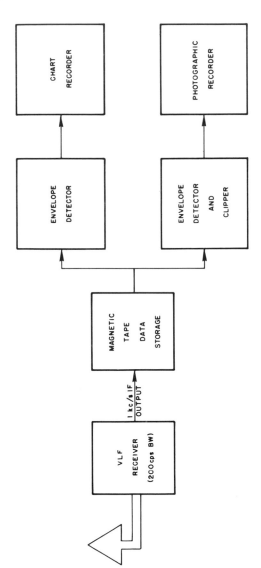

FIG. 5-1. Block diagram of receiver for fixed-frequency pulse sounding of the magnetosphere.

TABLE 5-1
CHARACTERISTICS OF VLF TRANSMITTERS

Station	Location	Frequency[c], kc/s	Approx. Power Output, kw	Geomagnetic Latitude	Pulse Width, msec	Pulse Repetition[a] Period, sec	Pulse Schedule[a] (min after the hour)
NAA	Cutler, Maine, U.S.A.	14.7	1000	56° N	200	2	30–34
NBA	Summit, Canal Zone	18.0	17	20° N	300	1	Continuous[b]
NPG	Jim Creek, Washington, U.S.A.	18.6	200	54° N	200	2	40–44
NPM	Lualaulei, Oahu, Hawaii	19.8	80	22° N	100	1	50–54
NSS	Annapolis, Maryland, U.S.A.	15.5[d] 22.3	80 136	51° N	200	2	50–54

[a] Characteristics change from time to time; those listed apply on May 1, 1963.
[b] Time signals; pulses omitted on every 5th second, and on the 56th, 57th, and 58th seconds.
[c] Personal communication, W. E. Garner, Naval Res. Lab., May 29, 1963.
[d] Changed to higher frequency in January 1961.

illustrated in Fig. 5-2a, shows the amplitude as a function of time; the second, shown in Fig. 5-2b, is made by intensity-modulating an oscilloscope sweep that is photographed on slowly moving film. Shown in Fig. 5-2c is a spectrogram of a one-hop whistler that occurred during the pulse schedule.

Frequency-modulation method. Another method of echo detection employs the same principle as frequency-modulated radar (Terman, 1955). A block diagram of the necessary apparatus is shown in Fig. 5-3a. The frequency of the transmitted signal is made to vary according to some simple periodic function, such as the saw-tooth shown in Fig. 5-3b. The echo shows the same modulation pattern, but is delayed in time with respect to the ground wave by the group delay. When the echo and the ground wave are mixed, two difference frequencies, which are linear functions of the group delay, are obtained.

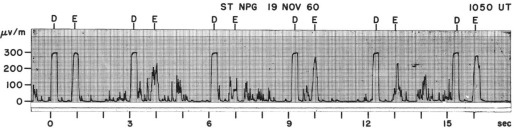

FIG. 5-2a. Amplitude-versus-time display of direct (D) pulse and a two-hop whistler-mode echo (E) from NPG, observed on Nov. 19, 1960, at Stanford. Direct pulse is shown clipped.

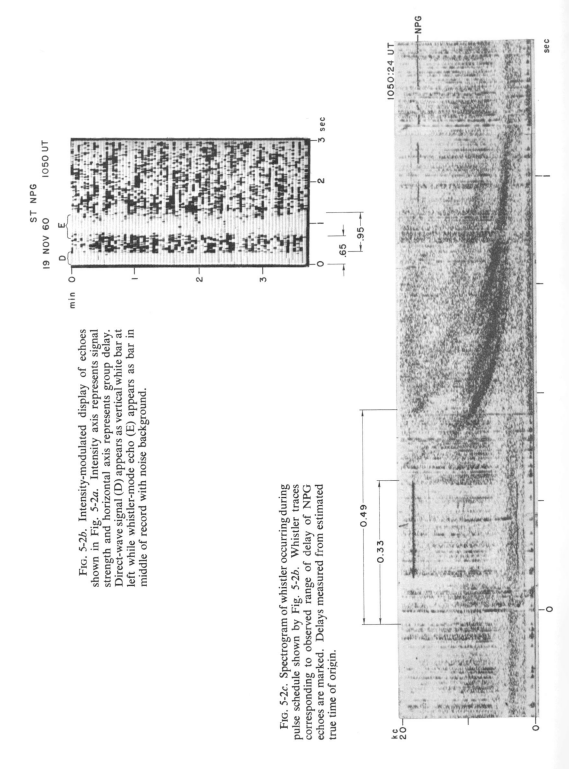

FIG. 5-2b. Intensity-modulated display of echoes shown in Fig. 5-2a. Intensity axis represents signal strength and horizontal axis represents group delay. Direct-wave signal (D) appears as vertical white bar at left while whistler-mode echo (E) appears as bar in middle of record with noise background.

FIG. 5-2c. Spectrogram of whistler occurring during pulse schedule shown by Fig. 5-2b. Whistler traces corresponding to observed range of delay of NPG echoes are marked. Delays measured from estimated true time of origin.

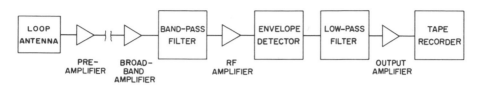

FIG. 5-3a. Block diagram of equipment for whistler-mode echo detection using frequency-modulated transmitter.

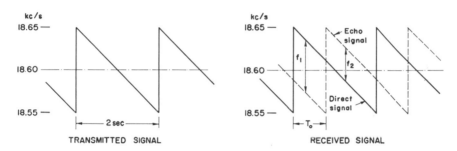

FIG. 5-3b. Characteristics of frequency-modulated signals at transmitter and receiver. Group delay is represented by T_0. Echo signal and direct signal are envelope-detected to produce difference frequencies f_1 and f_2.

These difference frequencies can be recorded on magnetic tape for spectrum analysis later. In this method, resolution of multipath echoes depends primarily on the resolution of the spectrum analyzer and the stability of the signals. The difference-frequency spectrum is broadened somewhat by the change in group delay with frequency.

A typical record of direct-wave amplitude as a function of time is shown in Fig. 5-4 for a frequency-modulated signal transmitted by NPG. Because of the narrow bandwidth of the transmitting antenna, the amplitude decreases as the frequency of the transmitted wave departs from the resonant frequency of the transmitting antenna. The narrow bandwidth of VLF transmitting stations limits the use of the FM technique to frequencies with small percentage deviations.

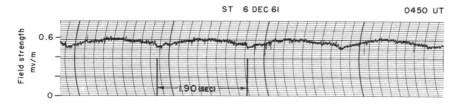

FIG. 5-4. Amplitude versus time of direct wave of FM signals from NPG as recorded at Stanford.

A spectrogram showing a whistler-mode echo signal obtained by the frequency-modulation method is shown in Fig. 5-5. Two echo traces, corresponding to difference frequencies of approximately 40 and 60 cps respectively, are shown. The first corresponds to the smaller difference frequency obtained when the two saw-toothed waves are mixed. The second trace corresponds to the second of the two possible difference frequencies. The 60- and 120-cps components are believed to be generated in the frequency modulator itself, since they did not occur when the station was transmitting traffic. The relative displacement of

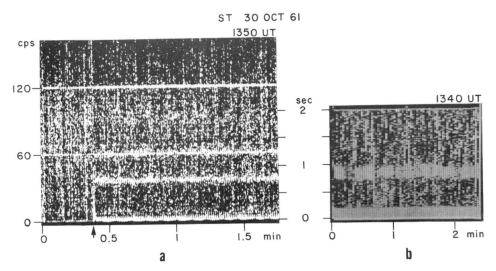

FIG. 5-5. Comparison of FM method (*a*) and pulse method (*b*). Whistler-mode echo appears at approximately 40 and 60 cps in FM method, corresponding to group delay of about 0.8 sec. FM transmissions begin at point marked with arrow. At 60 and 120 cps are spurious components originating in the equipment.

these echo traces is simply proportional to the relative group delay of the echo signal. A record of the echo signal taken ten minutes earlier by the pulse method is also shown in Fig. 5-5. Both records show effective group-delay scales, and it can be seen that the measured delays are equal within experimental error. The FM method, however, even in its crude form, is capable of greater sensitivity and time resolution than the pulse method because of its inherently greater signal-to-noise ratio.

5.2   *Types of Fixed-Frequency Echoes*

A considerable quantity of data has been acquired by means of the pulse method, and the intensity-modulated display of the type illustrated in Fig. 5-2*b* has shown an interesting and wide variety of echo patterns. An attempt has been made to classify these echo types and to illustrate them with actual records. Each principal type of echo pattern is defined in Figs. 5-6 through 5-12.

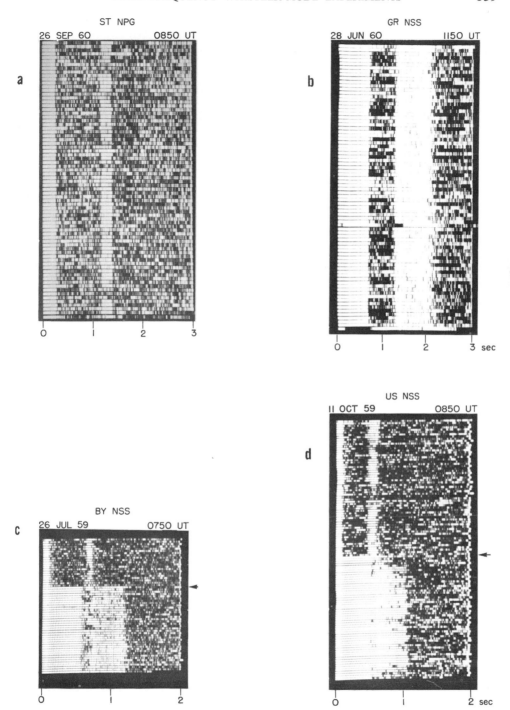

Fig. 5-6. Single-path echoes. Echo whose duration is approximately equal to length of the transmitted pulse. In *c* and *d*, width of transmitted pulse changes from about 100 ms to 600 ms at point marked by arrow.

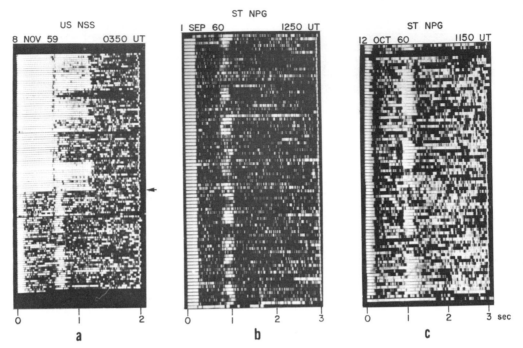

FIG. 5-7. Echo fading. Echoes show marked, quasi-periodic amplitude variations with time. In *a*, pulse length changes from 800 ms to 200 ms at arrow.

Discussion of echo types.   Most of the echo types described thus far in this chapter can be interpreted in terms of the models used to describe whistler propagation. It is probable that the single-path echo propagates along a well-defined discrete path or duct aligned with the earth's magnetic field. The delay depends on the effective geomagnetic latitude of the path as well as upon the distribution of electron density along the path. When two ducts are excited, two echoes with different group delay will be received in the opposite hemisphere. When this difference is sufficiently large, discrete multipath echoes will be observed, as shown in Fig. 5-8. Sometimes, as in this figure, the two echoes differ markedly in duration. Of particular interest in Fig. 5-8*a* is the fact that the echo of shorter duration appears for only two minutes during the four-minute run. Though rare, this effect has been observed on more than one occasion. It suggests that there is some mechanism that causes whistler-mode transmission to start and stop very suddenly. Run *b* shows at least three echoes of quite different amplitude. Run *c* shows two one-hop echoes of the multipath type that could easily be mistaken for a one- and a two-hop echo if the locations of receiver and source were not known. Run *d* shows multipath echoes that change in relative amplitude during the four-minute period.

When whistler ducts are closely spaced in latitude, or when the pulse duration is long, individual echoes are no longer separated on the records. The component echoes may combine in several ways. When each echo contribution is detectable by itself, the combination produces a single echo of increased duration.

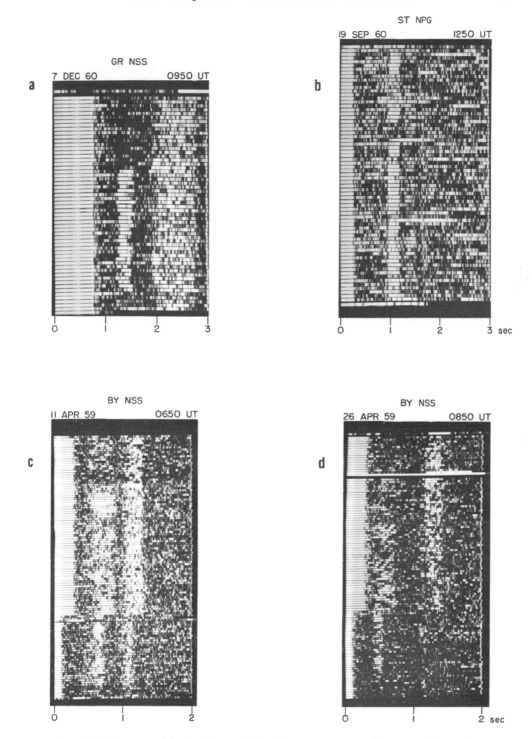

FIG. 5-8. Discrete multipath echoes. Each echo trace corresponds to a one-hop path.

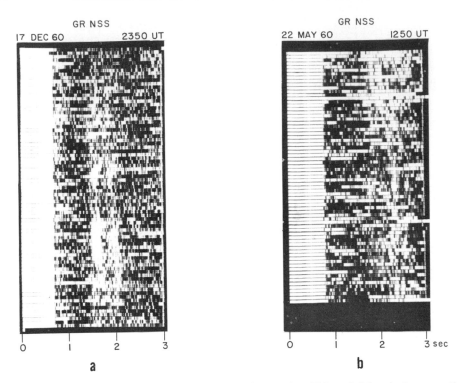

FIG. 5-9. Irregular echoes. Echoes show marked changes in width and delay during recording period.

Examples are shown in Fig. 5-10. On the other hand, when each individual contribution is below the level of detection, it is hypothesized that the over-lapping energy builds up in a pyramid fashion to produce a detectable echo of shorter duration than the source pulse. The mechanism of this multipath combination is described in Sec. 3.11. Examples of the reduced pulse length are shown in Figs. 5-9 and 5-12. The "pyramid" hypothesis is supported by the fact that the apparent echo duration increases somewhat with tape playback level.

Another explanation for the reduced echo pulse length is that the echoes are in fact short, triggered emissions that exceed the whistler-mode echo in strength. It is shown in Chap. 7 that dashes, but not dots, often trigger relatively strong discrete emissions. The "reduced-duration" echoes have been seen only in association with pulses exceeding the length of the dash, in agreement with the triggering hypothesis. Furthermore, the frequency range of the triggered emissions is usually much greater than the bandwidth (100 cps) of the fixed-frequency receiver, so that the "echo" duration would appear shorter than the transmitted pulse duration for a sufficiently great change of emission frequency with time. In Chap. 7 are shown spectra of artificially triggered emissions in which there appear emissions whose duration in a 100-cps bandwidth is clearly less than the length of a dash.

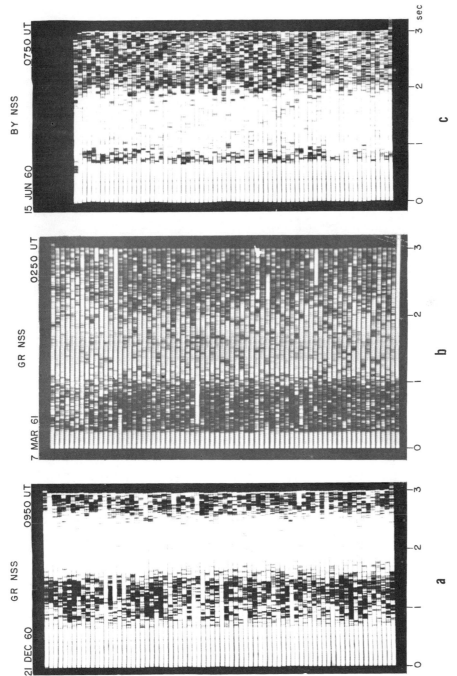

Fig. 5-10. Spread echoes. Echo duration exceeds that of transmitted pulse, probably as result of multipath propagation.

ST NPG

12 OCT 60   1250 UT

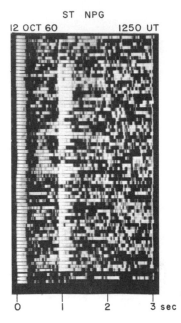

0   1   2   3 sec

FIG. 5-11. Hybrid echoes. Two-hop echoes preceded by weak one-hop hybrid echoes with half the two-hop delay.

GR NSS

24 DEC 59   0950 UT

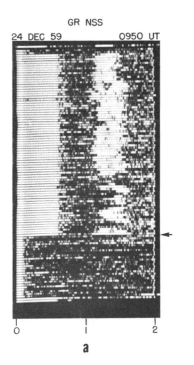

0   1   2

a

BY NSS

24 DEC 59   2350 UT

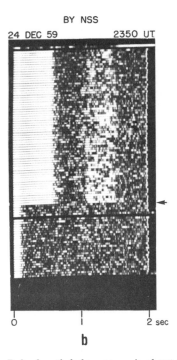

0   1   2 sec

b

FIG. 5-12. Variation of echo intensity with pulse length. Pulse length below arrow is about 100 ms; pulse length above arrow is about 600 ms. Only the 600-ms pulse produces detectable echoes.

A number of whistler ducts that show nearly the same group delay may produce different types of records. If the relative delay of the ducts varies slowly with time, the relative phases of the individual contributions will change in a systematic way. The result is amplitude fading. The smaller the number of ducts contributing to the sum, the deeper will be the null on the fading cycle. The depth of the null determines whether or not fading can be detected by the intensity-modulated display illustrated by Fig. 5-2b.

For more rapid changes in relative phase of individual components, fading may appear with greater rapidity and with different phases in different parts of the resulting pulse. This may result in a ragged-appearing pulse pattern like the one illustrated in Fig. 5-9.

5.3   Echo Occurrence

Activity index.   The absence of whistler-mode echoes during much of the recording time reduces the usefulness of the echo amplitude as a measure of activity. Furthermore the nature of the intensity-modulated records precludes any very accurate measure of the relative echo intensity. Because of these difficulties, a different index of echo amplitude was devised. It is obtained simply by counting the number of identifiable echoes in each hourly recording and dividing this number by the total number of pulses transmitted during the same period. The result is an echo index n_E ranging from 0 to 1. Hence an echo index of 0.2 at a particular hour means that there were echoes detected on the film records of 20 per cent of the available transmitted pulses. This index is believed to be related to the average intensity, since the echoes often show marked fading within a single run (and usually show marked changes in strength between runs) that is often sufficient to cause the intensity to drop below the detection level.

Diurnal and seasonal variations.   Diurnal and seasonal variations of the echo index have been examined for any systematic variations. Data from three transmitting stations, NSS, NAA, and NPG, have been used. Echoes from NSS have been observed at Greenbank, West Virginia; Ushuaia, Argentina; and Byrd Station, Antarctica. Two-hop echoes from NPG were observed at Stanford, California. From NAA, one-hop echoes have been received at Ushuaia, the U.S.N.S. *Eltanin*, Byrd Station, Eights Station, and Wellington. Two-hop echoes from NAA have also been observed at Stanford. Diurnal curves of echo index for different times of year are shown in Figs. 5-13 and 5-14.

These diurnal curves all show a pronounced difference in activity between night and day. The period of low-activity index is generally confined to the time when the end points of the path are in daylight. This seems to indicate that absorption in the ionosphere associated with solar radiation is of major importance. To illustrate this effect, the times of ground sunrise and sunset at the receiver and at its Vestine conjugate (Vestine, 1959) are shown. Sunrise and sunset times were taken from *The Air Almanac* (1960, 1961).

The diurnal behavior of NSS echo activity for stations located on roughly the same geomagnetic meridian is illustrated in Fig. 5-14. The curves show that

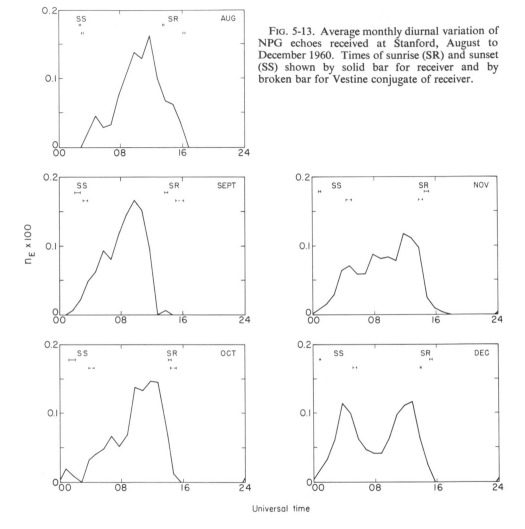

FIG. 5-13. Average monthly diurnal variation of NPG echoes received at Stanford, August to December 1960. Times of sunrise (SR) and sunset (SS) shown by solid bar for receiver and by broken bar for Vestine conjugate of receiver.

for both Greenbank and Byrd the average level of activity is lower during the December solstice than during the June solstice. The corresponding variation of whistler rate at Byrd is shown by the dotted curve. Although the daytime activity is low, both whistlers and NSS echoes are received at Byrd Station every hour of the day, even when the receiver is in continuous daylight. It is interesting to note that the diurnal curves of whistler occurrence and of NSS whistler-mode activity are substantially the same in character. It is concluded, therefore, that the diurnal variations of whistlers are controlled mainly by propagation factors rather than by thunderstorm activity.

The seasonal differences may be explained by considering the duration of daylight at the opposite ends of the path that originates in Greenbank. The ground sunset and sunrise times shown on the graphs indicate that during the

June solstice there is an appreciable period of darkness at both ends of the path, during which activity is high. (The diurnal curve at Greenbank is shown for only twelve hours because of limitations of the recording schedule.) During the December solstice, the conjugate point to Greenbank, although just outside the Antarctic Circle, is in continuous daylight because of refraction. This implies that D-region absorption occurs at the southern end of the path throughout the twenty-four hours. This fact is believed to account for the marked reduction in whistler-mode activity during the December solstice period at both Greenbank and, particularly, Byrd Station.

This interpretation bears on the question of the location of the reflection points of the two-hop whistler-mode signals. The similarities in the diurnal and seasonal behavior of the one-hop echoes recorded at Byrd and the two-hop echoes recorded at Greenbank show that reception at both stations is affected by absorption at the Southern Hemisphere termination of the path. Reflection must then take place either at the ground or somewhere in the lower regions of the ionosphere where the refractive index varies rapidly in the space of a wavelength (see Fig. 3-29).

Figure 5-14 is consistent with an earlier suggestion that most whistlers observed at high-latitude stations come from lower latitudes via the earth–ionosphere waveguide (Martin, 1958; Allcock, 1960a). The June solstice curves for Byrd Station exhibit a minimum that corresponds well with the sunrise time at the conjugate to Greenbank. Since Byrd itself is then in complete darkness, this decrease implies that the whistler-mode signals received at Byrd exited from the ionosphere near the Greenbank conjugate. This conclusion is supported by data on the group delay of fixed-frequency echoes. During the December solstice, the Greenbank conjugate is in nearly constant sunlight, so that on the basis of this explanation the maximum diurnal activity (near 0600 UT) should be considerably reduced. This expected behavior is shown by the Byrd data for the December solstice (Fig. 5-14).

Propagation factors other than D-region absorption undoubtedly affect the occurrence of whistler-mode echoes, but these factors have not yet been clearly resolved. It has been suggested by Laaspere et al. (1963) that the decrease in whistler-mode activity at sunrise might be partially explained in terms of the occurrence of spread F, which shows a diurnal variation similar to that of whistler-mode activity. Spread F is thought to be caused by field-aligned irregularities in the ionosphere, and these in turn may be linked to the postulated whistler ducts.

A detailed study of the month-to-month variation in the diurnal activity curve (Fig. 5-13) was made for station NPG observed at Stanford. In each month shown, the sunrise drop begins very close to 1300 UT. In most cases this time is close to the time of first sunrise regardless of whether this time occurs first at the receiver or at its conjugate point. This result supports the conclusion reached previously that D-region absorption occurs at both ends of a two-hop path. The second interesting point to be noted on these curves is the systematic change in the shape of the nighttime portion during the five-month period from August to December 1960. In August, activity is low prior to local midnight

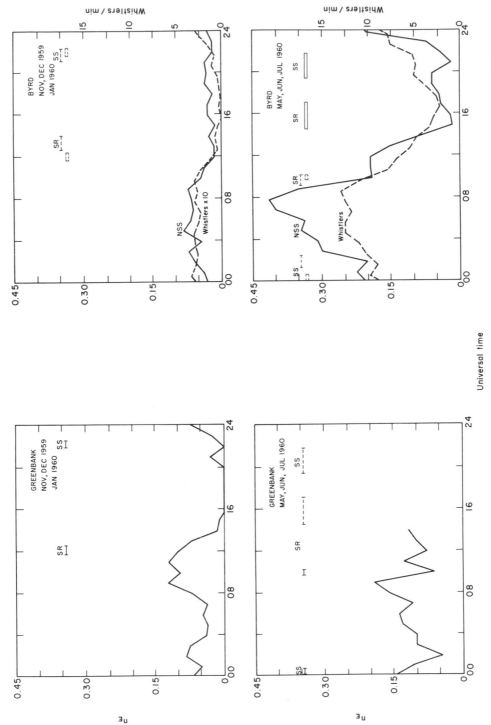

FIG. 5-14. Average diurnal variation of NSS echo occurrence at Byrd and Greenbank during solstice periods. Times of sunrise (SR) and sunset (SS) shown by solid bar for receiver and by broken bar for Vestine conjugate of receiver. Absence of bars indicates no sunrise or sunset during all or part of observation. On curves for Byrd, times of sunrise and sunset at Greenbank are shown by double broken bars, and at Greenbank conjugate by double solid bars.

and reaches a pronounced maximum just before dawn. By December the pre-midnight peak is relatively strong, leaving a marked depression in activity around local midnight.

The cause of the variations in nighttime activity is unknown. A probable cause is a variation in the occurrence of geomagnetic ducting, which should depend on the presence of field-aligned enhancements of ionization and also on horizontal gradients of ionization in the F2 region. With the appropriate horizontal gradients it is possible in principle to alter the direction of the wave normal so that it approaches more closely the direction of the geomagnetic field, thereby reducing the enhancement factors required for trapping of the electromagnetic energy.

Day-to-day activity. Whistler-mode propagation shows a remarkable, un-explained variation in level from day to day. This behavior is illustrated in Fig. 5-15 by the daily activity index for station NPG observed at Stanford over the period September 1960 to December 1961. From the marked variation in activity and the knowledge that background noise level does not vary radically from day to day, we conclude that the over-all transmission loss in the whistler mode varies widely from day to day. Since the observed variations in trans-mission loss cannot readily be attributed to an absorption effect, we must look for some other explanation. One possibility is a day-to-day variation in the enhancement factors of the postulated ducts.

Recently a remarkable correlation was found between NPG whistler-mode echoes and high frequency F-region backscatter observed at Stanford (Carpenter and Colin, 1963). The backscatter was observed on both 12 mc/s and 23 mc/s, and has been interpreted as reflections from meter-scale field-aligned irregulari-ties located in the same area of the F region through which the paths of the whistler-mode echoes could have passed. The correlation, determined from a comparison of activity on a night-to-night basis, was extremely high, as the graph of Fig. 5-16 shows. No correlation was found between whistler-mode echoes and E-region backscatter. The hour-to-hour correlation was also very high on the few nights when sufficient data were available.

This correlation suggests the possibility that the postulated whistler-mode ducts are related to the relatively small F-region irregularities which produce high-frequency backscatter.

5.4   Echo Fading

Whistler-mode echoes from fixed-frequency stations often show pronounced and regular fading in amplitude. This effect was first reported in 1958 (Helliwell and Gehrels). From records such as Fig. 5-7 the fading period has been measured over a considerable length of time. The distributions of echo fading periods from stations NPG and NSS are shown in Fig. 5-17.

One source of the fading of VLF signals observed in point-to-point propaga-tion experiments on the ground is variation in the properties of the earth–ionosphere waveguide. However, Bowhill (1956) has reported that the fading periods of VLF signals propagating in the earth–ionosphere waveguide average about seven minutes. Since the prominent fading periods in the whistler-mode

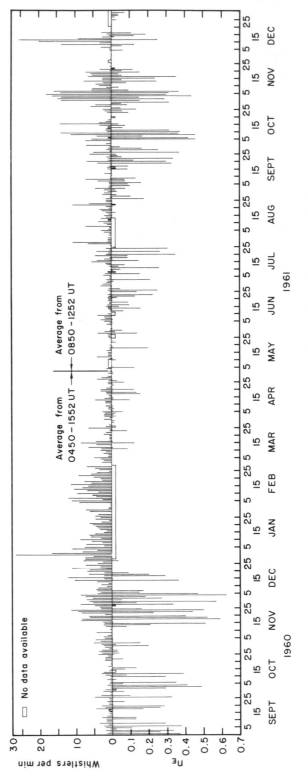

Fig. 5-15. Day-to-day variation in NPG echo activity and whistler rate at Stanford.

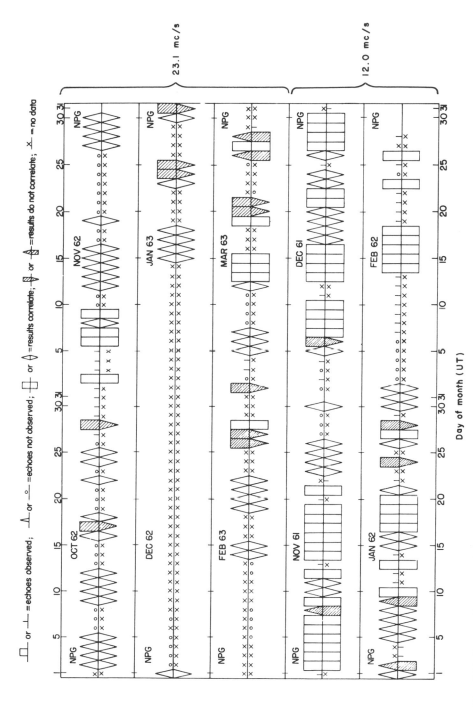

FIG. 5-16. Day-to-day correlation of NPG echo occurrence (upper section of each graph) with occurrence of backscatter (lower section). Days in which data show no correlation are shown shaded.

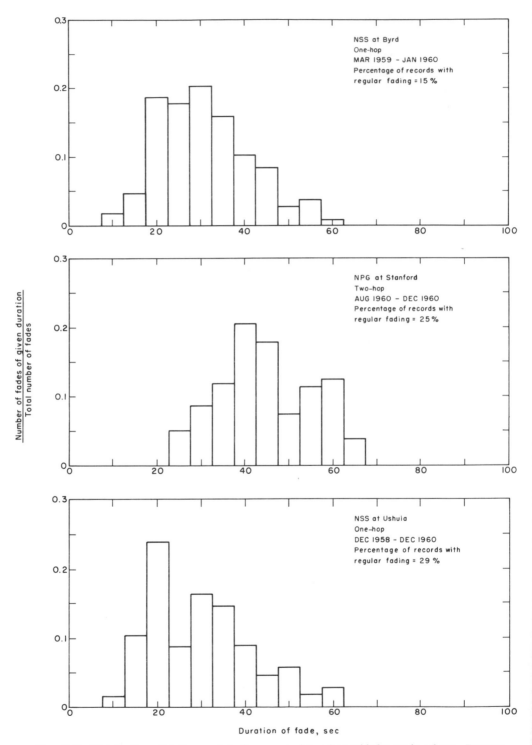

FIG. 5-17. Distribution of fading periods for one- and two-hop whistler-mode echoes. Because of the long pulse repetition period, observations are limited to a minimum fading period of about 5 sec.

signals of Fig. 5-17 are less than one minute, it seems reasonable to rule out waveguide variations as a significant factor in the observed fading pattern. Bowhill notes further that typical ionosphere waveguide fading is shallow and not especially regular. The whistler-mode fading, on the other hand, is systematic and remarkably deep, with the minima often dropping 20 db below the maxima.

The nature of the observed fading suggests the interference of two relatively stable signals of approximately equal amplitude and slowly varying phase. Two discrete field-aligned paths with nearly the same group delay could account for the observations.

5.5   *Group Delay Distributions*

Group delay is closely related to electron density and path latitude. It can be measured readily by using the method described in Sec. 5.1. Statistical data on group delay measured at Stanford, Greenbank, Ushuaia, and Byrd will now be examined and interpreted in terms of paths of propagation. For data taken at Ushuaia and Byrd, a correction of 0.03 seconds was added to the measured group delay to account for the time required for the ground pulse to reach the receiver. Delays measured at Stanford and Greenbank were divided by two to give the equivalent one-hop delay. Where the group delay varied within a four-minute run, the minimum delay was used.

The distribution of group delays for certain pairs of stations is plotted in Fig. 5-18. In spite of statistical uncertainties, the following significant trends have been noted.

1. The group delays at Byrd show a much greater range than those at Ushuaia, and, significantly, include the range of delays observed at Ushuaia. This result is taken to mean that virtually all echoes exiting at latitudes between Byrd and Ushuaia are received at Byrd, whereas Ushuaia receives only those exiting at latitudes equal to or lower than Ushuaia. This in turn suggests that coupling between the duct and the earth–ionosphere waveguide is best when the receiver is located on the high-latitude side of the duct.

2. The average group delays at Stanford (44° N) are much lower than those at Greenbank (50° N), even though the NPG transmitter is higher in geomagnetic latitude (54° N) than the NSS transmitter (50° N). The difference in frequency of the transmitters is not significant in this comparison, since it could account for no more than 10 per cent of the observed difference. This result suggests that with respect to the group delay, the location of the receiver may be more important than that of the transmitter. The relation between the Greenbank and the Stanford delay is in fact roughly that predicted from the latitudes of the receivers. It is also possible that the difference in the longitudes of Greenbank and Stanford contributes to the observed difference in delay.

Marked decreases in echo delay occur during magnetic storms as in the case of whistlers (see Chap. 6). For example, the magnetic disturbance of December 1–3, 1961, was accompanied by a marked decrease in the NPG two-hop echo delay from the normal value of 0.75 sec to a minimum value of 0.4 sec. No whistlers were observed at Stanford during this period.

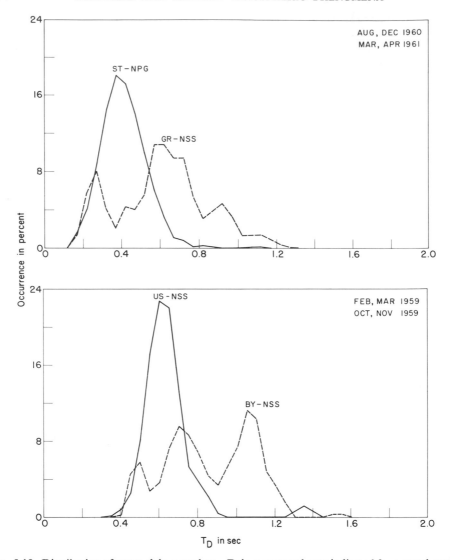

FIG. 5-18. Distribution of group delays per hop. Delays averaged over indicated four-month period.

5.6   *Transmission Loss*

It is difficult to measure transmission loss in the whistler mode accurately with conventional single-channel receiving equipment because of uncertainties in polarization and direction of arrival of the received wave. Furthermore, interpretation of the field at the receiver in terms of the basic loss factors is difficult because the location of the path of propagation is generally not known. In spite of these limitations it is possible to estimate roughly the transmission loss in certain special cases. Hence when the whistler-mode signal is very strong and associated whistler data indicate that the path latitude is close to the latitude of the receiver, it is reasonable to assume that the end point of the duct is near the receiver. An example of a whistler-mode echo that meets these requirements is shown in Fig. 5-2. The median field intensity is estimated to be 200 μv/m. The direct wave from the transmitter (1100 km distant) is about 4000 μv/m. Hence the ratio of echo to direct wave at the receiver is -26 db.

Using this echo intensity and the methods of Sec. 3.11, we can estimate the apparent cross-sectional area of this duct. Taking $P = 250$ kw, $T_d = 1.0$, and other parameters as given in the illustrative example, we obtain an apparent area of about 2600 km², assuming that there is no ionospheric absorption or leakage at the conjugate point. This relatively large area could be interpreted either as a single duct or as a number of smaller ducts.

At Stanford the weakest detectable whistler-mode signal, observed during local winter, is about 5 μv/m, 32 db below the strong signal in Fig. 5-2.

Transmission loss should be low when both transmitter and receiver are close to the duct. The only case in which this condition can be approximately realized is the NSS-Greenbank pair. Strong two-hop echoes with field intensities as high as 800 μv/m at 15.5 kc/s have in fact been observed at Greenbank. This value exceeds the strongest echoes received at Stanford from NPG, which has 4 db more power, and therefore it is consistent with the prediction.

5.7 Satellite Observations

Observations of fixed-frequency whistler-mode propagation were made in the LOFTI I satellite (Leiphart et al., 1962; Rorden et al., 1962). Pulses on a frequency of 18.0 kc/s were transmitted from both NBA in the Canal Zone and NPG near Seattle, and were received in the satellite on a small-loop antenna feeding a narrow-band receiver (25-cps bandwidth). Signals received in the satellite were observed to fade and to show group delays ranging from a few milliseconds to over 650 milliseconds. The carrier frequency was often doppler-shifted several cycles per second. The pulse envelope usually showed little distortion, but occasionally multiple pulses were observed. Signals were strong at night and generally weak during the daytime, but were present over much of the observable portion of the satellite orbit. Signals were observed as far away as Woomera, Australia. Signals from NPG were generally stronger than those from NBA during daytime when the sub-satellite field intensities from the two stations were about the same. The data obtained from NBA in the LOFTI I satellite are illustrated in Fig. 5-19 (reproduced from Rorden et al., 1962). Multiple whistler-mode signals of short and long delay are shown; they are labeled "initial pulse" and "echo," respectively.

One of the most significant results of the LOFTI I experiment was the observation of whistler-mode signals at virtually every location of the satellite. No evidence for whistler ducts was found. This result is not as paradoxical as it might seem, since the observation of whistlers on the ground requires not only the excitation of a whistler-mode signal but its transmission across the lower boundary of the ionosphere back into the earth–ionosphere waveguide. The satellite, on the other hand, observed only the transmitted whistler-mode signal. Even if the satellite had been in a whistler duct, the related changes in wave-normal direction and field intensity might well have gone undetected.

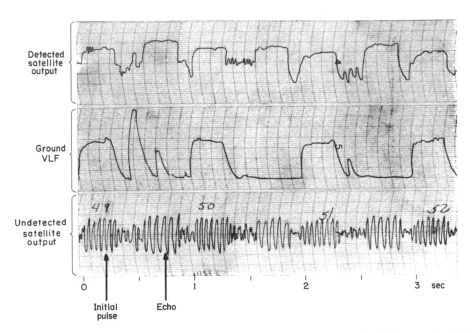

FIG. 5-19. Satellite data taken during nighttime showing whistler-mode signals from station NBA on 18.0 kc/s. Telemetry from LOFTI I showing detected output (top record) and undetected output (bottom record) of satellite receiver together with signal received on ground at Fort Myers, Florida (middle record). Short-delay signals labeled 49, 50, and 51 are each followed by a long-delay echo signal. (Traces darkened for better reproduction.)

    The virtually continuous observation of whistler-mode signals in LOFTI I is evidence against the presence of irregularities capable of cutting off whistler-mode propagation. Hence the suggestion by Budden (1959) that irregularities in the lower ionosphere might affect the constitutive relations and thus cut off VLF propagation is not supported by these results. If irregularities of the type postulated by Budden do in fact exist, and if they have the predicted effect on the constitutive relations, then their size must be such as to produce relatively little effect at a frequency of 18.0 kc/s.

    Let us now consider why non-ducted whistler-mode signals are not detected on the ground. As pointed out in Sec. 3.7, the wave-normal direction of a ducted wave with respect to the direction of the earth's field must lie within a certain cone that depends on the increase of electron density in the duct. If any of these wave normals falls within the transmission cone, energy will propagate across the boundary and be received on the ground. Furthermore, the restriction of this angle limits the magnitude of the collisional absorption. On the other hand the wave normals of non-ducted whistler-mode signals of the type observed in LOFTI I can deviate markedly from the direction of the earth's magnetic field, as shown by Yabroff (1961). Such a deviation has two effects. First, a large wave-normal angle greatly increases the absorption, as shown in Fig. 3-32. Second, a large wave-normal angle tends to increase the reflection at the lower boundary of the ionosphere, so that little energy is transmitted to the ground. Thus we have a consistent interpretation of both the LOFTI I results and the ground results. In this picture the whistler duct acts simply to control the wave normal and has only a second-order effect on the strength of the signal as observed in the satellite.

On the basis of this interpretation one might expect careful observations in a satellite to show only a slight increase in field strength in a whistler duct compared with that in adjacent regions. On the other hand, under corresponding conditions the wave-normal direction should show a marked change in the hemisphere opposite the location of the transmitter.

With the inclusion of non-ducted transmission, several types of ray path are possible, depending on the altitude and the geographical location of the satellite. One of these, of course, is the so-called "ducted" mode, in which the energy is assumed to be trapped in ducts of increased ionization aligned with the earth's magnetic field. This type of ray path has been assumed in order to explain the multipath character of whistlers (Smith, 1961a).

The average spacing between the ducts is typically a few hundred kilometers, which is large compared with the estimated duct diameter of 10 km. The probability that a satellite would encounter a duct is therefore very low. LOFTI I often observed whistler-mode signals continuously over distances greater than 1000 km. It is concluded, therefore, that ducts are not responsible for the signals observed in the satellite.

It then follows that the effective ray paths need not be aligned closely with the earth's magnetic field (Yabroff, 1961), but, of course, they must still lie within the limiting ray cone around the magnetic field, as shown by Storey (1953) and Smith (1960b).

The principal types of ray paths expected at very low frequencies under quasi-longitudinal conditions are diagrammed in Fig. 5-20. In the diagram, T represents a VLF transmitter on the earth's surface; points labeled R represent receivers in the ionosphere, with the ionosphere-boundary altitude shown exaggerated. Paths 1, 2, and 3 lie predominantly in the earth–ionosphere waveguide, and result in the shortest possible delays. These three paths differ mainly in the position of the receiver. For path 1, the receiver is in the same magnetic hemisphere as the transmitter, but at higher latitude; for path 2, it is in the same hemisphere but at lower latitude; and for path 3, it is in the opposite hemisphere. Paths 4, 5, and 6 are characterized by strong magneto-ionic guiding and return of the ray from an altitude maximum. These are usually called whistler-mode paths, although they do not necessarily follow ducts of increased ionization. Paths 4 and 5 can be called one-hop paths, since they go through one altitude maximum. They are shown ending in the hemisphere opposite their entrance to the ionosphere. It is possible (but not very likely) that the entire ionospheric path will lie in one hemisphere. Path 6 represents a two-hop whistler-mode path in which a one-hop signal (6a) is reflected in the lower ionosphere and returns (6b) to the hemisphere of origin.

We can interpret the multiple signals shown in Fig. 5-19 in terms of the possible ray paths sketched in Fig. 5-20. To explain the relatively great strength

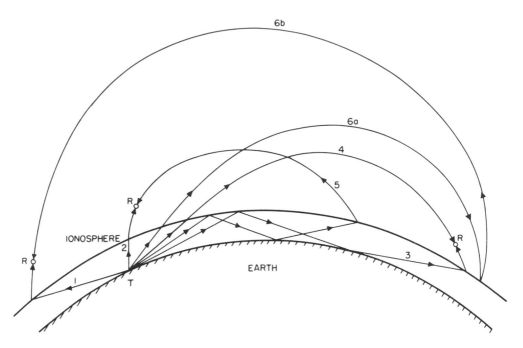

FIG. 5-20. Principal paths involved in satellite reception of VLF transmissions. The letter *T* represents a VLF transmitter and *R* represents positions of satellite-borne receiver. Altitude of earth–ionosphere boundary is shown exaggerated.

of the second signal or "echo," it is necessary to postulate that the first segment of the path begins close to but south of the transmitter (path 6*a* of Fig. 5-20). Input-field strength is then high and D-region absorption is not excessive because of the favorable wave-normal direction. The signal is reflected at the lower boundary of the ionosphere* and returns to the satellite along path 6*b*. A group-delay analysis for these low-latitude paths shows that variations in the assumed path have relatively little effect on the integrated time delay. Hence it is possible to deduce an effective scale height for the upper region of the ionosphere. For the LOFTI I group-delay data, the scale height of the upper part of the F region, assuming a Chapman distribution, was found to be 85 km during the night and 120 km during the day, in reasonable agreement with other estimates (Wright, 1960).

The interpretation of LOFTI I results is consistent with that suggested for the Vanguard III whistler observations described in Sec. 4.6. In both cases it appears that energy reaches the satellite along a ray path that is defined by the distribution of the refractive index. This ray path is close to the direction of the earth's field but not exactly the same as in the case of whistler ducts. This interpretation implies that whistler energy is being transmitted into the ionosphere continuously from all the thunderstorms over the surface of the earth.

---

* Alternatively, reflection might occur at a layer of sporadic E ionization.

Most of this energy remains within the ionosphere as a result of absorption or total internal reflection at the lower boundary of the ionosphere. Only those signals that happen to enter a whistler duct will partially emerge from the opposite end to be observed as ordinary whistlers. Thus, to a first approximation the ionosphere becomes an effective electromagnetic energy trap for very-low-frequency sources on the ground. Essentially all energy that enters the ionosphere remains there.

What becomes of this ionosphere-trapped energy? On the daylight side of the earth the observed attentuation rates suggest that most of the absorption takes place in the D and E regions and thus that lightning energy contributes something to the heating of the lower ionosphere through the process of collisional absorption. At night, however, attenuation in the lower layers is obviously small, judging from the relatively low decrement of whistler echo trains and the LOFTI I results. Hence a number of hops can occur before the whistler has decreased appreciably in intensity. There is therefore a greater opportunity for the upper regions of the magnetosphere to extract energy from the whistler. When the gyro-frequency is close to the wave frequency, dissipation is likely to increase. Thus at night we can expect absorption of whistler energy in the region near the top of the magnetic field-line path, where the wave frequencies approach the gyro-frequency. The absorption mechanism is not fully understood, but it may be similar to Landau damping (Scarf, 1962; Liemohn and Scarf, 1962a, b), or it may be related to acceleration of electrons in the manner of the proposed geocyclotron (Helliwell and Bell, 1960). The latter type of absorption could account in part for a component of the radiation belts. At the same time it is important to note that the exchange of energy between electromagnetic waves and the ambient plasma may not always be from the wave to the plasma. As we point out in Chap. 7, conditions under which the plasma transfers its energy to the electromagnetic wave can be visualized.

The interpretation of the multiple signals shown in Fig. 5-20 suggests that the path of propagation of non-ducted signals may tend to move toward the poles with each successive reflection. This concept was considered in connection with certain observed properties of whistlers before the idea of whistler ducts was developed (Storey, 1953; Helliwell, 1956b). The result of this behavior is that if attenuation in the lower regions is not too severe, most of the energy of a whistler will eventually reach high latitudes, where it will be absorbed near the top of the paths of propagation.

For example, consider a frequency of 5 kc/s, at which whistler energy tends to peak. The region of absorption at 5 kc/s will necessarily lie at an altitude below that at which the minimum gyro-frequency is equal to 5 kc/s. This altitude occurs at about five to six geocentric earth radii (see Appendix). Thus if the outer ionosphere is heated appreciably by whistlers, the heated region might be expected to lie between roughly four and six earth radii.

Chapter Six

Electron-Density Measurements Using Whistlers

From the theory of whistlers outlined in Chap. 3, we find that the group delay is influenced by the number of electrons along the path of propagation. Hence it should be possible, in principle, to extract information about the electron-density distribution from the integral equation for group delay. In this chapter methods for finding the distribution are discussed and one of them, based on the work of Smith (1960a, 1961a), is developed in detail.

We shall show that the shape of a whistler trace is relatively insensitive to the shape of the electron-density distribution, and that therefore a solution of the integral equation for a single trace is difficult to apply to experimental data. We shall develop a practical method of analysis in which the variation of dispersion with latitude is used, and shall make an approximate correction for the F region of the ionosphere. We shall present quantitative results that define the electron density in the equatorial plane at geocentric distances of from two to five earth radii, and shall show that this method of analysis is nearly independent of the shape of the distribution along a particular field-line path. We shall then describe the variations of the electron density with time and with magnetic activity.

6.1 Nose Whistler Analysis

Group-delay integral. The group delay at a given frequency can be determined when the group ray refractive index μ_r' and the path of propagation are known. In general the delay is given by

$$T = \frac{1}{c} \int_{\text{path}} \mu_r' \, ds \; . \tag{6.1}$$

For this problem the approximate form of the group refractive index given by (3.13) is applicable. The group ray refractive index is then given by (3.30). When (3.30) is substituted into (6.1) the group delay becomes

$$T = \frac{1}{2c} \int_{\text{path}} \frac{f_0 f_H}{f^{1/2}(f_H - f)^{3/2}} \, \phi(\theta, \Lambda) \, ds \; , \tag{6.2}$$

where

$$\phi(\theta, \Lambda) = \frac{(1 - \Lambda)^{3/2}}{\left[\frac{1}{4} \tan^2 \theta (\cos \theta - \Lambda) + \dfrac{(\cos \theta - \Lambda)^3}{\cos^2 \theta} \right]^{1/2}} \; .$$

The quantity $\phi(\theta, \Lambda)$ is plotted in Fig. 3-14.

Equation (6.2) defines the group delay in general, under the approximations developed in Chap. 3, for any signal traveling through the whistler medium. However, computation of (6.2) is complicated by the dependence of the path of integration on the distribution of electron density. In general, machine calculations (Yabroff, 1961) for particular models of the magnetosphere must be performed in order to obtain numerical results.

To obtain the distribution of electron density from a single whistler it is necessary to solve the integral equation (6.2) for the distribution of plasma frequency f_0. No analytical solution to this problem has yet been developed. In addition, as we shall see shortly, the available experimental data are not sufficiently accurate for this approach to the problem. Practical solutions to this problem are based on a knowledge of the path of propagation and a simplification in the expression for the group ray refractive index.

Path of propagation. In Chap. 4, we presented experimental evidence which indicated that whistlers travel along paths of propagation aligned with the earth's magnetic field. Hence the path of propagation is known to the same accuracy as the earth's magnetic field, which can be described with sufficient accuracy by the dipole approximation. This approximation has been supported by satellite and probe measurements which show that the earth's magnetic field is dipole in form out to at least six or seven earth radii from the center of the earth (E. J. Smith *et al.*, 1960).

Near the surface of the earth, higher-order terms must be included to describe accurately the location of a line of force. These terms lose significance rapidly with increasing altitude, so that near the top of a whistler path the field is well described by the dipole approximation. It is convenient, therefore, in whistler analysis to use the concept of the effective dipole latitude, which is the latitude of the path in the dipole field at which the nose frequency would be the same as the actual nose frequency. Hence there may be a discrepancy between the effective latitude and the actual latitude of the endpoint of a particular path of propagation. Since a single whistler component covers an effective area of about a thousand kilometers in diameter, this discrepancy is difficult to detect simply by measuring relative intensity at spaced stations.

The locus of a dipole magnetic-field line is given in polar coordinates by

$$\frac{R}{R_0} = \frac{\cos^2 \phi}{\cos^2 \phi_0},\tag{6.3}$$

where R_0 is the radius of the earth and ϕ_0 is the latitude of the effective dipole field line at the earth's surface.

From the dipole approximation to the earth's field, we get for the gyrofrequency f_H at any point in space

$$\frac{f_H}{f_{H_0}} = \left(\frac{R_0}{R}\right)^3 \sqrt{1 + 3 \sin^2 \phi},\tag{6.4}$$

where f_{H_0} is the gyro-frequency at the geomagnetic equator on the earth's surface. Its value is approximately 886 kc/s. The minimum value of the gyro-frequency, given by

$$f_{H_1} = f_{H_0} \cos^6 \phi_0 , \qquad (6.5)$$

occurs at the top of the path.

Longitudinal approximation. We have demonstrated the plausibility of the field-aligned duct as an explanation of the observed properties of whistlers. Let us assume that whistlers propagate in such ducts and that their propagation characteristics are described accurately by the ray theory developed in Chap. 3 There it was found that the average group ray velocity in a duct of enhanced ionization was described closely by the purely longitudinal expression for group ray velocity. The error in this assumption for reasonable enhancement factors is less than 1 per cent. It is justifiable, therefore, to make the approximation that the group ray refractive index is described by the purely longitudinal expression. Thus in Eq. (6.2) the factor $\phi(\theta, \Lambda)$ becomes 1 and the group-delay integral reduces to

$$T = \frac{1}{2c} \int_{\text{path}} \frac{f_0 f_H \, ds}{f^{1/2}(f_H - f)^{3/2}} . \qquad (6.6)$$

Equation (6.6) can be simplified for purposes of analysis by multiplying both sides by $f^{1/2}$, which gives

$$Tf^{1/2} = D(f) = \frac{1}{2c} \int_{\text{path}} \frac{f_0 f_H \, ds}{(f_H - f)^{3/2}} . \qquad (6.7)$$

The quantity $D(f)$ is called the dispersion of the whistler. As f approaches zero, D approaches a constant equal to the dispersion constant used by Storey (1953). By substituting (6.4) into (6.7), we can express the dispersion in terms of the field-line coordinates by

$$D(f) = \frac{R_0}{cf_{H_0}^{1/2} \cos^5 \phi_0} \int_0^{x_0} \frac{f_0(x)(1 - x^2)^{3/2}(1 + 3x^2)^{1/4} \, dx}{\left[1 - \Lambda_1 \dfrac{(1 - x^2)^3}{(1 + 3x^2)^{1/2}}\right]^{3/2}} , \qquad (6.8)$$

where

$$x = \sin \phi , \qquad x_0 = \sin \phi_0 , \qquad \Lambda_1 = \frac{f}{f_{H_1}} .$$

Dispersion at low frequencies. At frequencies low compared with the gyro-frequency and the plasma frequency, (6.8) reduces to

$$D = Tf^{1/2} = \frac{R_0}{cf_{H_0}^{1/2} \cos^5 \phi_0} \int_0^{x_0} f_0(x)(1 - x^2)^{3/2}(1 + 3x^2)^{1/4} \, dx . \qquad (6.9)$$

In this approximation D is a constant that is measured from the whistler trace itself. If the latitude of the field-line path and the form of $f_0(x)$ are given, the scale factor of $f_0(x)$ can be determined from (6.9). If, in addition, D is given over a range of latitudes, the scale factor of $f_0(x)$ is defined for the same range of latitude. Alternatively, the variation of base-level ionization with latitude can be assumed and then the shape of the distribution can be adjusted to fit the data.

Using this approach, Allcock (1959) computed a distribution of electron density from one to two earth radii above the earth. As we shall show later, the resulting distribution is consistent with that determined by using nose whistlers. A problem in Allcock's method is that the path of propagation cannot be determined readily without additional information. Allcock assumed that the average path latitude of the whistlers from one location was in fact equal to the geomagnetic latitude of the receiver. In his study, the principal stations are close to the belt of maximum whistler activity, and therefore his assumption is probably valid. However, the effective area of a whistler covers an appreciable range of latitudes, so that the average dispersion at a station may correspond to a substantially different latitude.

Direct integration of the dispersion integral. Equation (6.8) can be directly integrated for the whistler dispersion by using integral tables for two simple models of plasma frequency variation. These are $f_0 = $ constant and $f_0 = \kappa \sqrt{f_H}$. If we make the following substitutions

$$1 - y^2 = \frac{(1 - x^2)^3}{(1 + 3x^2)^{1/2}} = \frac{f_{H_1}}{f_H}, \tag{6.10}$$

$$h(y) = \frac{2}{9} \frac{(1 + 3x^2)^{5/3} y}{(1 + \frac{5}{3}x^2)(1 - y^2)^{1/6} x}, \tag{6.11}$$

$$A(x_0) = \frac{R_0}{c f_{H_0}^{1/2}(1 - x_0^2)^{5/3}} = \frac{R_0 f_{H_0}^{1/3}}{c f_{H_1}^{5/6}}, \tag{6.12}$$

and

$$g(y) = f_0(y) h(y), \tag{6.13}$$

then (6.8) is given by

$$D(f) = A(x_0) \int_0^{y_0} \frac{g(y)\, dy}{(1 - \Lambda_1 + \Lambda_1 y^2)^{3/2}}. \tag{6.14}$$

The function $h(y)$ contains the integrable factor $(1 - y^2)^{-1/6}$, and is in general well behaved. In the two examples that follow we shall approximate $h(y)$ as a constant. The upper limit of integration y_0 is approximately 1 for most latitudes of interest. Thus for a latitude of 50°, y_0 is 0.98. For our purpose it is sufficient to approximate y_0 by 1. Carpenter (1962a, b) has found that the errors in these two approximations tend to cancel one another.

Consider the model for constant plasma frequency; then $g(y)$ becomes a constant (G), and Eq. (6.14) reduces to

$$D(f) = A(x_0) G \int_0^1 \frac{dy}{(1 - \Lambda_1 + \Lambda_1 y^2)^{3/2}} = \frac{A(x_0)G}{1 - \Lambda_1} = \frac{A(x_0)G}{1 - f/f_{H_1}}. \tag{6.15}$$

Solving (6.15) for the group delay and differentiating with respect to frequency, we find that the nose frequency is simply $f_{H_1}/3$.

For the second model, we have $f_0 = \kappa \sqrt{f_H}$, and therefore

$$g(y) = G(1 - y^2)^{-1/2} ,$$

where G is a constant. The integral of (6.14) then becomes

$$D(f) = A(x_0)G \int_0^1 \frac{dy}{(1 - y^2)^{1/2}(1 - \Lambda_1 + \Lambda_1 y^2)^{3/2}} . \qquad (6.16a)$$

Smith (1960a) has shown that this expression may be integrated by using the transformation $y = x(1 - \Lambda_1)^{y_2}(1 - \Lambda_1 x)^{-y_2}$. With substitution, Eq. (6.16a) becomes

$$D(f) = \frac{A(x_0)G}{(1 - \Lambda_1)} \int_0^1 \frac{(1 - \Lambda_1 x^2)^{1/2}}{(1 - x^2)^{1/2}} \, dx = \frac{A(x_0)G}{(1 - \Lambda_1)} E(\Lambda_1^{1/2}) , \qquad (6.16b)$$

where E is the complete elliptic integral of the second kind with modulus $\Lambda_1^{1/2}$. For this model, the so-called gyro-frequency model, the nose frequency is approximately $0.39 f_{H_1}$.

In these two elementary examples the path of propagation can be determined from the nose frequency. When the path is known, the scale factor of the distribution can be determined.

These examples are useful as illustrations, but are not suitable for solving the electron-density problem, since there is no a priori basis for assuming any particular shape for the distribution. What is needed is a method for determining the shape of the distribution from the experimental data.

Solution of the whistler integral equation. The whistler integral equation (6.6) can be considered to be a purely analytical problem in which we wish to extract the plasma frequency distribution for a given variation of group delay with frequency. Various approaches to this problem have been outlined by different authors. These approaches have been summarized by Smith (1960a), who developed one approach based on the use of the Stieltjes transform. This solution requires knowledge of all the derivatives of the dispersion function, and hence is of little practical use because of the difficulty of obtaining the data. Another approach, considered by both Smith (1960a) and Storey (1957a, b), is to expand the function $g(y)$ in a power series. Unfortunately it appears to be very difficult to evaluate the coefficients in the power series with sufficient accuracy from experimental whistler data.

The basic difficulty in attempting to invert the whistler integral equation arises from the fact that the experimental function $T(f)$ is relatively insensitive to the plasma frequency distribution $f_0(x)$. Error analysis for the inversion process itself is a complicated problem, and even if successfully performed, it appears to be of little practical use.

6.2   Method of Assumed Models

Relation of model shape to dispersion function. Because of the difficulties encountered in attempting to solve the whistler integral equation for the electron-density distribution, a different method based on assumed models has been used (Smith, 1960a, 1961a; Pope, 1961a). The function $D(f)$ is

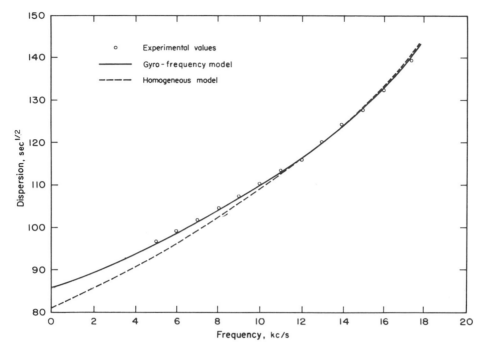

FIG. 6 1. Curves of dispersion versus frequency calculated for the homogeneous model given by (6.17) and for the "gyro-frequency" model given by (6.18). Circles represent data scaled from a whistler recorded at Seattle, 5 Feb 58, 1336 UT. Curves were normalized to fit the whistler at its nose frequency of 14.75 kc/s. (For another example of the comparison of the theoretical and experimental results, see Fig. 4-18.)

calculated for various assumed model distributions and the results are compared with the data. In one extreme model all of the ionization is assumed to be concentrated at the top of the path. This is equivalent to a homogeneous model in which the gyro-frequency is equal to the actual gyro-frequency at the top of the path. The dispersion for this model is then given by

$$D_\triangle = \frac{K}{(1 - \Lambda_1)^{3/2}}, \tag{6.17}$$

where $\Lambda_1 = f/f_{H_1}$.

In another simple model the electron density is proportional to the strength of the magnetic field and hence most of the ionization is near the end points of the path. The dispersion for this model is given approximately by

$$D_H = \frac{2}{\pi} \frac{K}{(1 - \Lambda_1)} E(\Lambda_1^{1/2}). \tag{6.18}$$

To compare these two models the scale factors were chosen such that the delay at the nose would be the same. Path latitudes were chosen to make the nose frequencies for these two distributions the same. Curves of dispersion versus frequency for these two models are shown in Fig. 6-1. The difference in dispersion at zero frequency is only about 4 per cent. The lowest frequencies observable on middle-latitude nose whistlers are usually not much lower than 5 kc/s, where the difference in dispersion for the two models is only 2 per cent. Since the experimental error of measurement of the best whistlers is not much less than 2 per cent, it is clear that recovery of the shape of the plasma frequency distribution from a single nose whistler trace would be difficult.

Use of latitude variation of whistlers. Because the shape of the nose whistler is relatively insensitive to the shape of the electron-density distribution, single nose whistler traces have been used to provide only a single parameter of the electron-density distribution. Additional information is provided by multiple nose whistlers whose individual components propagate over paths of different geomagnetic latitude. From each component two measurements are made— the nose frequency and the group delay at the nose. The latitude of the path is derived from the nose frequency, while the delay defines one parameter of the distribution along that particular path. From statistically significant quantities of data, the characteristic variation of delay at the nose is obtained as a function of latitude. A model of the electron-density distribution in the magneto-sphere can be fitted to this variation after a correction is made for the lower ionosphere.

Experimental data. Samples of nose whistlers obtained from spectrograms have been scaled for nose frequency and group delay. The nose frequency is plotted as a function of group delay at the nose in Fig. 6-2 (Smith, 1960a, 1961a). The trend of these data is simple and well defined, suggesting the feasibility of representation by a simple model of electron density. Two pronounced groupings are obvious, one around the December and one around the June solstice, indicating an annual variation, which is discussed in Sec. 6.4.

Effect of the lower ionosphere. Because of its high electron density, the F region of the ionosphere has a significant effect on whistler dispersion, especially at low latitudes (20° to 30°). At middle and high latitudes, however, the portion of the total dispersion attributable to the F region is relatively small because of the short length of path and the high values of gyro-frequency in the F region.

Because of the high gyro-frequency, the dispersion for a single passage through the F layer can be approximated by

$$D_{\mathrm{F}} = \frac{1}{2c} \int \frac{f_0 \, ds}{f_H^{1/2}} \, . \tag{6.19}$$

Since the gyro-frequency f_H is substantially constant in the F region, the integral of (6.19) reduces simply to

$$D_{\mathrm{F}} = \frac{1}{2c f_H^{1/2}} \int f_0 \, ds \, . \tag{6.20}$$

To compute (6.20) we require a model of the F layer. It is convenient and

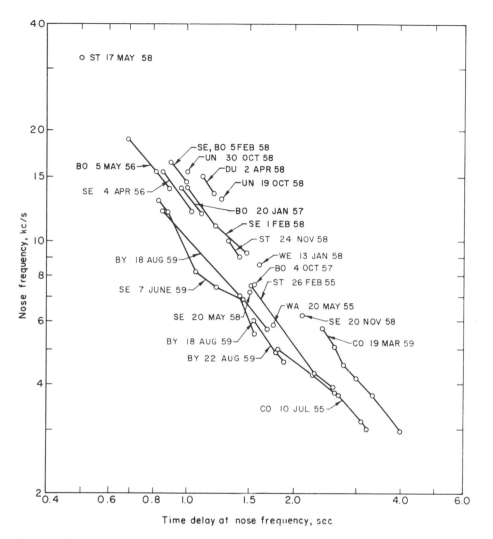

FIG. 6-2. Frequency versus delay at whistler nose. Solid lines connect components from the same source.

accurate enough for this purpose to represent the plasma frequency in the F layer by a double parabolic distribution with a lower semi-thickness of 100 km and an upper semi-thickness of 500 km. For this model, (6.20) becomes

$$D_{\mathrm{F}} = \frac{f_0 \mathrm{F}2}{2 c f_H^{1/2}} \left\{ \int_{-100}^{0} \left[1 - \left(\frac{h}{100} \right)^2 \right]^{1/2} dh + \int_{0}^{500} \left[1 - \left(\frac{h}{500} \right)^2 \right]^{1/2} dh \right\}, \quad (6.21)$$

where h is the height in km with respect to the maximum, and $f_0\mathrm{F}2$ is the "ordinary" critical frequency of the F layer.

Performing the indicated integrations, we get from (6.21),

$$D_F = \frac{f_0 F2}{2cf_H^{1/2}} \times 150\pi .\tag{6.22}$$

A typical value for (6.22) when $f_0 F2 = 3$ mc and $f_H = 1$ mc, is $D \approx 2.4$ sec$^{1/2}$. This value must, of course, be doubled for a one-hop whistler that passes twice through the F region.

Choice of models—normalized nose frequencies. From the appearance of the data in Fig. 6-2, a two-parameter model would seem satisfactory. The following models are considered:

Dungey's model: On thermodynamical grounds Dungey (1954) proposed that collisions cause the density of particles to be distributed in isothermal equilibrium irrespective of the presence of the earth's field. If we assume only protons and electrons at a temperature of 1500°K, the electron density in Dungey's model is given by

$$N = N_0 e^{2.5/R} ,\tag{6.23}$$

where N_0 is the electron density at infinity and R is the distance from the earth's center in earth radii. Johnson (1960) has derived a similar model, with a centrifugal force term added.

Johnson-Smith model: Johnson (1959) and Smith (1960a), independently suggested a model in which the Dungey model of (6.23) is multiplied by the gyro-frequency. The density is then given by

$$N = N_0 f_H e^{2.5/R} .\tag{6.24}$$

Gyro-frequency model: If we consider the spiral motion of individual charged particles in the earth's field, we see that they enclose a constant amount of flux (Alfvén, 1950). Hence the electron density tends to be proportional to the strength of the earth's field. This model, called the gyro-frequency model, has been used by several authors (Storey, 1953; Gallet, 1959a; Smith, 1960a, 1961a) in the study of whistlers, and recently has been given a theoretical basis by Dowden (1961a). This model is particularly attractive because it simplifies the calculation of the group delay.

Model forms: It is convenient to maintain a constant base level for the models containing gyro-frequency by introducing the factor

$$g = \frac{1}{(1 + 3 \sin^2 \phi_0)^{1/2}} .$$

This factor has a relatively small effect, since ϕ_0 varies from roughly 45 deg to 65 deg, giving a corresponding variation in this factor of about 8 per cent.

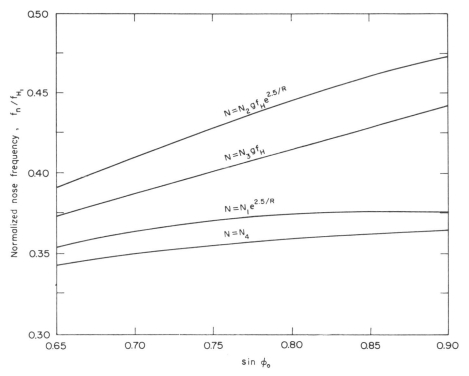

FIG. 6-3. Normalized nose frequency versus latitude for selected electron-density models.

The electron-density variations for the different models used in the calculations are given by

Dungey Model	$N = N_1 e^{2.5/R}$,	(6.25)
Johnson-Smith Model	$N = N_2 g f_H e^{2.5/R}$,	(6.26)
Gyro-frequency Model	$N = N_3 g f_H$,	(6.27)
Constant-density Model	$N = N_4$.	(6.28)

For each of these models there is a characteristic variation of $\Lambda_n = f_n/f_{H_1}$ with latitude. Smith (1960a, 1961b) has computed curves showing this variation; they are shown in Fig. 6-3. Although differences in the normalized wave frequency are not large, they are of sufficient magnitude to be considered in the calculations of f_n versus t_n for the models.

Fitting a model to the data. The final step in selecting a model is to compute the f_n versus t_n curve for the test models. The three models given by (6.25), (6.26), and (6.27) are substituted into (6.8), which is then solved numerically for the nose frequency at appropriate latitudes. The nose frequency for any latitude is obtained from Fig. 6-3 and Eq. (6.5). The resulting values of $D(f_n)$ are then corrected for F-layer dispersion, after which the delay at the nose is computed from $D(f_n) = t_n \sqrt{f_n}$.

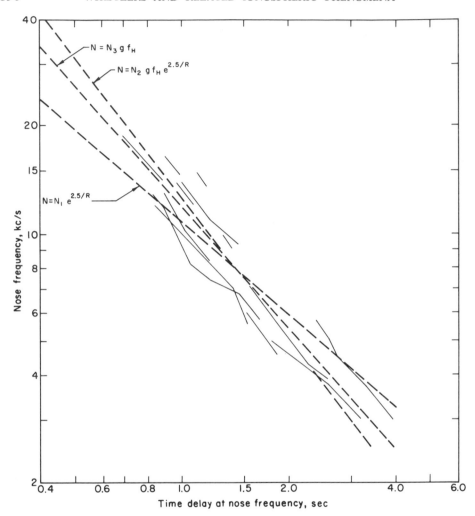

FIG. 6-4. Frequency versus delay at whistler nose predicted from models of the outer ionosphere and from whistler data of Fig. 6-2.

The undetermined scale factor of the electron-density distribution is obtained simply by sliding the computed f_n versus t_n curves parallel to the t_n axis to obtain a best fit with the experimental data. In Fig. 6-4 the three models are compared with the experimental data of Fig. 6-2. The solid lines represent the experimental data and the dashed lines are the computations. The best fit is clearly with the gyro-frequency model, which has therefore been chosen to describe the electron density. The best fit would be with the Dungey model if the exponent were changed such that

$$N = N_0 e^{8/R} . \tag{6.29}$$

However, this change requires a temperature of 500°K if hydrogen is the main constituent. Since the temperature of the outer ionosphere estimated from other measurements (Harris and Jastrow, 1959; Bourdeau et al., 1962). is in the vicinity of 1500°K, the Dungey model seems untenable.

Smith (1960a) has derived an average model based on the gyro-frequency model and the data from Fig. 6-2, which are characteristic of solar maximum. It is given by

$$N = 1.2 \times 10^4 f_H , \qquad (6.30)$$

where N is the number of electrons per cubic meter and f_H is the gyro-frequency in cps.

It is sometimes useful to compare the total electron content over a particular path through the ionosphere with the columnar density obtained from certain high-frequency experiments. For example, Garriott (1960) employed Faraday rotation and doppler techniques to determine the total electron content between the ground and a satellite. The values he obtained are of the order of $10^{17}/m^2$ up to a height of 1000 km. Another method (Eshleman et al., 1960), based on phase path and group path measurements on moon echoes, provides data on the total electron content between earth and moon, in the so-called cislunar medium. Definite values from this measurement are not yet available.

From whistler data we can estimate the total electron content of the magneto-sphere on a radial path in the equatorial plane. From (6.30) we find the base-level electron density to be about $10^{10}/m^3$. Since the density drops off inversely with the cube of the radial distance, the electron content in a column of one square meter cross section is simply

$$N_c = \int_{R_0}^{\infty} \frac{10^{10} \, dR}{(R/R_0)^3} = 3.2 \times 10^{16}/m^2 . \qquad (6.31)$$

6.3   Nose Extension Methods

When nose whistlers are available, the method described in Sec. 6.2 will yield a model. However, most whistlers do not exhibit the nose, and hence some other method is needed for their analysis. One approach to this problem, developed by Smith and Carpenter (1961), is to estimate the nose frequency and delay from the observable portion of the whistler trace. The problem is to find a reasonably simple function to approximate Eq. (6.8). We use the fact that the dispersion function is relatively insensitive to the shape of the distribution. Smith has suggested a function to approximate (6.8). It is given by

$$D(f) = tf^{1/2} = D_0 S_0(f/f_{H_1}) = D_0 \frac{2}{\pi} \frac{E(\sqrt{f/f_{H_1}})}{1 - f/f_{H_1}} , \qquad (6.32)$$

where

$$D_0 = \frac{1}{2c} \int_{\text{path}} \frac{f_0}{f_H^{1/2}} \, ds ,$$

f_{H_1} is the minimum gyro-frequency on the path of propagation, and E is a complete elliptic integral of the second kind.

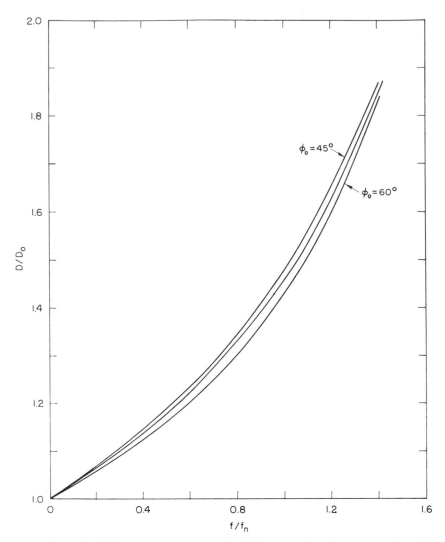

FIG. 6-5. Normalized dispersion versus normalized frequency, showing a comparison of the simplified dispersion function (middle curve) and the full latitude-dependent calculation for latitudes of 45° and 60°.

   To illustrate its accuracy, this approximation is compared in Fig. 6-5 with the complete expression of Eq. (6.8). The curves are plotted for two latitudes (45° and 60°) and the gyro-frequency model of (6.30), and they show that the error in the approximation is nowhere greater than 2 per cent. This error is believed to be smaller than the experimental errors. The relatively small error in this approximation results from the fact that the effects of the two approximations used in deriving Eq. (6.32) nearly cancel each other in the middle of the range of latitudes of high whistler activity (Carpenter, 1962c).
   Since the approximation of (6.32) involves the minimum gyro-frequency, it

can be transformed into a more useful form, in which f_n appears explicitly, by calculating dt/df from (6.32) and setting it equal to zero. Solving for Λ in the resulting equation, we obtain $\Lambda_n = f_n/f_{H_1}$, so that

$$D(f) = D_0 S_1(f/f_n),\qquad(6.33)$$

where

$$S_1(f/f_n) = \frac{2}{\pi}\frac{E(\sqrt{\Lambda_n f/f_n})}{1 - \Lambda_n f/f_n}$$

and $\Lambda_n = 0.386$ for the gyro-frequency model.

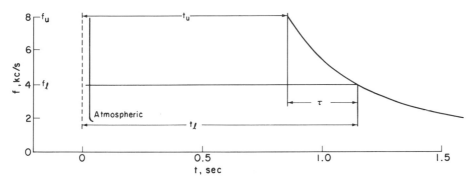

FIG. 6-6. Sketch of whistler spectrogram illustrating measurements required in nose extension method.

Since (6.33) contains two unknowns, D_0 and f_n, we require two independent measurements of $D(f)$ from the whistler trace. It is fairly obvious that these can be the group delays at two frequencies, say 16 kc/s and 8 kc/s. The measurements to be made from the whistler are illustrated in Fig. 6-6, which shows a typical middle-latitude, one-hop whistler trace. A delay of about 30 milliseconds has been assumed for the recorded atmospheric to account for the propagation time from the conjugate point to the receiver. Measurements are made of t_u and t_l, the time delays at the upper and lower frequencies of measurement, respectively.

One of the unknowns, D_0, can be eliminated from Eq. (6.33) by writing the dispersion equation for two frequencies of measurement and dividing one by the other. Thus we have

$$\frac{D(f_u)}{D(f_l)} = \frac{t_u f_u^{1/2}}{t_l f_l^{1/2}} = \frac{S_1(f_u/f_n)}{S_1(f_l/f_n)} = S_2(f_l/f_u; f_u/f_n),\qquad(6.34)$$

where t_u and t_l are the time delays at the upper and lower frequencies of measurement, f_u and f_l. The function S_2 is a new function of the ratios f_l/f_u and f_u/f_n.

From Eq. (6.34) the function S_2 is computed for different values of the independent variables. Curves of S_2 as a function of f_u/f_n parametric in f_l/f_u

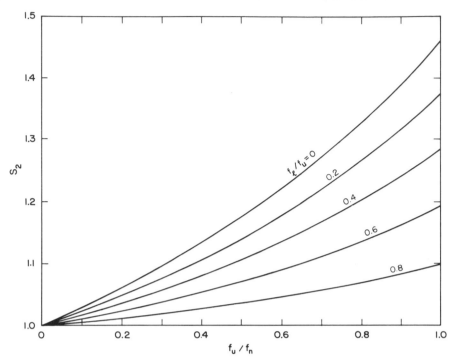

FIG. 6-7. The parameter S_2 versus f_u/f_n parametric in f_l/f_n.

are shown in Fig. 6-7. As we might expect, this figure shows that the ratio f_u/f_n is poorly defined at low values. However, experience has shown that extrapolations from values of f_u/f_n as small as $\frac{1}{4}$ can be made with sufficient accuracy.

To obtain f_n, the delays and frequencies are measured at two points on the whistler trace and substituted in Eq. (6.34) to obtain the function S_2. The value f_l/f_u is experimentally determined, and therefore Fig. 6-7 yields the value f_u/f_n, from which f_n is calculated.

By substituting $f = f_n$ in Eq. (6.33), we find that the nose delay is given by

$$t_n = \frac{D_0}{f_n^{1/2}} S_1(1) , \tag{6.35}$$

where $S_1(1) = 1.456$ (from tables of the complete elliptic integral).

Alternatively we can derive an equation for t/t_n by substituting (6.35) into (6.33), which gives

$$\frac{t}{t_n} = \frac{0.678}{(f/f_n)^{1/2}} \frac{2}{\pi} \frac{E(\sqrt{\Lambda_n f/f_n})}{1 - \Lambda_n f/f_n} . \tag{6.36}$$

The function defined by Eq. (6.36) is plotted in Fig. 6-8. Hence when f_u/f_n has been determined from Fig. 6-7, it can be substituted into Fig. 6-8 to obtain the ratio t/t_n from which t_n is calculated.

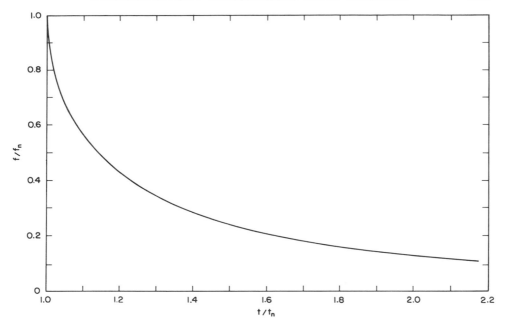

FIG. 6-8. Graph of f/f_n versus t/t_n, based on Eq. (6.36).

Errors in the extension method outlined above are not readily analyzed. The method has been tested by Smith and Carpenter (1961), who measured the actual nose frequency and delay from a number of nose whistlers and compared these values with those obtained independently by the extension method outlined above. The ratio of upper frequency to nose frequency varied from 0.26 to 0.899 in the examples that they computed. Errors in the nose frequencies were less than 5 per cent, and the errors in group delay were even less. Carpenter (1962c) discusses in detail the errors in the extension method.

Other methods for determining the path of propagation can be defined. Measurements of the group delay and the slope of the whistler at a particular frequency provide two independent numbers. However, experience has shown that the measurement of two group delays at widely spaced frequencies is as good as any other method and is easy to apply.

In applying the extension methods outlined above, it is important to obtain maximum precision in the measurement of group delay at the chosen frequencies f_u and f_l. The main problem, identification of the causative atmospheric, is discussed in Secs. 4.2 and 4.3.

6.4   Annual Variation of Electron Density

The distribution of the multipath nose whistlers plotted in Fig. 6-2 shows a distinct annual variation. Group delays are longest near December and shortest near June. The total annual variation in group delay is estimated from June and July data, representing the minimum, and October to March

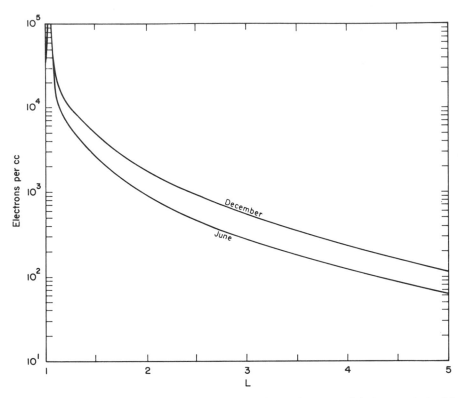

FIG. 6-9. Gyro-frequency model of the electron density in the equatorial plane as derived from nose whistler data.

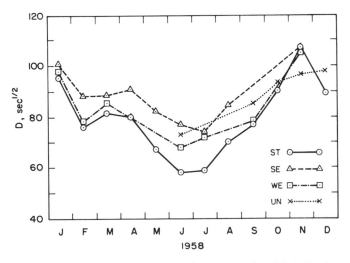

FIG. 6-10. Annual variation of whistler dispersion measured at 5 kc/s for the year 1958.

data, representing the maximum. The resulting density distributions in electrons per cubic meter have been determined by Smith (1960a) and are given by $N = 17,000f_H$ (October–March), and $N = 8,900f_H$ (June–July).

These distributions, including the effect of an average nighttime F layer, are plotted against height in the geomagnetic equatorial plane in Fig. 6-9. Height, denoted by L, is measured in units of earth radii.

Additional data on the annual variation can be obtained from the usual type of whistler that does not exhibit a nose. Monthly average dispersions from four IGY stations for the year 1958 are plotted in Fig. 6-10. Three of the stations—Stanford, Seattle, and Unalaska—are in the Northern Hemisphere, and one—Wellington—is in the Southern Hemisphere. The annual variation is clearly apparent at each of the four stations. It has the same phase in both hemispheres, unlike f_0F2 at sunspot maximum. The minimum dispersion occurs in either June or July, and the maximum in November, December, or January, depending on the station and year. These data are in general agreement with the nose whistler results. More detailed data on the annual variation are given by Carpenter (1962b, c).

The times of minimum and maximum electron density correspond, respectively, to the aphelion (July 3) and perihelion (January 3) positions in the earth's orbit about the sun. Hence the phase is reasonably consistent with an explanation in which the electron-density maximum in December is caused by increased solar radiation, or increased density of the solar corona. However, the magnitude of the annual variation in electron density is greater than 1.5 to 1 in 1958, while the corresponding change in solar radiation, based on the inverse square law, is only about 6 per cent. Clearly if the eccentricity of the earth's orbit about the sun is the cause of the annual variation, the outer ionosphere must be very sensitive to changes in solar radiation, or the density of the solar corona must vary rapidly with distance in the vicinity of the earth's orbit.

Another quantity that in general shows an annual variation is the geomagnetic latitude of the sub-solar point at a particular geomagnetic longitude. At the two geomagnetic longitudes where geographic and geomagnetic equators intersect, the sub-solar point will show the same latitude excursion above and below the geomagnetic equator, giving a strong semi-annual variation at these longitudes. At intermediate longitudes this excursion will have its maximum absolute value at a solstice (December 22 or June 22). On the opposite side of the earth the phase is reversed.

If the geomagnetic asymmetry described above is the controlling factor, the annual variation in electron density should reverse its phase in the eastern hemisphere of the earth. If, on the other hand, the orbit-eccentricity hypothesis is correct, the phase and magnitude of the annual variation should be independent of longitude and there should be no semi-annual component. The available data suggest that the annual variation is independent of longitude favoring the orbit-eccentricity hypothesis. Data from the Eastern Hemisphere are needed to obtain conclusive results on this point. Another explanation for the annual variation, advanced by Paetzold (1959) to explain a similar variation in satellite drag data, is that the solar system is moving through interstellar material, creating a kind of wind. This wind distorts the solar corona in which the earth is embedded, causing an annual variation in gas density.

6.5 Correction for Duct Enhancement

The values of electron density deduced from whistler group delays apply, of course, only to the ducts in which the whistlers propagate. Densities in regions adjacent to the ducts would be expected to be somewhat lower. The minimum enhancement in electron density required for trapping is about 5 to 10 per cent. Hence the electron density obtained from whistlers need not be more than 10 per cent above the minimum density. Evidence that the mean enhancement is probably small is found in the fluctuation of points from the mean slope of a typical multipath nose whistler train. These are thought to correspond to fluctuations in density of about 10 per cent, but little work has been done on this problem. However, much larger departures are sometimes observed. For example, the two middle points in the train labeled SE: 7 June 59 in Fig. 6-2 correspond to roughly 40 per cent reduction in density with respect to the regions described by the other four points. Further study of such deviations to determine their cause should be useful.

6.6 Solar-Cycle Variation

Using the extension methods described in Sec. 6.3, with available nose whistlers, Carpenter (1962b) has investigated the variation of average magneto-spheric electron density with solar activity. He finds that the average electron-density level in the magnetosphere for the January through June period in 1961 is 75 to 80 per cent of that for the same period in 1958. These data show some evidence that the larger part of the reduction occurs near the December solstice.

The solar-cycle variation is illustrated in Fig. 6-11 by the monthly average values of dispersion of Stanford whistlers at 5 kc/s from the period July 1957 through November 1961. The general trend of this curve is the same as that derived from nose whistler data. Carpenter finds that the long term decrease in D_5 (whistler dispersion at 5 kc/s) shown in Fig. 6-11 is augmented by a slow drift of the whistler paths toward the equator. The total movement for the period from 1958 to 1961 is about one degree in latitude. The annual variation is shown by the curves of Fig. 6-11, which also include a significant in-phase path variation. These data indicate that the magnitude of the annual variation decreases with decreasing solar activity.

Over the same period the electron density of the F region, as measured by the 12-month running mean of f_0F2 at Washington, D.C., shows the same general trend. However, the indicated change in f_0F2 corresponds to a reduc-tion in the electron density at the F-layer maximum of roughly 60 per cent as

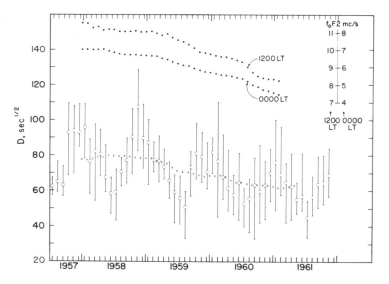

Fig. 6-11. Average monthly values of dispersion of Stanford whistlers at 5 kc/s together with 12-month running means of f_0F2 at Washington, D.C. The X's show 12-month running means of dispersion, and flags show the 90 percentile range of daily values during the month.

compared to about 20 per cent for the magnetosphere. Extrapolating these trends to the sunspot minimum gives a value of the magnetospheric electron-density level of about 60 to 70 per cent of the 1958 value, while the corresponding density of the F-layer maximum is in the range from 15 to 30 per cent of the 1958 value. Hence it appears that the magnetosphere is less sensitive than the F region to the long-term variations of solar activity.

6.7 Diurnal Variation of Electron Density

The diurnal variation of electron density is not easily determined because of the scarcity of daytime whistlers. Iwai and Outsu (1958b) found that the dispersion of whistlers observed at low geomagnetic latitudes follows closely the variations in f_0F2. The integrated density appears to vary less than the value of f_0F2, indicating a smaller diurnal variation in the upper parts of the path. Kimpara (1962c) found that at low latitudes (25° to 35°) diurnal variation is large during December at solar maximum, but is small in June. Data from middle latitudes (Rivault and Corcuff, 1960; Allcock, 1960b) also show a definite diurnal variation in dispersion with an afternoon maximum and a post-midnight minimum. The magnitude of this variation is about 25 per cent, corresponding to a change in the electron density over the entire path of 50 per cent, assuming no change in form of distribution. After the estimated F-region component is removed, the corresponding change in integrated magnetospheric electron content is roughly 20 to 30 per cent.

6.8   Effect of Magnetic Storms on Electron Density in the Magnetosphere

Using nose whistlers and the extension methods outlined above, one can measure the effect of magnetic storms on electron density in the magnetosphere. Carpenter (1962b) has found that the electron density typically drops by about 20 per cent sometime after the onset of a storm that has a K_p level of 6 or more.

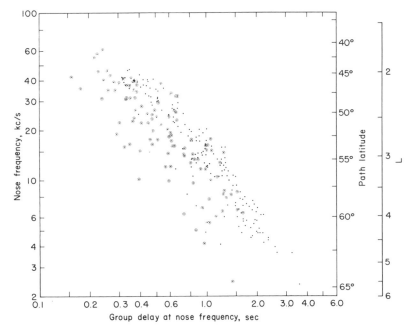

FIG. 6-12. Whistler data for period October 1957 through April 1961, showing storm effects, Circled points indicate observations preceded within 72 hours by at least one 3-hour K_p level of 6 or more.

In Carpenter's study data were obtained either directly from nose whistlers below 15 kc/s or by the extension methods described in Sec. 6.3. Values of nose frequency versus group delay at the nose for the period October 1957 through April 1961 are plotted in Fig. 6-12. On the right of each graph is a scale of ϕ_0, the effective geomagnetic latitude of the whistler-path endpoint. The relation between the nose frequency and the path latitude was obtained from Fig. 6-3, using the gyro-frequency model. However, this relation is relatively insensitive to the electron-density distribution, as Fig. 6-3 shows.

The values of f_n versus t_n in Fig. 6-12, representing a single UT day, were taken from at most one whistler per day from each of two Whistlers-West stations (Carpenter, 1962b). No more than three values were taken from a single multipath whistler. Those taken were the highest and lowest values of f_n, and the intermediate value falling nearest the mid-point between the other two on the logarithmic scale. Thus the maximum number of points for a single day is six. When several whistlers were available from a station for a given day, that whistler showing the widest spread in f_n values was selected.

Over the latitude range of roughly 45° to 60° the values of t_n at a fixed f_n vary over a range of nearly 4 to 1. It is clear from the figures that the distribution of t_n values is skewed, with the upper limit of t_n being well defined, while the lower values are more scattered. The 90 per cent range of variation in t_n at fixed f_n for the "quiet" data of Fig. 6-12 is about 1.5 to 1.

Figure 6-12 illustrates clearly the deep depressions associated with some severe storms. A typical value of density reduction is about 20 per cent in 1958, and about 15 per cent in 1961 (Carpenter, 1962c). Interpreting the reductions in t_n observed during big storms in terms of electron-density depressions might be criticized on the basis that the same effect could be produced by appropriate distortion of the earth's magnetic field. However, evidence from satellites indicates that the gyro-frequency and the shape of the earth's field are virtually independent of magnetic disturbance out to distances of the order of eight earth radii (Cahill and Amazeen, 1963). This distance covers most of the data obtained in this study. In addition there is no evidence that the nose frequency varies markedly with magnetic disturbance.

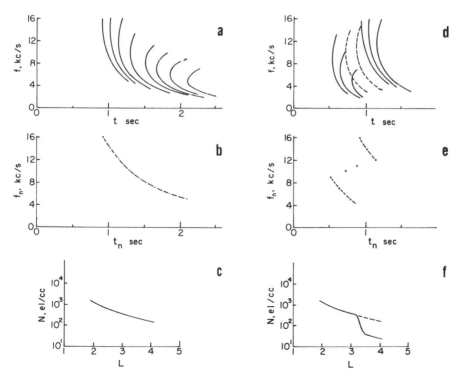

FIG. 6-13. Spectra and analysis of knee whistler compared with those of normal whistler. Parts *a* and *b* show, respectively, a normal whistler and its related f_n, t_n curve. Part *c* shows a typical electron-density profile in the equatorial plane for a normal whistler. Comparative sketches for the knee whistler are shown in parts *d*, *e*, and *f*, respectively.

Reductions in electron density during magnetic storms as measured by whistlers are comparable in magnitude to those reported by Yeh and Swenson (1961) and by others using satellite Faraday rotation and doppler data. In the satellite observations, electron content was measured between the ground and the satellite, which orbited at altitudes near 1000 km. Hence these data are restricted mainly to the F2 region of the ionosphere. The fact that the whistler results indicate comparable reductions in density during storms suggests that the magnetosphere is subject to the same depletion mechanism as the F region. We might postulate that the expansion of the F region during magnetic storms, resulting from the storm-associated heating of the F1 region, could have the effect of increasing the rate of recombination of magnetospheric electrons that flow into the upper F region.

Magnetospheric density depressions during magnetic storms have recently been linked to a new class of whistler, called the "knee whistler" (Carpenter, 1963a). This class of whistler is characterized by a reversal in the normal progression of multipath components. In ordinary trains of nose whistlers, the group delay increases relatively smoothly with decreasing nose frequency, as illustrated by Figs. 4-17 and 4-19 of the Atlas. In the knee whistler, on the other hand, the portion of the train below some particular frequency appears to have been translated to the left on the frequency–time plane, so that the group delays in this translated portion are much less than normal. One frequent result of this translation is the crossing of some of the whistler traces, as illustrated by the knee whistlers of Fig. 4-28. Sketches illustrating the knee whistler and its analysis are shown in Fig. 6-13.

Carpenter has deduced that the discontinuity in the whistler-trace structure corresponds to a "knee" in the profile of magnetospheric electron density, that is, a region at several earth radii beyond which the electron density is substantially depressed below the normal level. He suggests that the knee is always present in the magnetosphere, but that it moves inward with increasing magnetic activity. Evidence of the knee has been found at geomagnetic latitudes as low as about 50°. Knee whistlers account for many of the deep density depressions during magnetic storms.

Chapter Seven

VLF Emissions

From 200 to 30,000 cps there is observed, in addition to whistlers, another class of natural radio phenomena known as VLF emissions (or VLF ionospheric noise). These phenomena are less well understood than whistlers, but are believed to originate in the ionosphere or magnetosphere. In this chapter we shall present a comprehensive Atlas of the spectra of VLF emissions, a description of their known characteristics, and a discussion of current theories of their generation.

Very-low-frequency emissions can be detected and recorded with the same equipment employed in the study of whistlers. In fact, several types of emissions are often observed in close association with whistlers. Emissions appear in a wide variety of spectral forms; an emission may appear to be relatively steady for several minutes, or even hours, or it may occur in discrete bursts as short as a fraction of a second. To the ear an emission may resemble a hissing sound or a relatively musical tone. The amplitude of emissions frequently fluctuates in a periodic or quasi-periodic manner, with periods ranging from less than a second to more than a minute.

The intensity of emissions is comparable to that of whistlers. Emission spectra are characterized by a tendency for both the steady and the discrete forms to appear in well-defined and sometimes relatively narrow frequency bands. These bands may remain relatively constant in frequency, or they may show a systematic drift in frequency, either positive or negative. The width of these individual bands may range from about thirty cycles to as high as twenty kilocycles or more. Separate and distinct bands may appear simultaneously, but seldom do they appear to be harmonically related. The frequency limits of the noise bands may vary slowly or rapidly with time.

Regular diurnal variations have been found in the occurrence of VLF emissions, with the phase of the diurnal variation showing a systematic variation with geomagnetic latitude. Very-low-frequency emissions, like whistlers, are localized geographically and are observed most commonly at middle and high latitudes. At locations that are geomagnetically conjugate to one another, emissions are often closely related in form as well as in time of occurrence.

As a function of magnetic activity, emission activity generally increases at low latitudes and decreases at high latitudes. The latitude of peak activity descends with increasing K_p. A close association exists between auroral phenomena and certain types of VLF emissions.

Although the mechanism of their generation is not yet understood, there is strong evidence that emissions propagate to the earth in the whistler mode from a region of generation within the earth's ionosphere. Emissions frequently echo between the hemispheres in the whistler mode, and are often observed to be excited or "triggered" by whistlers or other emissions. Recently it has been discovered that emissions are sometimes triggered by Morse code whistler-mode signals from VLF transmitters. Mechanisms of emission generation have been proposed that are based on (1) Čerenkov radiation, (2) an analogy with the traveling-wave tube, (3) cyclotron radiation, and (4) the transverse resonance instability. In each mechanism the electromagnetic energy is obtained by converting some of the kinetic energy of charged particles (electrons or protons) as they spiral along the lines of force of the earth's magnetic field.

The study of particle–wave interaction in the magnetosphere has led to a proposal for a "geocyclotron" that would employ strong whistler-mode waves to accelerate relativistic electrons through the mechanism of gyro-resonance (Helliwell and Bell, 1960; Bell, Helliwell, Mlodnosky, Smith, 1963). More recently it has been proposed (Bell, 1964a) that this mechanism could be reversed so as to reduce the energy density in the radiation belts. Other mechanisms by which the energy of trapped particles may be increased or decreased by whistlers have been proposed (Parker, 1961; Dungey, 1963b).

7.1   Emission Atlas

We have prepared an Atlas of emissions using a system of classification that is a modification and an extension of that proposed by Gallet (1959a).* Each type of emission is described below and is illustrated with one or more selected spectrograms. Sketches of model spectral forms are shown in Table 7-1. Examples have been selected to illustrate for each basic form the typical variations in frequency, bandwidth, duration, period, dispersion, and so forth. Where significant differences appear in the noise recorded simultaneously at spaced stations, particularly at conjugate pairs, the simultaneous spectra are often shown.

The spectra in the Atlas were prepared at Stanford University with the aid of the Rayspan spectrum analyzer described in Chap. 4. Because of the variability in signal levels and background noise, no attempt was made to calibrate the intensity of the display relative to the field strength of the emission. In each case the tape playback level and the intensity of the beam of the recording oscilloscope were adjusted to provide maximum spectral information of the natural phenomena being illustrated. On some records a high-pass filter was employed on playback to reduce the level of power-line interference at the lower frequencies.

Except as noted, simultaneous spectrograms of spaced-station recordings have been accurately synchronized with the aid of a selected VLF transmitter signal that is included in the broad-band information recorded on the tapes. The frequency conversion of this signal places it at the bottom of the spectrogram in a narrow band from which the background noise has been removed with a high-pass filter. The same technique has been used in some illustrations to provide absolute time reference using station NBA, which transmits 300-msec

---

* For additional collections of spectra, see Dinger (1956) and Jones *et al.* (1963).

pulses whose leading edges mark the beginning of each second, on the schedule shown in Table 5-1.

Because of variations among tape playback machines and differences in field-station power frequencies, the time intervals shown by the scale at the bottom of a group of records may not agree exactly with the time interval defined by the time signals on the record itself. This error is usually less than one-half of one per cent and may appear in the periods given in the legends.

Some spectra are marked to draw attention to certain features. The meanings of the symbols are given in Chap. 4. If the exact time of the beginning of the spectrogram has been measured, this time appears above the record in minutes and seconds. Otherwise it is shown to the nearest minute.

On spectra illustrating periodic emissions of the non-dispersive type a single period is given, while for the dispersive type the periods at two or more frequencies may be given. The period at frequency f is denoted by the symbol $P(f)$ and in the interpretation given in the text, it corresponds to a two-hop traverse of the path by the triggering wave packet. Quasi-periodic emissions are denoted by the symbol $QP(f)$.

The visual appearance of the spectra is naturally affected by the ratio of the frequency and time scales chosen for their presentation. An illustration of this effect is seen by comparing Fig. 7-8 with the same record shown in time-compressed form in Fig. 7-35.

TABLE 7-1

MODEL SPECTRAL FORMS OF VLF EMISSIONS

Type and Name	Model Spectral Form
I. *Hiss*	
II. *Discrete emissions* A. Rising tone	
B. Falling tone	
C. Hook	
D. Combinations	
III. *Periodic emissions* A. Dispersive	
B. Non-dispersive	
C. Multiphase	
D. Drifting	
IV. *Chorus*	
V. *Quasi-periodic emissions*	
VI. *Triggered emission*	

CLASSIFICATION OF VLF EMISSIONS

I. *Hiss:* Figs. 7-1 to 7-5. An emission whose spectrum resembles that of band-limited thermal or fluctuation noise is called hiss. It can be identified aurally by a hissing sound. Hiss often shows no substantial change in its spectrum for periods of minutes or even hours, and is then called "steady" hiss. Occasionally hiss exhibits marked variations in amplitude over periods of the order of a second, and is then called "impulsive" hiss.

II. *Discrete emissions:* Figs. 7-6 to 7-14. Transient emissions usually with a duration of a few seconds or less, are called discrete. They may be pure-toned (well-defined trace) or swishy (broad, fuzzy trace). The principal elementary types are *rising tones* (risers), *falling tones,* and *hooks* (Gallet, 1959a). A riser is an emission whose spectral trace shows an increase of frequency with time whereas a falling tone shows a corresponding decrease. A hook is a discrete tone that in its usual form first falls and then rises in frequency, its spectrum resembling a hook. Some hooks consist of two falling tones joined at their lower frequencies. Elements with these three basic forms may be joined in various ways to form *combinations* of discrete emissions. Combinations may consist of single, continuous traces or of multiple traces joined at branch points. A single-trace combination that shows a relatively small change in frequency with time is often called a quasi-constant tone. Occasionally several discrete emissions not joined together, will appear in a clearly definable grouping that is called a "cluster."

III. *Periodic emissions:* Figs. 7-15 to 7-29. A sequence of discrete events or clusters of discrete events showing regular spacing is called a set of periodic emissions. Usually their time separation is constant, but it may on occasion change slowly. The period usually falls in the range from two seconds to six seconds, and unless noted, corresponds to two hops. If the period varies with the frequency, the periodic emissions are called *dispersive.* If there is little or no variation with frequency, periodic emissions may be called *non-dispersive.* Two or more interleaved sets with the same period are called *multiphase* periodic emissions. In this type of emission the number of phases equals the number of sets. The frequencies of the sets may or may not be the same. If the frequency within a set changes significantly, the set is called *drifting.* The measured period is then the average over the set, with the frequency of measurement being given as the frequency of the midpoint of the set. Notation is based on that used for whistler echo trains, with each element (or cluster) marked with a capital letter (A, B, C, etc.) indicating the set and a subscript (0, 1, 2, 3, etc.) indicating the number of labeled hops preceding it.

IV. *Chorus:* Figs. 7-30 to 7-38. A sequence of closely spaced, discrete events, often overlapping in time, is called chorus (originally called the dawn chorus (Isted and Millington, 1957)). Some forms of chorus have been compared to the sounds of a flock of birds. The most common form consists of a multitude of rising tones in the range 1 to 5 kc/s, with rates of change of frequency with time averaging about 3 kc/s/s (Pope, 1963). Often a background continuum of hiss is present. Chorus frequently consists of the superposition of different sets of periodic emissions.

V. *Quasi-periodic emissions:* Figs. 7-39 to 7-45. A sequence of repeated noise bursts of relatively long period, in which each burst may consist of a number of discrete events, periodic emissions, or chorus, is called a quasi-periodic emission. The period between bursts is usually measured in tens of seconds and is relatively irregular compared with that of the periodic emissions.

VI. *Triggered emissions* (interactions): Figs. 7-46 to 7-67. Any emission that appears to have been initiated, or triggered, by another event is called a triggered emission or interaction. Triggering sources include whistlers, discrete emissions, and signals from VLF transmitters. Most triggered emissions follow the apparent source. However, one type known as a precursor precedes the associated whistler. Closely related to triggered events are changes in the spectral shape associated with the presence of another discrete event.

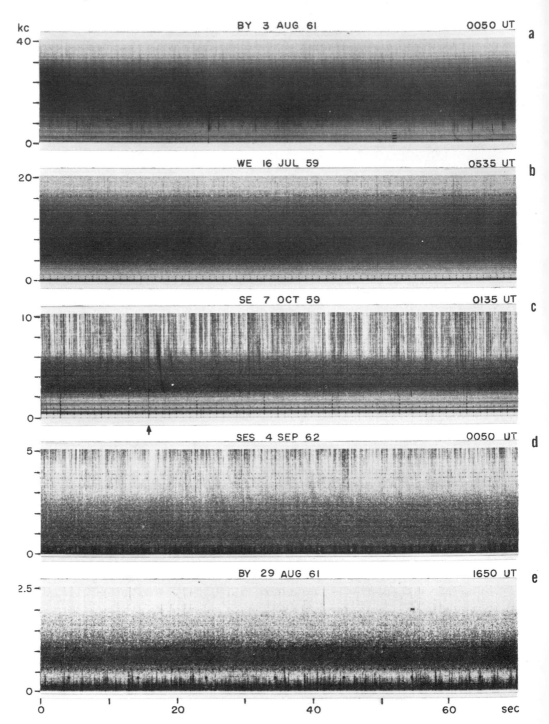

FIG. 7-1. Variation in upper cutoff frequency of hiss. *a*, Decrease in amplitude above 32 kc/s corresponds to decrease in high-frequency response of equipment. *b*, Station NPM just above 16 kc/s. *d*, VLF station interference at 3.7 and 3.9 kc/s believed to result from cross-modulation in the equipment. The lower cutoff of hiss in *b*, *c*, and *e* may be due to station response. Upper-cutoff frequencies of hiss are, from parts *a* through *e*, >34, 17, 6, 3, and 2 kc/s. *e*, Note band of discrete rising tones between 500 and 1200 cps.

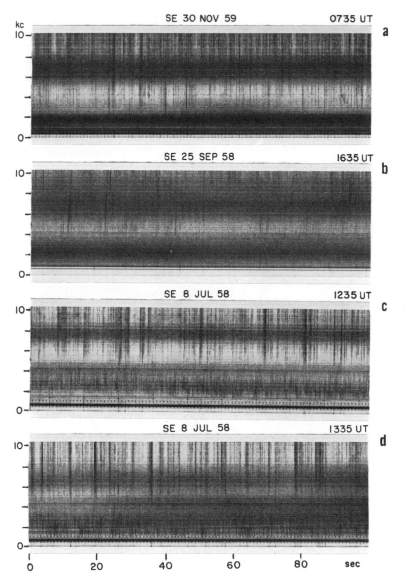

FIG. 7-2. Multiband hiss. *a*, *b*, Two hiss bands at 2 and 7 kc/s. *c*, Two
hiss bands, 2 to 5 kc/s, and 8 kc/s; discrete falling tones superimposed on
lower band. *d*, Hiss from below instrumental cutoff at 1 kc/s to 5 kc/s and
at 7 kc/s; discrete falling tones superimposed on lower band.

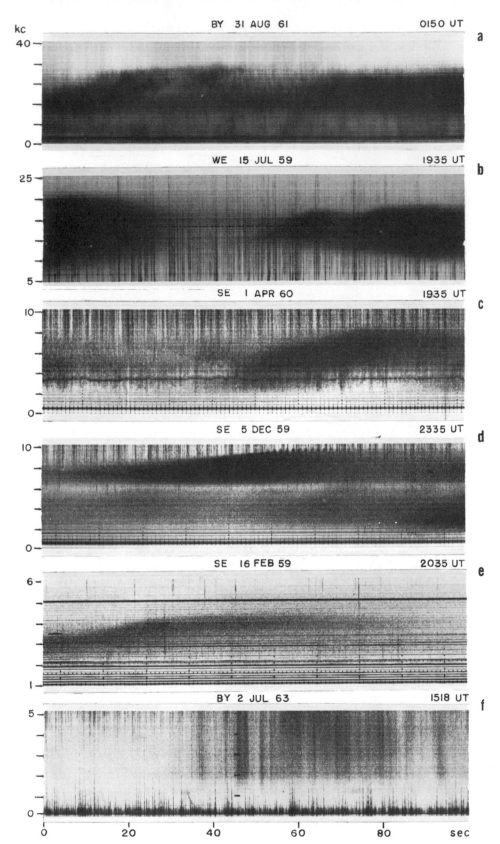

FIG. 7-3. Growth and decay of hiss at different frequencies. *d*, Weak evidence of a periodic event (P = 1.46 sec) extending above the hiss band. *f*, Impulsive hiss, with low-frequency cutoff at 2.0 kc/s.

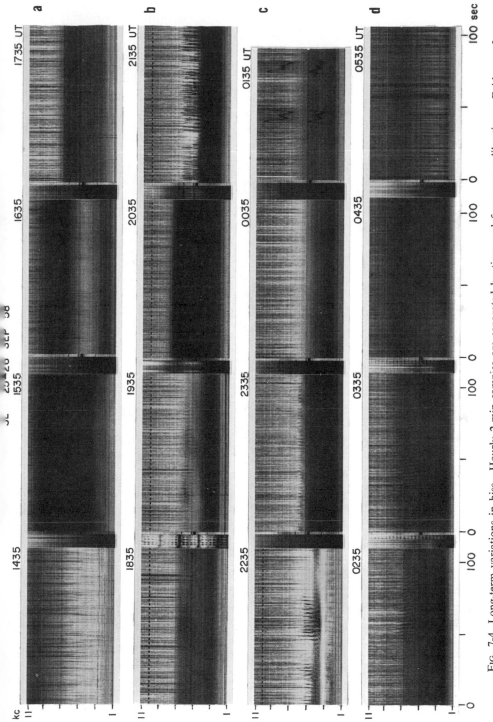

Fig. 7-4. Long-term variations in hiss. Hourly 2-min samples are separated by time and frequency calibrations. Evidence of whistler echo trains may be seen in the 1835 (2 kc/s), 2335 (3.5 kc/s), 0235 (6 kc/s), and 0335 (6 kc/s) runs. Trains of discrete events, possibly periodic, are readily identified in the 2135, 2235, and 2335 runs. The slowly varying discrete event in the 0135 run is man-made interference.

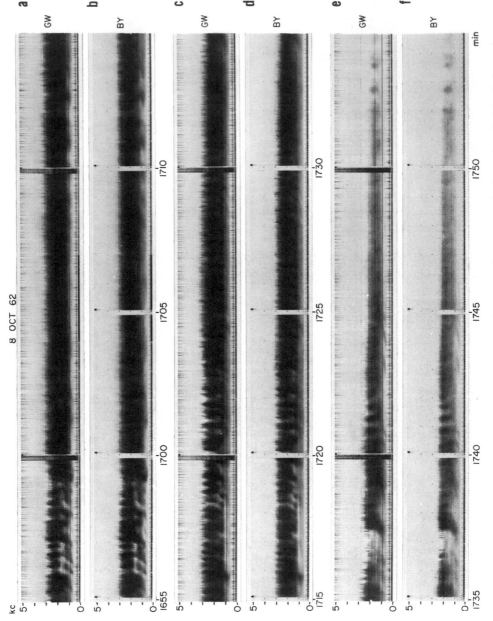

Fig. 7-5. Temporal variations in hiss at conjugate stations. Continuous records show virtually identical structure at conjugate points. Periodic events occur at 1657 and 1737 UT. Records are interrupted for ten seconds every 5 min at BY and every 10 min at GW. Station NBA was inserted at bottom of both records for timing.

212

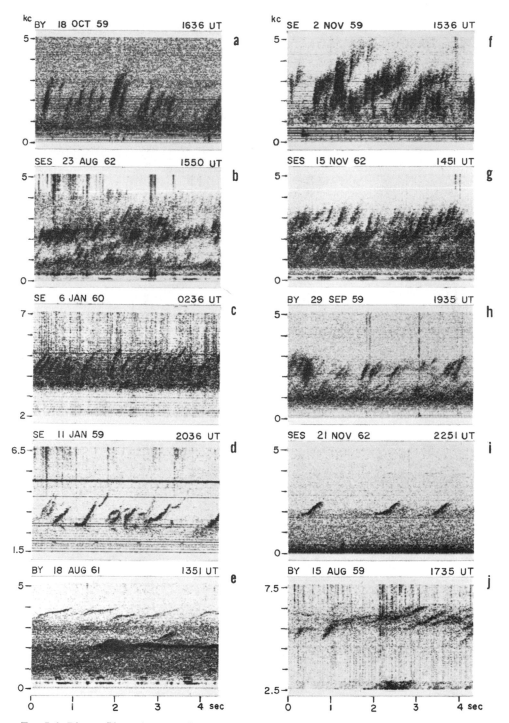

FIG. 7-6. Risers. Slope decreases from top to bottom. *b*, Bands of risers with positive drift in frequency. *e*, Closely spaced risers of irregular form characteristic of chorus. *g*, *h*, Forms resembling partially developed hooks. *i*, Riser that develops into quasi-constant tone at 2.0 kc/s. *j*, Break in riser slope occurring at approximately 5.6 kc/s; slope below this frequency averages 2.5 kc/s per sec; slope above this frequency averages 0.75 kc/s per sec.

213

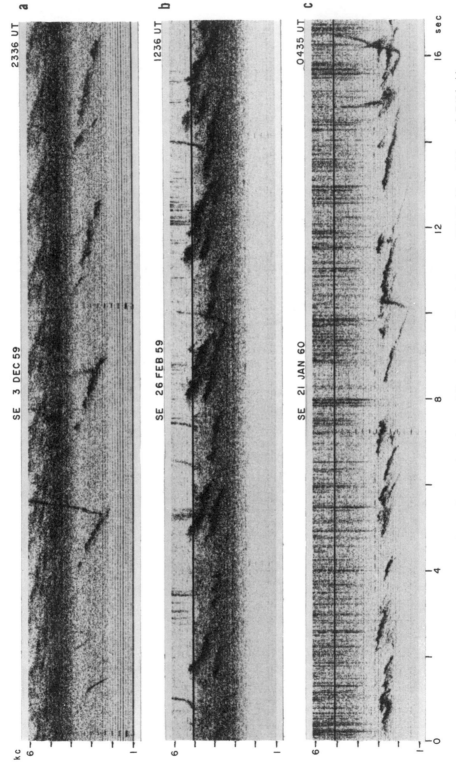

FIG. 7-7. Falling tones. Each element is a member of a set of dispersive periodic emissions. *a*, P(3.5 kc/s) = 3.28 sec. *b*, P(5 kc/s) = 3.22 sec. *c*, P(1.6 kc/s) = 4.56 sec. Several risers and hooks can be seen.

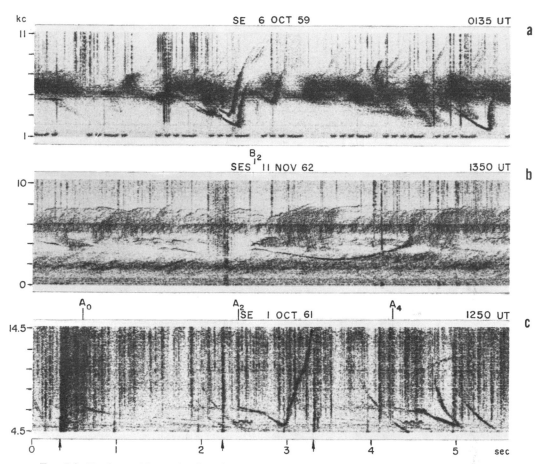

FIG. 7-8. Hooks. *a*, Note pair of hooks beginning at 2.2 sec. *b*, Hook of unusually long duration (1.88 sec) that begins in element B_2 of a periodic emission; record is an expanded version of the section of Fig. 7-35 lying between 53 and 59 sec. *c*, Hook originating in second element (A_2) of periodic emission, $P(6.9 \text{ kc/s}) = 1.82 \text{ sec}$; hook echoes with same period as that of the periodic emission; sources of three two-hop whistlers are marked, all having the same period as the emissions; periodic emission believed to be associated with the remnants of a preceding whistler echo train; (additional parts of the same run are shown in Fig. 7-55); VLF station interference appears at 4.9 kc/s at approximately 2.4 and 4.5 sec.

215

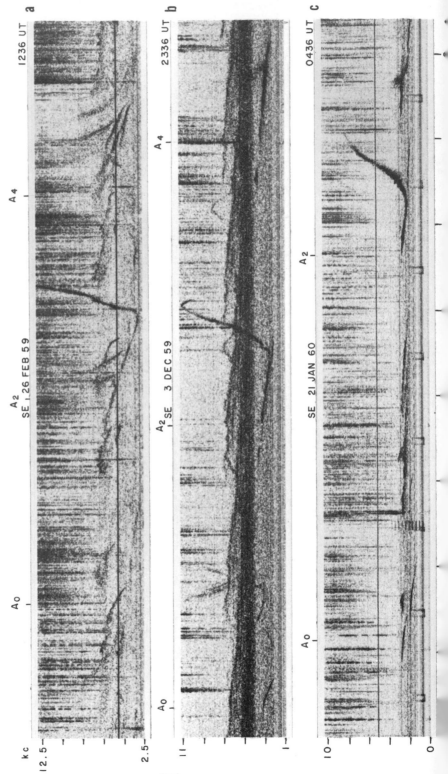

216

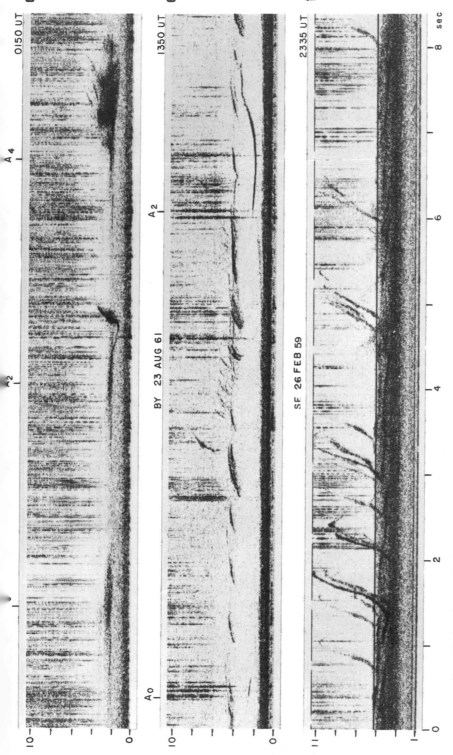

Fig. 7-9. Hooks. Typical variations in hook shape. *a–e*, Each hook appears to originate in a falling tone that is an element of a periodic emission; the phase of the periodic emission related to the hook is marked. Note that *e* is an expanded section of Fig. 7-20*a* in the period 67 to 75 sec. *f*, Risers, in addition to hooks, appear to originate in falling tones that may be elements of periodic emissions.

217

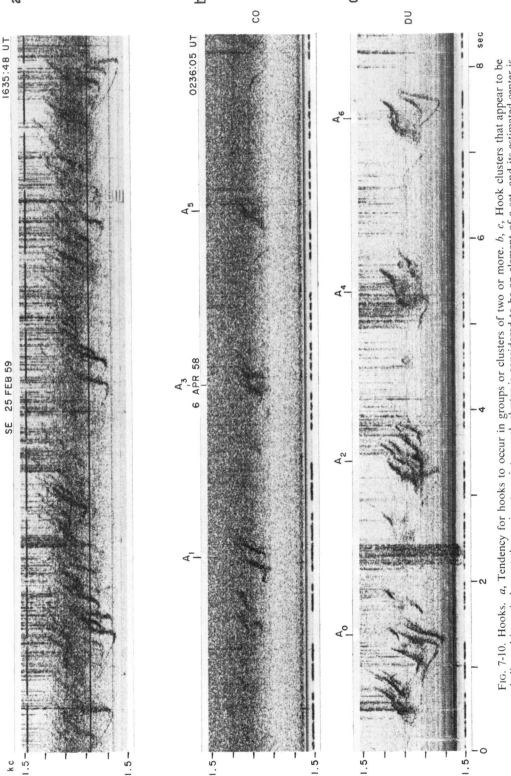

FIG. 7-10. Hooks. *a*, Tendency for hooks to occur in groups or clusters of two or more. *b*, *c*, Hook clusters that appear to be periodic and in anti-phase at the conjugate points; each cluster is considered to be an element of a set, and its estimated center is marked; P(7.3 kc/s) = 2.0 sec. Note absorption band from 4 to 6 kc/s at CO that is not evident at DU.

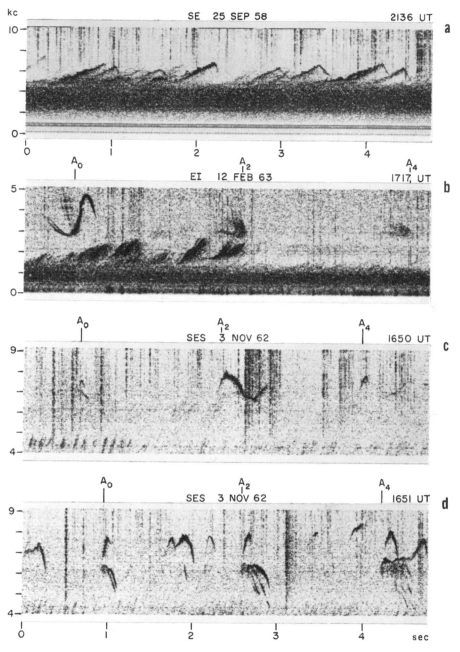

Fig. 7-11. Combinations of discrete emissions. *a*, Examples of riser followed by falling tone, sometimes called "inverted hook," beginning in band of hiss. *b*, Hook followed by falling tone; lower portions of hook echo; P(3.0 kc/s) = 3.95 sec; sequence of risers in band below hook is a segment of a quasi-periodic emission; a band of hiss lies below about 1300 cps. *c*, Riser followed by hook is part of a periodic set (A); P(7.6 kc/s) = 3.31 sec. *d*, Complex combinations; most emissions are elements of periodic sets; one set (A) marked for illustration; P(6.3 kc/s) = 3.27 sec; sets show a slight positive drift in frequency.

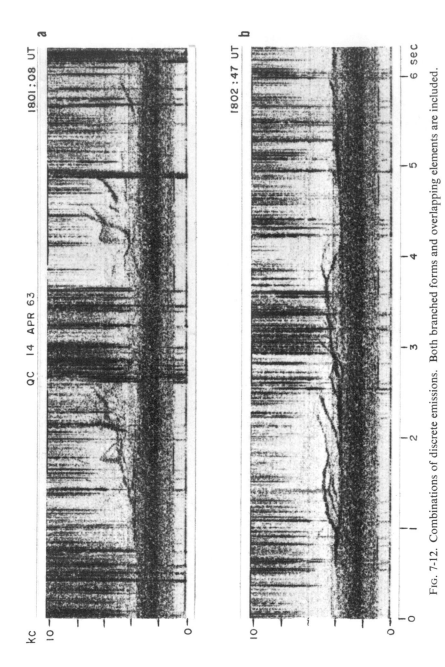

Fig. 7-12. Combinations of discrete emissions. Both branched forms and overlapping elements are included.

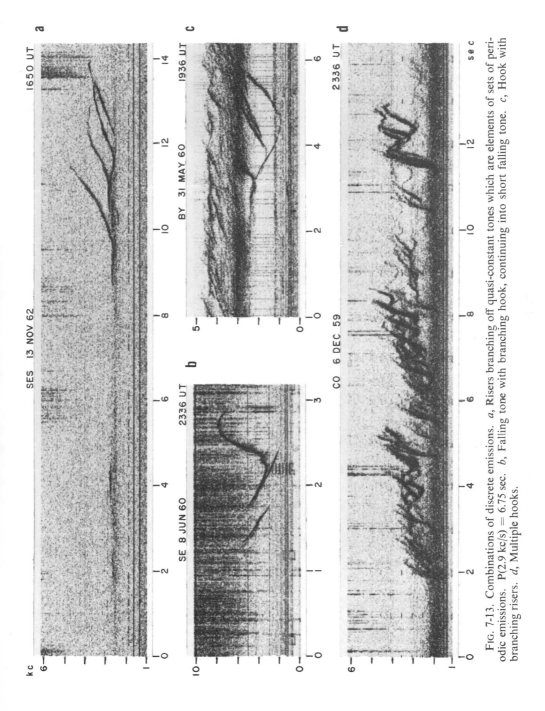

Fig. 7-13. Combinations of discrete emissions. *a*, Risers branching off quasi-constant tones which are elements of sets of periodic emissions. $P(2.9 \text{ kc/s}) = 6.75$ sec. *b*, Falling tone with branching hook, continuing into short falling tone. *c*, Hook with branching risers. *d*, Multiple hooks.

221

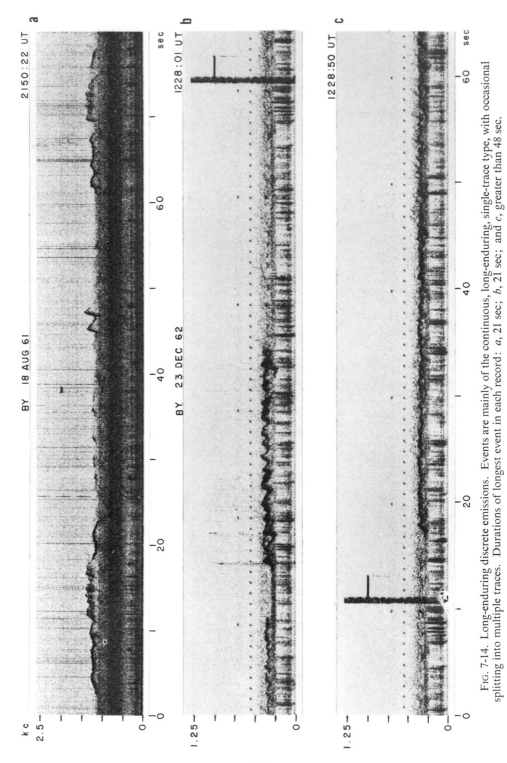

FIG. 7-14. Long-enduring discrete emissions. Events are mainly of the continuous, long-enduring, single-trace type, with occasional splitting into multiple traces. Durations of longest event in each record: *a*, 21 sec; *b*, 21 sec; and *c*, greater than 48 sec.

222

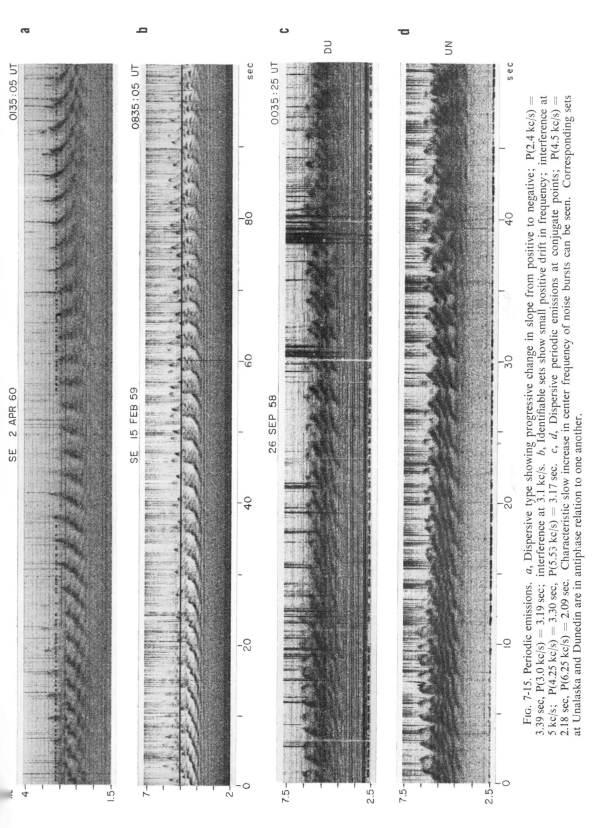

FIG. 7-15. Periodic emissions. *a*, Dispersive type showing progressive change in slope from positive to negative; P(2.4 kc/s) = 3.39 sec, P(3.0 kc/s) = 3.19 sec; interference at 3.1 kc/s. *b*, Identifiable sets show small positive drift in frequency; interference at 5 kc/s; P(4.25 kc/s) = 3.30 sec, P(5.53 kc/s) = 3.17 sec. *c, d*, Dispersive periodic emissions at conjugate points; P(4.5 kc/s) = 2.18 sec, P(6.25 kc/s) = 2.09 sec. Characteristic slow increase in center frequency of noise bursts can be seen. Corresponding sets at Unalaska and Dunedin are in antiphase relation to one another.

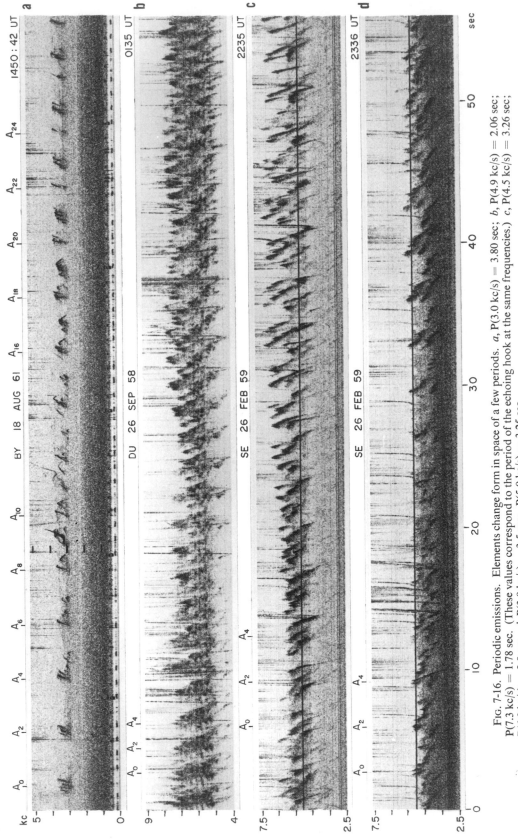

Fig. 7-16. Periodic emissions. Elements change form in space of a few periods. *a*, P(3.0 kc/s) = 3.80 sec; *b*, P(4.9 kc/s) = 2.06 sec; P(7.3 kc/s) = 1.78 sec. (These values correspond to the period of the echoing hook at the same frequencies.) *c*, P(4.5 kc/s) = 3.26 sec; P(6.0 kc/s) = 2.9 sec. *d*, P(3.9 kc/s) = 3.5 sec; P(5.0 kc/s) = 3.25 sec.

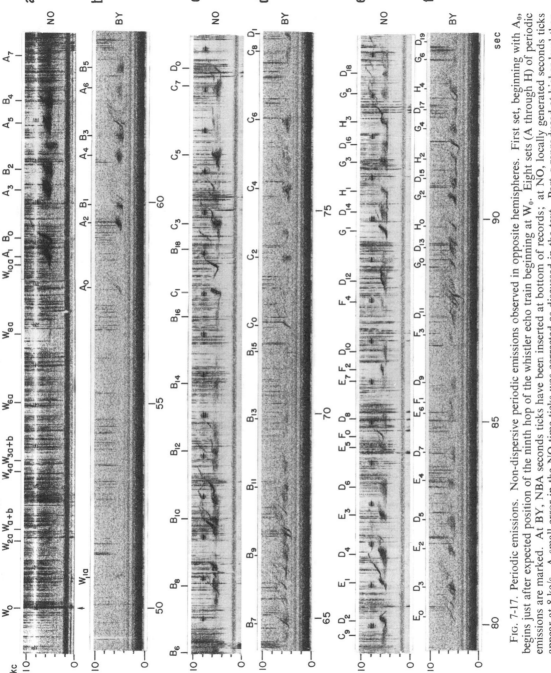

Fig. 7-17. Periodic emissions. Non-dispersive periodic emissions observed in opposite hemispheres. First set, beginning with A_0, begins just after expected position of the ninth hop of the whistler echo train beginning at W_0. Eight sets (A through H) of periodic emissions are marked. At BY, NBA seconds ticks have been inserted at bottom of records; at NO, locally generated seconds ticks appear at 8 kc/s. A small error in the NO time ticks was corrected as discussed in the text. Part *a* reproduced at higher level than other panels to bring out details of whistler echo train; narrow-band filter employed at 8 kc/s to prevent overloading of spectrum analyzer by seconds ticks.

225

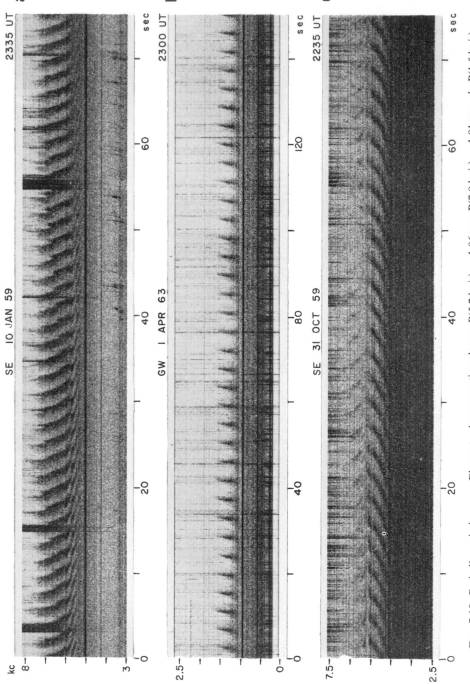

Fig. 7-18. Periodic emissions. *a*, Elements show negative slope; P(5.7 kc/s) = 1.96 sec, P(7.0 kc/s) = 1.91 sec. *b*, P(1.5 kc/s) = 4.33 sec. *c*, Strong periodic emissions between 4 and 6 kc/s show positive slope; weaker periodic emissions appearing above 5.7 kc/s show negative slope; P(4.9 kc/s) = 2.83 sec, P(5.5 kc/s) = 2.84 sec, P(6.3 kc/s) = 2.80 sec.

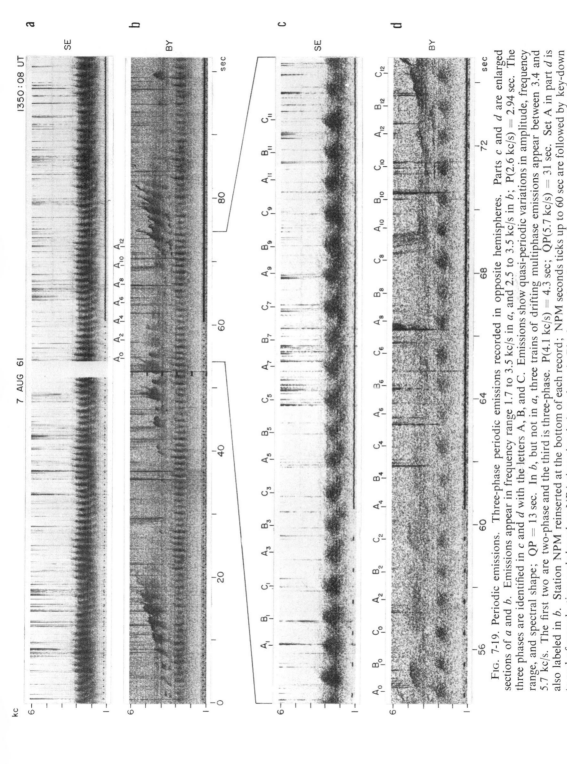

FIG. 7-19. Periodic emissions. Three-phase periodic emissions recorded in opposite hemispheres. Parts c and d are enlarged sections of a and b. Emissions appear in frequency range 1.7 to 3.5 kc/s in a, and 2.5 to 3.5 kc/s in b; $P(2.6 \text{ kc/s}) = 2.94$ sec. The three phases are identified in c and d with the letters A, B, and C. Emissions show quasi-periodic variations in amplitude, frequency range, and spectral shape; $QP = 13$ sec. In b, but not in a, three trains of drifting multiphase emissions appear between 3.4 and 5.7 kc/s. The first two are two-phase and the third is three-phase. $P(4.1 \text{ kc/s}) = 4.3$ sec; $QP(5.7 \text{ kc/s}) = 31$ sec. Set A in part d is also labeled in b. Station NPM reinserted at the bottom of each record; NPM seconds ticks up to 60 sec are followed by key-down to end of record; time scale based on NBA time signals (not shown). Blank space in a inserted to compensate for a break in the tape.

227

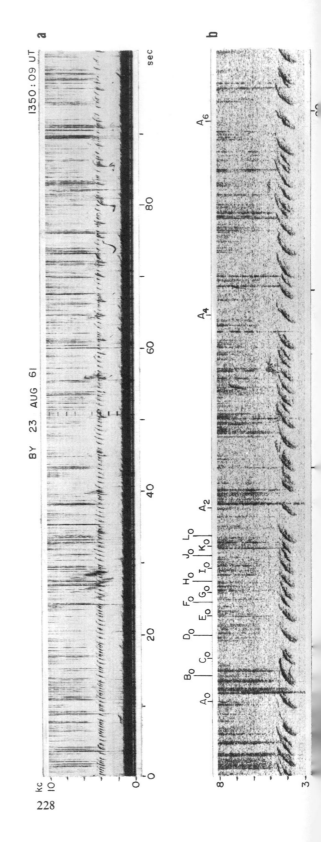

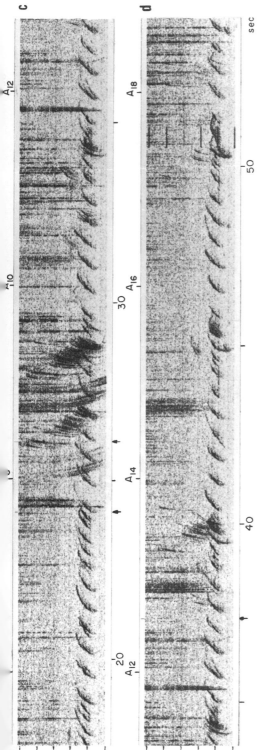

FIG. 7-20. Periodic emissions. Twelve-phase periodic emission with associated echoing nose whistlers and hooks. *b, c, d,* Segments, expanded in both frequency and time, of the *a* record between 1 and 54 sec. Each of the last two expanded segments of the record is shifted to the left with respect to the previous segment by exactly three cycles of the periodic emission. For clarity, each part repeats a small portion of the previous part; P(3.9 kc/s) = 5.40 sec. Period of echoing nose whistler components is equal to period of emission at 3.9 kc/s. Echoing hook, at 73, 79, and 85 sec of part *a*, also has a period equal to that of the periodic emissions, but at a frequency of 3.2 kc/s, indicating that the nose frequency for the path lies between 3.2 kc/s and 3.9 kc/s. Origin of echoing hook can be traced back through a series of short falling tones that have their origin in the whistler-mode echo of the multipath nose whistler originating at second arrow (part *c*).

229

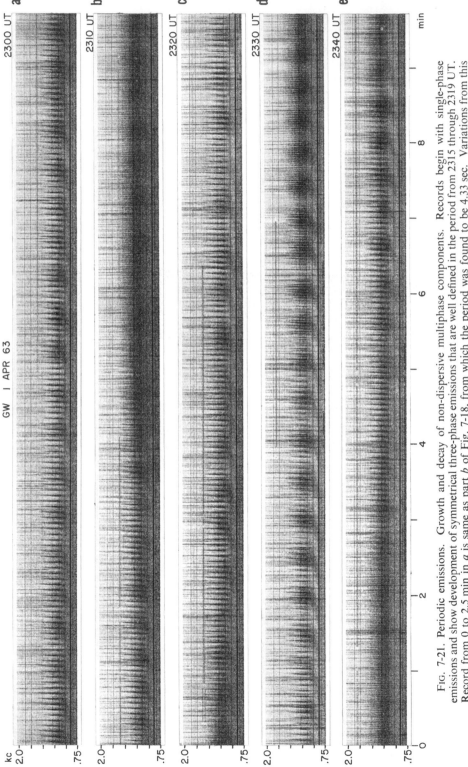

GW 1 APR 63

Fig. 7-21. Periodic emissions. Growth and decay of non-dispersive multiphase components. Records begin with single-phase emissions and show development of symmetrical three-phase emissions that are well defined in the period from 2315 through 2319 UT. Record from 0 to 2.5 min in *a* is same as part *b* of Fig. 7-18, from which the period was found to be 4.33 sec. Variations from this period of the order of 1 per cent are observable. Emissions also show quasi-periodic fluctuations in intensity and upper cutoff frequency, with an average period (QP) of 30.4 sec based on the 2300 and 2330 runs. Variable-intensity hiss tends to show the same quasi-periodic intensity fluctuations as the periodic emissions.

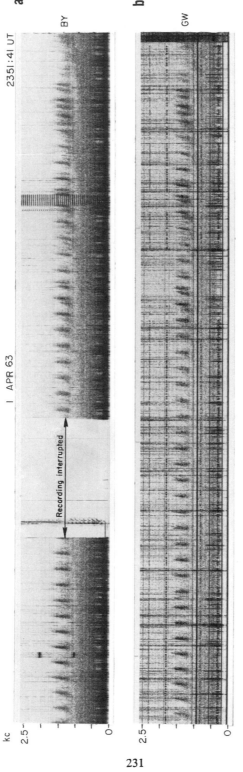

FIG. 7-22, a–b. For legend to Fig. 7-22, see p. 232.

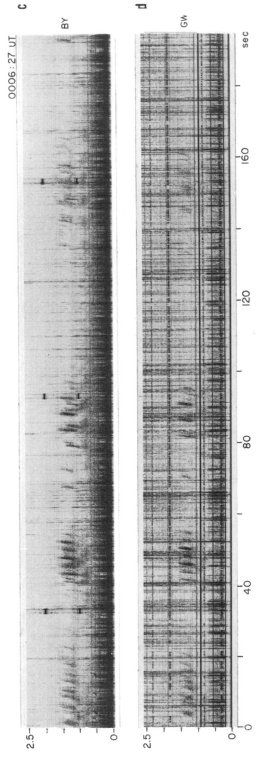

Fig. 7-22. Periodic emissions. Multiphase non-dispersive periodic emissions at conjugate points. *a, b,* Symmetrical two-phase emission appears between 160 sec and 180 sec; elements of the two phases are of roughly similar appearance. *c, d,* Symmetrical two-phase emission appears between 40 sec and 55 sec; elements of the two phases are of distinctly different appearance; emission sets show short-period growth and decay; the leading element of each set appears first at BY; P(1.3 kc/s) = 4.43 sec.

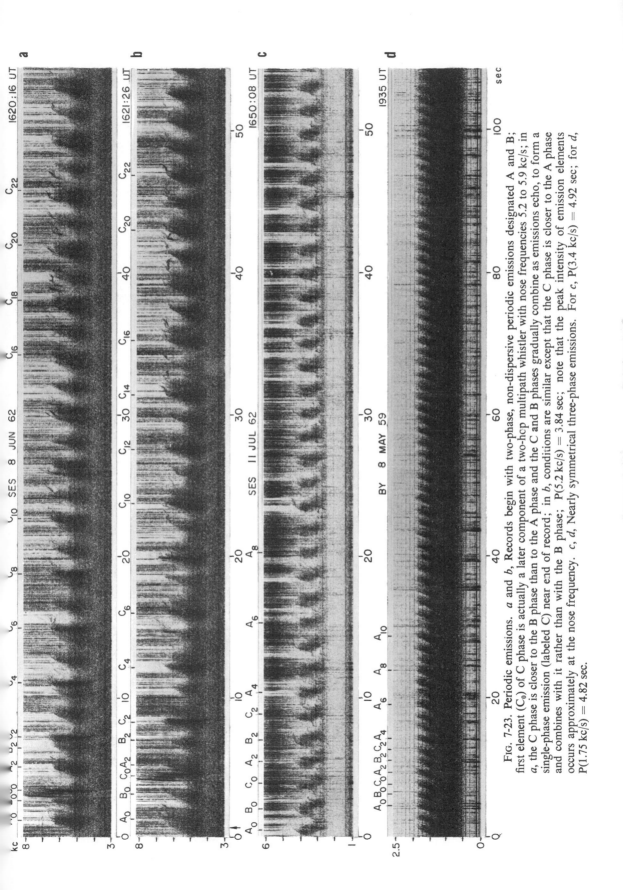

FIG. 7-23. Periodic emissions. *a* and *b*, Records begin with two-phase, non-dispersive periodic emissions designated A and B; first element (C_0) of C phase is actually a later component of a two-hcp multipath whistler with nose frequencies 5.2 to 5.9 kc/s; in *a*, the C phase is closer to the B phase than to the A phase and the C and B phases gradually combine as emissions mature, to form a single-phase emission (labeled C) near end of record; in *b*, conditions are similar except that the C phase is closer to the A phase and combines with it rather than with the B phase; note that the peak intensity of emission elements occurs approximately at the nose frequency. *c, d*, Nearly symmetrical three-phase emissions. For *c*, P(3.4 kc/s) = 4.92 sec; for *d*, P(1.75 kc/s) = 4.82 sec. P(5.2 kc/s) = 3.84 sec.

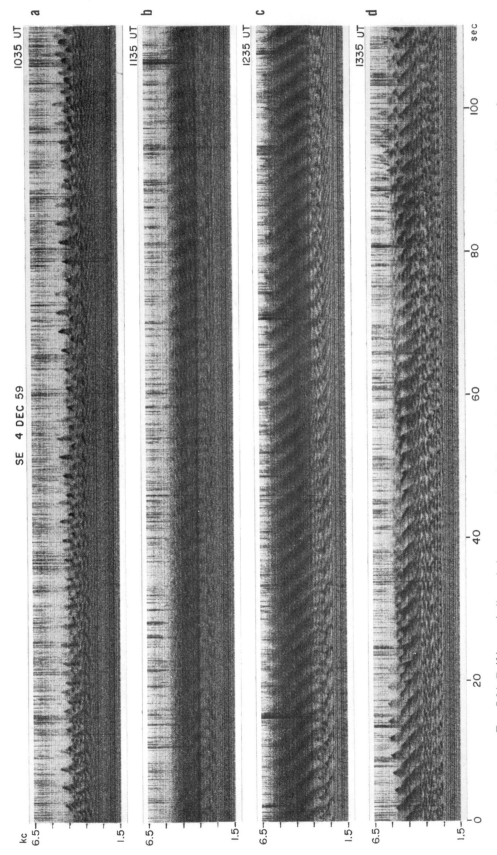

FIG. 7-24. Drifting periodic emissions. *a*, quasi-periodic variations in emissions frequently have period of about 15 sec. *d*, quasi-periodic variations in amplitude and frequency have a period of about 30 sec. P(2.6 kc/s) = 2.99 sec, P(5.6 kc/s) = 2.42 sec;

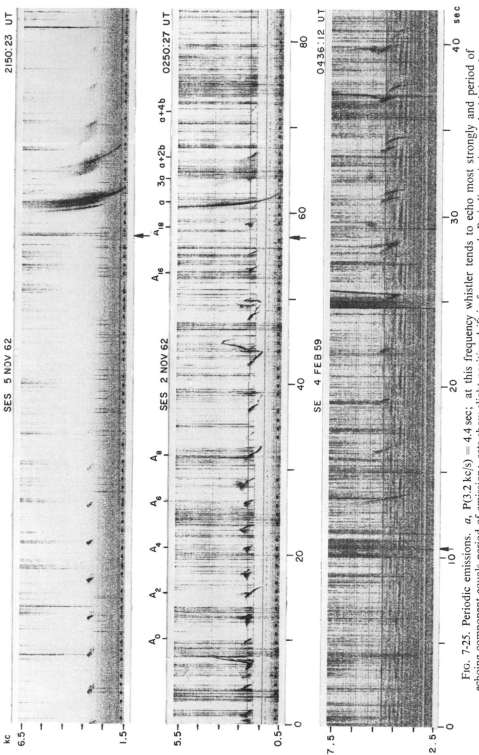

Fig. 7-25. Periodic emissions. *a*, P(3.2 kc/s) = 4.4 sec; at this frequency whistler tends to echo most strongly and period of echoing component equals period of emission; sets show slight positive drift in frequency. *b*, Periodic emissions and whistler echo train. Strong one-hop whistler on path "a" excites two- and four-hop echoes on path "b" of longer delay; two-hop echo period on path "b" is 5.24 sec at 2.1 kc/s; A-phase emission period is 5.37 sec at 2.1 kc/s. *c*, Dispersive, banded, drifting sets with whistler echo trains; P(5.0 kc/s) = 2.93 sec, P(4.0 kc/s) = 3.20 sec. The whistler periods at the corresponding frequencies are 2.86 sec and 3.11 sec, respectively. The emission periods thus exceed the whistler periods by an average of about 2.5 per cent, suggesting a small delay in the time of re-emission with respect to the arrival of the wave packet in the triggering region.

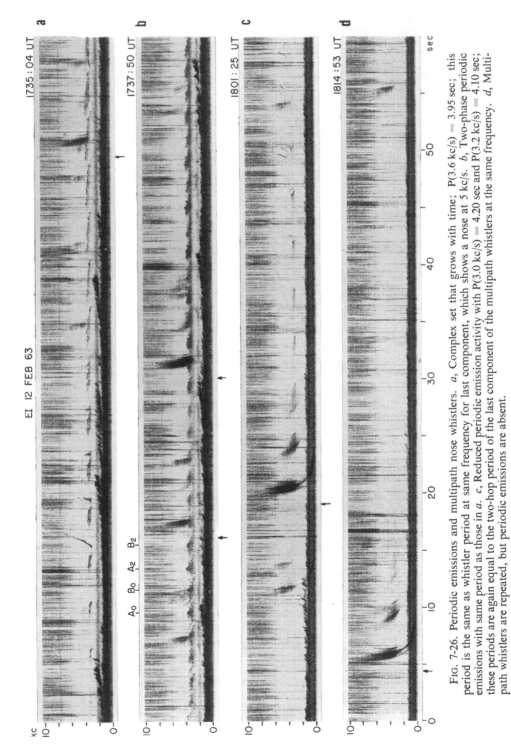

EI 12 FEB 63

FIG. 7-26. Periodic emissions and multipath nose whistlers. *a*, Complex set that grows with time; P(3.6 kc/s) = 3.95 sec; this period is the same as whistler period at same frequency for last component. *b*, Two-phase periodic emissions with same period as those in *a*. *c*, Reduced periodic emission activity with P(3.0 kc/s) = 4.20 sec and P(3.2 kc/s) = 4.10 sec; these periods are again equal to the two-hop period of the last component of the multipath whistlers at the same frequency. *d*, Multi-path whistlers are repeated, but periodic emissions are absent.

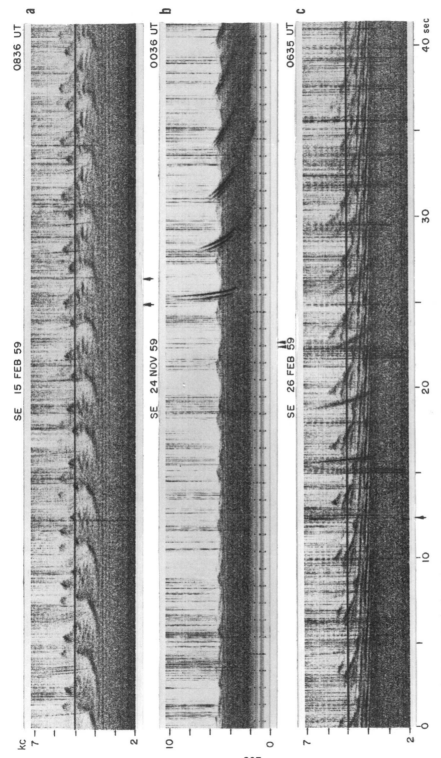

Fig. 7-27. Periodic emissions and whistler echo trains. Period of the emissions is equal to the whistler-mode period at the same frequency. *a*, Two of several whistler echo trains are indicated; P(4.5 kc/s) = 3.32 sec; P(5.7 kc/s) = 3.12 sec; emissions are banded, with each set showing positive drift in frequency. Interference at 5 kc/s. *b*, P(5.1 kc/s) = 3.02 sec. *c*, P(5.7 kc/s) = 3.33 sec; P(4.1 kc/s) = 3.66 sec.

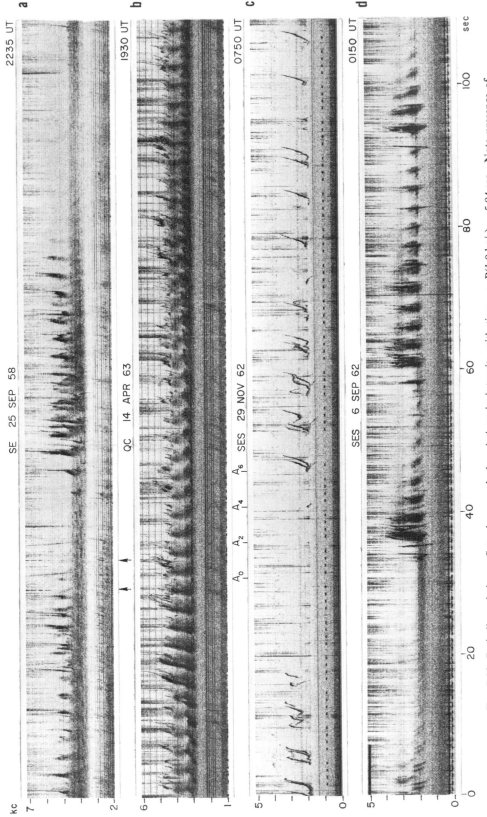

Fig. 7-28. Periodic emissions. Sets show marked variations in intensity with time. *c*, P(1.9 kc/s) = 5.04 sec. Note presence of non-dispersive sets associated with dispersive sets.

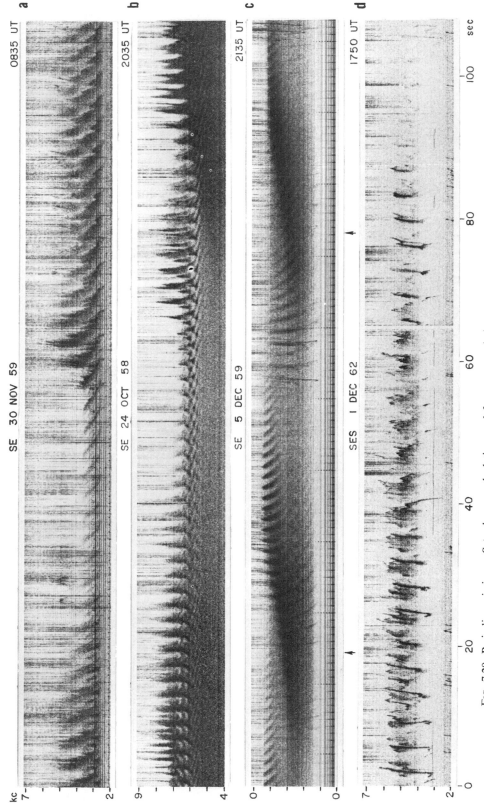

Fig. 7.29. Periodic emissions. Sets show marked time and frequency variations. *c*, Periodic emissions appear to be associated with whistler-like echo trains; hiss background appears to be associated with echo trains. *d*, Some evidence of dispersion at the lower frequencies.

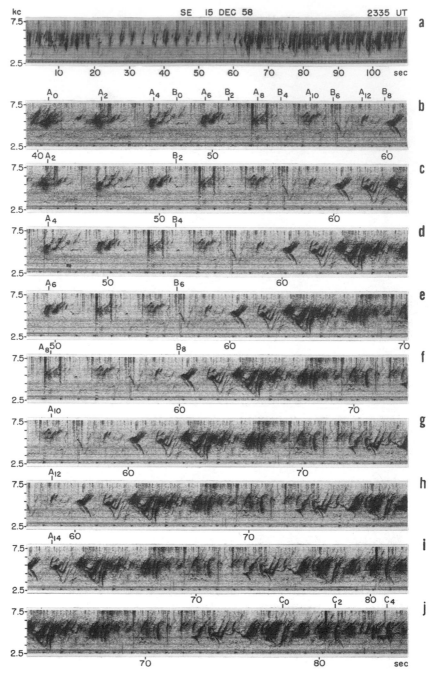

FIG. 7-30. Chorus. Superposition of multiphase non-dispersive periodic emissions. *a*, Transition from complex structure, ending at 20 sec, to relatively simple, well-defined periodic behavior until 60 sec, after which structure becomes complex again; portion from 39 sec to 85 sec shown in expanded form in *b* through *j*, with each part shifted to the left with respect to the preceding part by approximately one period. Two periodic sets, A and B, are marked. Set A consists of a cluster of elements, mainly of the rising type, while set B is a well-defined single element which develops a falling tail at B_6. Periodic sets show some variation in vertical alignment resulting from the method of aligning the strips, based on the clusters of set A. The basic period can be seen to persist throughout the complex chorus structure that begins at 60 sec. Emission elements that fall well below 5 kc/s tend to show dispersion. An example (set C) is labeled in *j*.

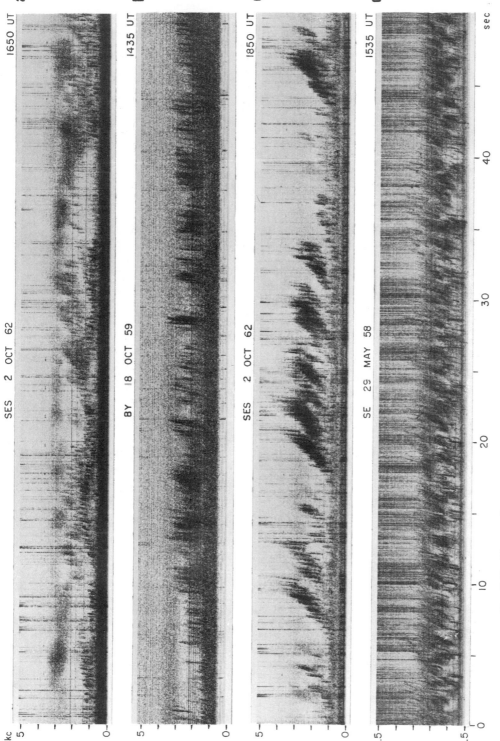

Fig. 7-31. Chorus. Burst type, with systematic positive drift in frequency especially pronounced in *c*.

241

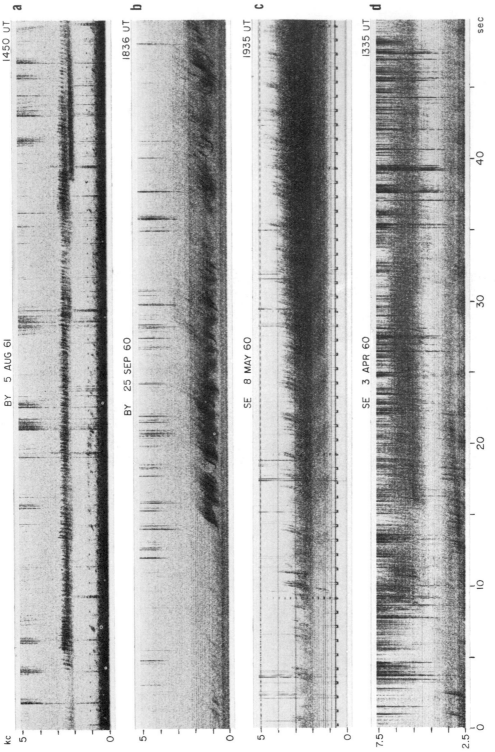

FIG. 7-32. Chorus, showing characteristic commencements. *a*, Relatively rapid onset of chorus at 4 sec; a second band starts at 39 sec. *b*, Sudden commencement of burst-type chorus at 14 sec. *c*, More gradual development of chorus with weak background of hiss; weak periodicity is suggested by the noise bursts in the beginning of the record; $P(2.3 \text{ kc/s}) = 3.1$ sec; weak whistler-mode echo train below chorus band apparently beginning at riser. *d*, Sudden commencement of a relatively uniform type of chorus at

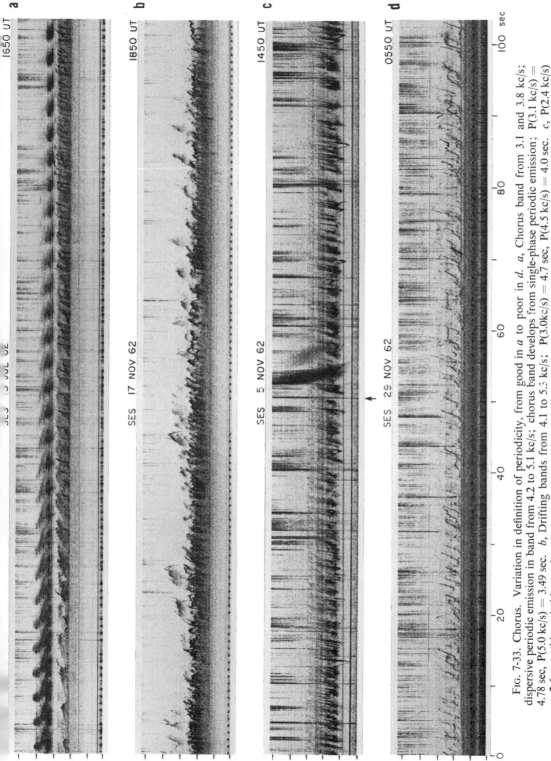

Fig. 7-33. Chorus. Variation in definition of periodicity, from good in *a* to poor in *d*. *a*, Chorus band from 3.1 and 3.8 kc/s; dispersive periodic emission in band from 4.2 to 5.1 kc/s; chorus band develops from single-phase periodic emission; P(3.1 kc/s) = 4.78 sec, P(5.0 kc/s) = 3.49 sec. *b*, Drifting bands from 4.1 to 5.3 kc/s; P(3.0kc/s) = 4.7 sec, P(4.5 kc/s) = 4.0 sec. *c*, P(2.4 kc/s) = 2.6 sec; this period is equal to the period of the whistler at the same frequency for one of the early traces of multipath whistler. *d*, Periodicity not readily determined but appears to be P(1.6 kc/s) = 4.4 sec.

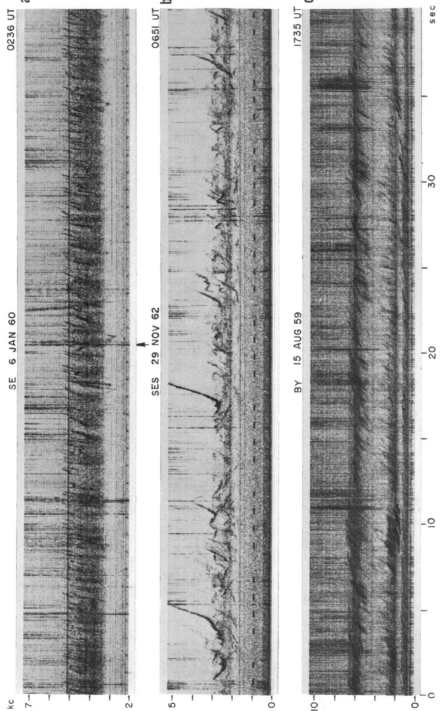

Fig. 7-34. Chorus. *a*, Strong banding with closely spaced, relatively simple elements; weak periodicity; P(3.2 kc/s) = 2.7 sec; two-hop whistler (source marked with arrow) shows same period at same frequency. *b*, More widely spaced elements of unusual complexity. *c*, Three distinct bands consisting mainly of risers.

244

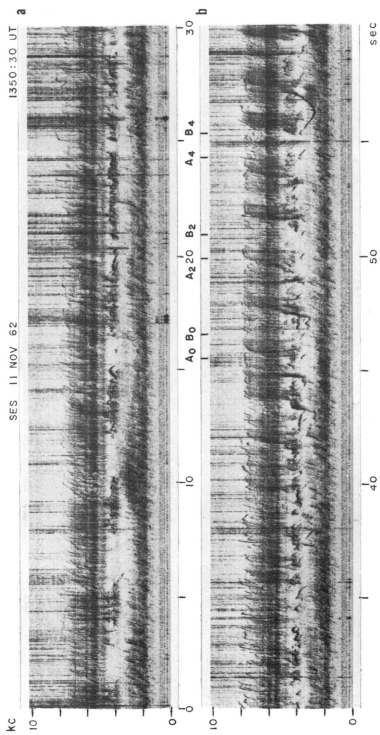

Fig. 7-35. Chorus. Three bands of activity; upper band, P(5.9 kc/s) = 4.0 sec; relatively strong periodicity in middle band, P(3.6 kc/s) = 4.39 sec (sets A and B); on basis of a periodic interpretation, upper band shows roughly 30 phases; lower band may also be periodic, but interpretation is ambiguous.

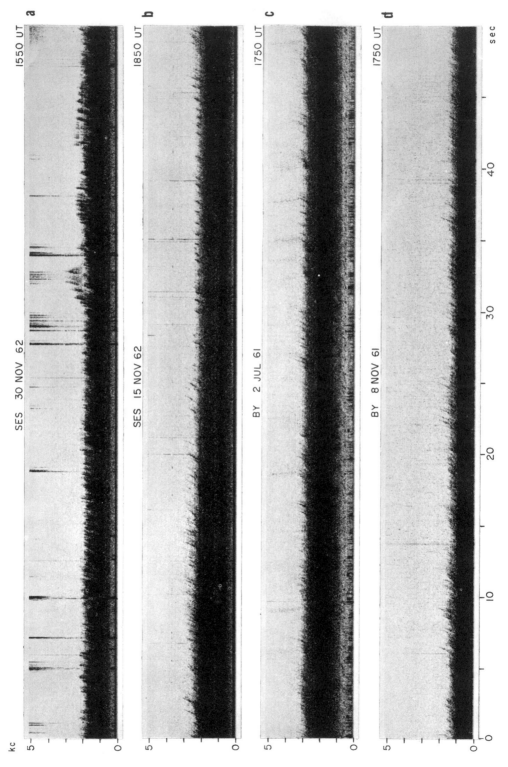

FIG. 7-36. Chorus. Elements appear to be superimposed on hiss background (this type often called polar chorus); multiple banding evident in *b*, *c*, and *d*.

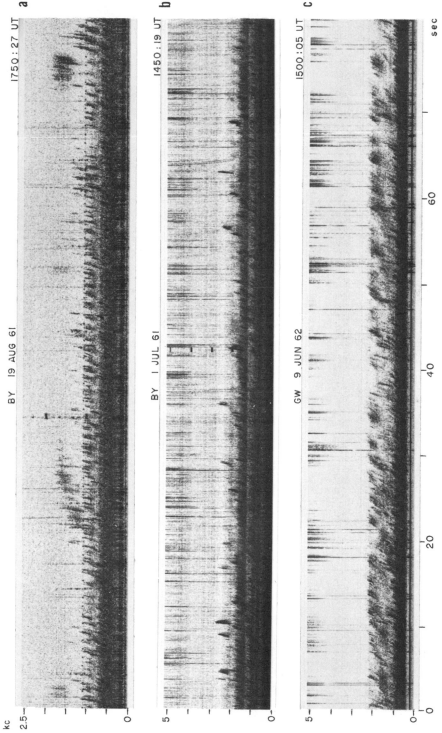

FIG. 7-37. Chorus. *a*, Chorus elements superimposed on hiss (polar chorus). *b*, Three chorus bands; occasional isolated bursts appear above the upper band. *c*, Strong chorus band with upper cutoff at 1 kc/s and relatively infrequent bursts at higher frequencies with upper cutoff at 2.2 kc/s.

247

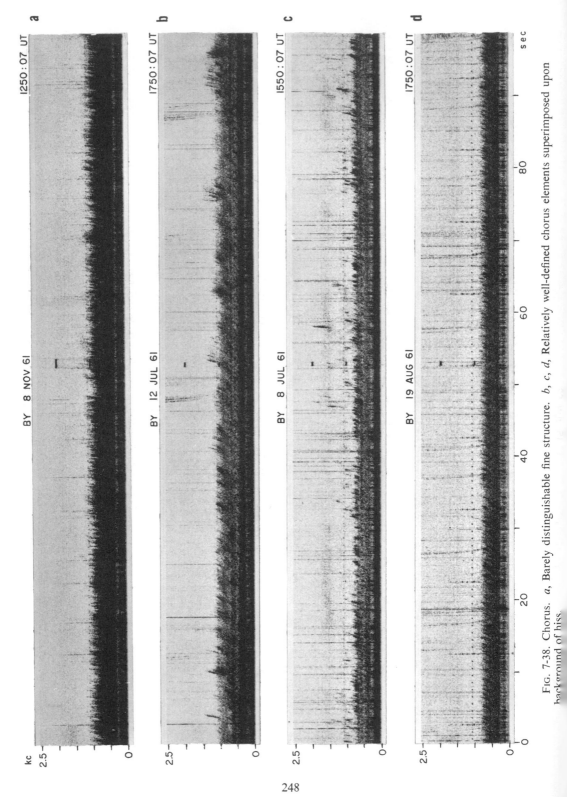

Fig. 7-38. Chorus. *a*, Barely distinguishable fine structure. *b*, *c*, *d*, Relatively well-defined chorus elements superimposed upon background of hiss.

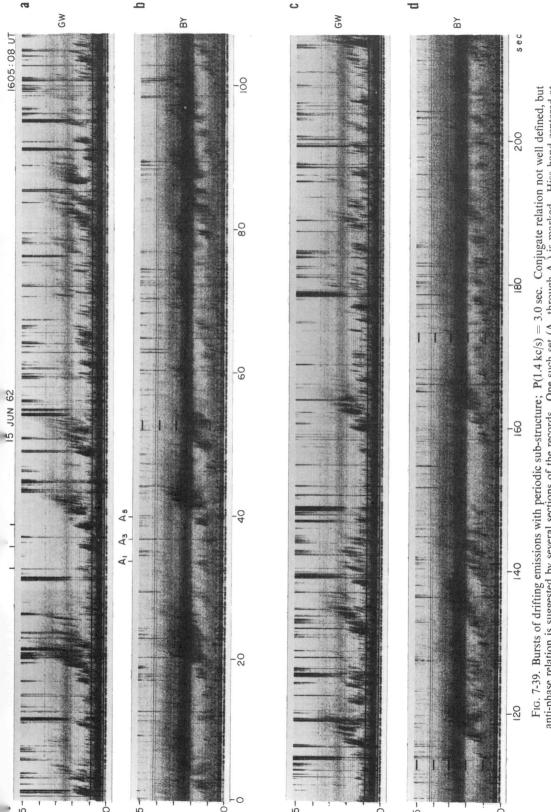

Fig. 7-39. Bursts of drifting emissions with periodic sub-structure; $P(1.4 \text{ kc/s}) = 3.0$ sec. Conjugate relation not well defined, but anti-phase relation is suggested by several sections of the records. One such set (A_0 through A_5) is marked. Hiss band centered at 2.3 kc/s is relatively strong at BY and weak at GW, whereas chorus band centered at 500 cps is relatively strong at GW and virtually absent at BY.

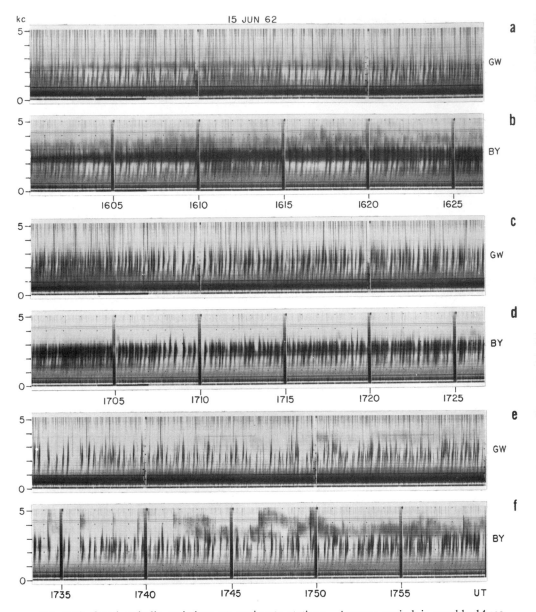

FIG. 7-40. Quasi-periodic emissions at conjugate stations. Average period is roughly 14 sec, based on samples taken between 1710 and 1720 UT and between 1740 and 1750 UT. Strong band of hiss below 1 kc/s evident at GW, whereas the hiss in this band at BY is relatively weak.

250

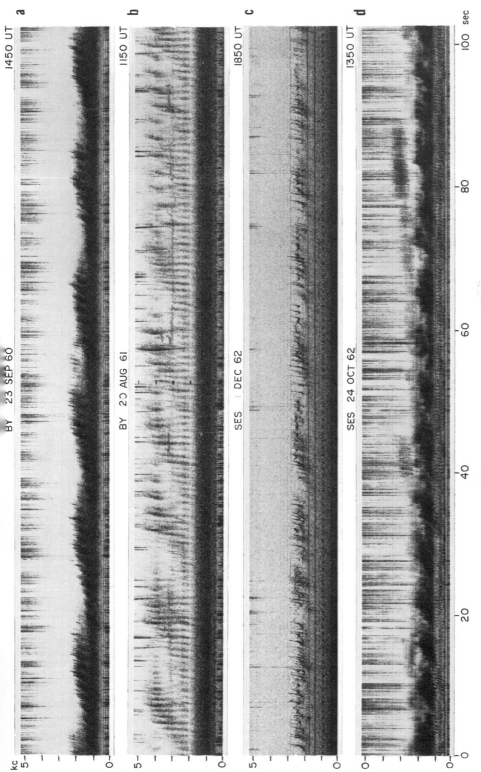

FIG. 7-41. Quasi-periodic emissions. *a*, QP(2.0 kc/s) = 17 sec; each group appears to contain a three-phase emission, P(1.6 kc/s) = 4.2 sec. *b*, QP(3 kc/s) = 12 sec, P(2.2 kc/s) = 2.8 sec, P(3.9 kc/s) = 2.3 sec. Note that drifting periodic band tends to level off at average frequency of about 3.9 kc/s. Some elements of quasi-periodic groups are connected to corresponding non-dispersive members of fixed-frequency sets at 2.2 kc/s through traces of whistler-mode echoes of previous elements. *c*, QP(2.0 kc/s) = 11 sec. *d*, QP(3 kc/s) = 7 sec.

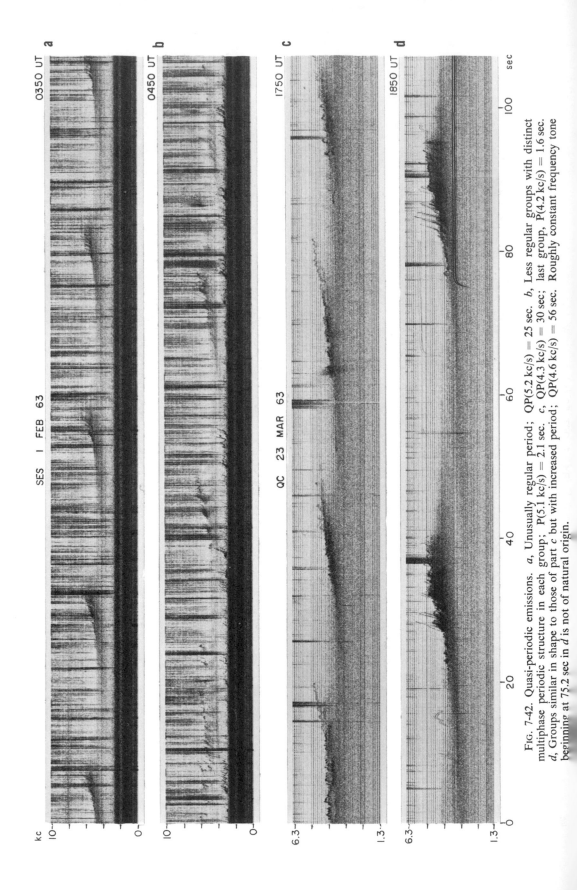

FIG. 7-42. Quasi-periodic emissions. *a*, Unusually regular period; QP(5.2 kc/s) = 25 sec. *b*, Less regular groups with distinct multiphase periodic structure in each group; P(5.1 kc/s) = 2.1 sec. *c*, QP(4.3 kc/s) = 30 sec; last group, P(4.2 kc/s) = 1.6 sec. *d*, Groups similar in shape to those of part *c* but with increased period; QP(4.6 kc/s) = 56 sec. Roughly constant frequency tone beginning at 75.2 sec in *d* is not of natural origin.

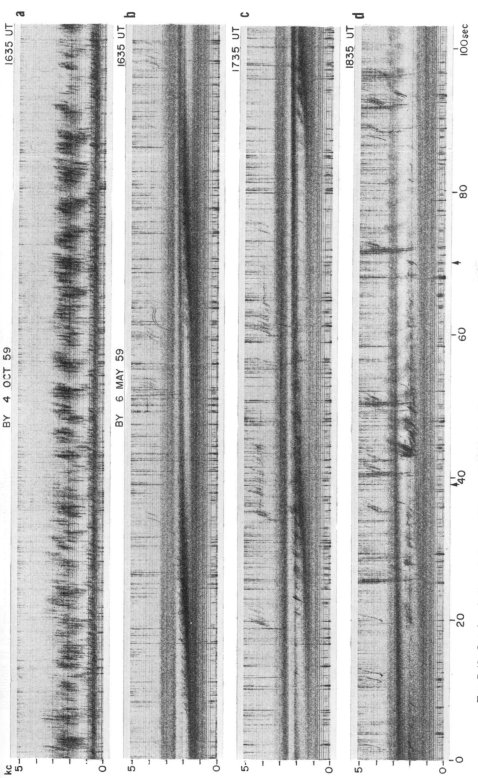

FIG. 7-43. Quasi-periodic emissions. *a*. Discrete elements in adjacent groups show tendency to reappear at regular intervals, suggesting that these groups may be highly damped sets of periodic emissions; P(2.0 kc/s) = 4 sec. *b*, QP(2.0 kc/s) = 53 sec. *c*, QP(1.9 kc/s) = 64 sec. *d*, QP(1.6 kc/s) = 50 sec. Note presence of several multipath whistlers with echo trains concentrated in the noise band centered on 3 kc/s; hooks and risers triggered by these whistlers can also be seen above the noise band. The same type of triggered emission occurs in part *c*, but is much weaker.

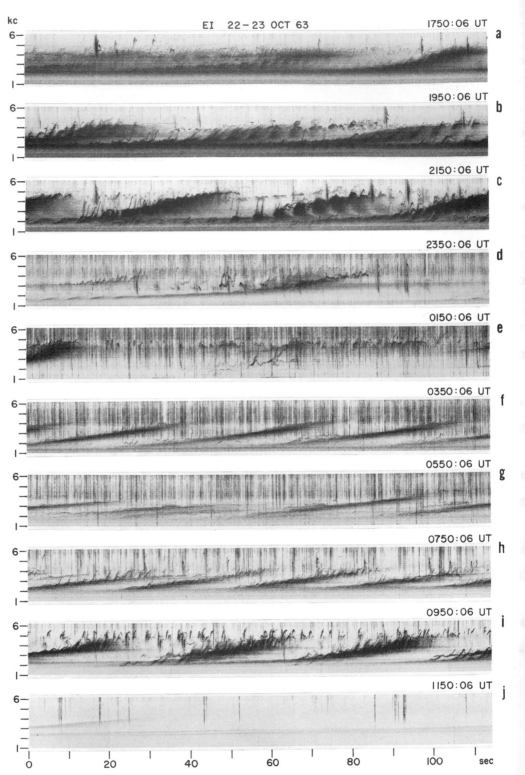

FIG. 7-44. Quasi-periodic emissions. *a–j*, Emissions observed continuously over a period of at least 18 hours. Periodicity of individual elements is evident in *a*, *b*, *c*, and *d*.

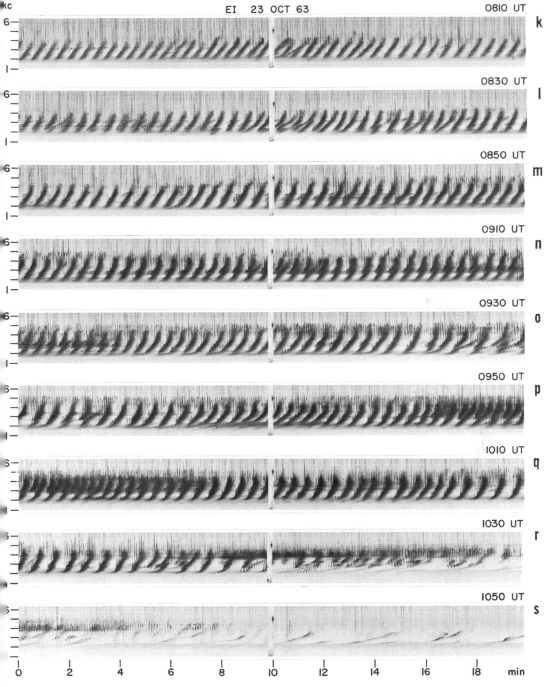

EI   23 OCT 63

0810 UT   k

0830 UT   l

0850 UT   m

0910 UT   n

0930 UT   o

0950 UT   p

1010 UT   q

1030 UT   r

1050 UT   s

FIG. 7-44. *k–s*, Continuous slow-speed recording showing progressive changes in the character of the emissions that were sampled in *i*. In *r* and *s*, a marked decrease in activity is accompanied by a decrease in slope and an increase in period of the noise bursts. QP(2.3 kc/s) = 32 sec based on *n*.

255

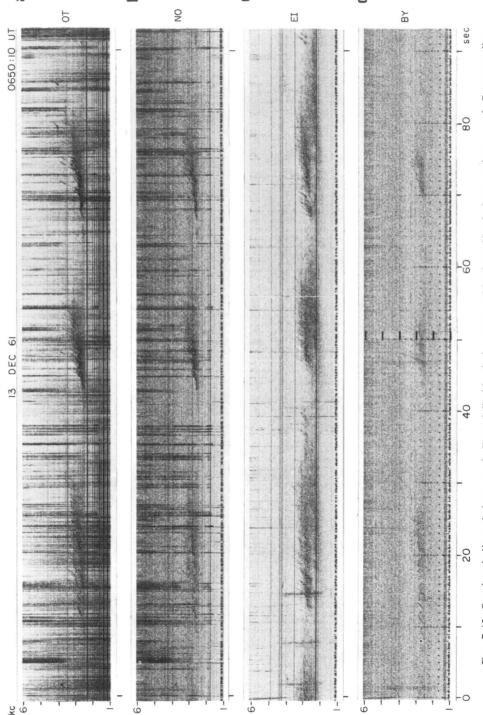

Fig. 7-45. Quasi-periodic emissions. *a*, *b*, Essentially identical groups at Northern Hemisphere stations. *c*, *d*, Corresponding groups at Southern Hemisphere stations. Although similar in general appearance, the latter groups tend to be delayed slightly with respect to those in the Northern Hemisphere and to contain more energy at lower frequencies; QP(2.8 kc/s) = 26 sec.

256

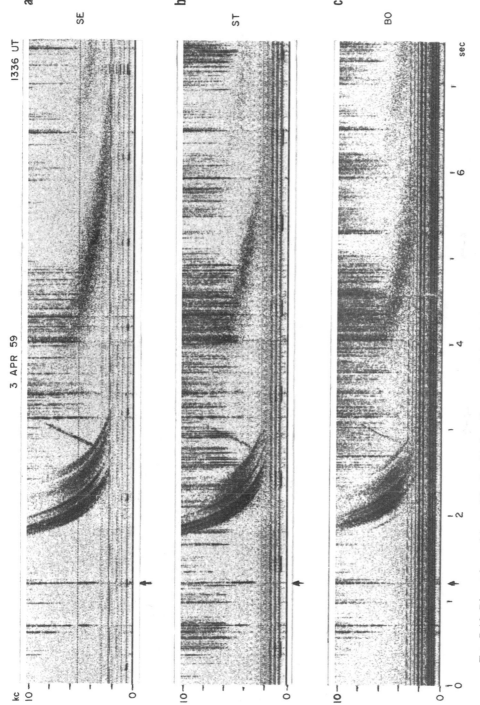

FIG. 7-46. Riser triggered by multipath whistler. Spectrum of riser is the same at the three stations, but the multipath structure of the whistler is distinctly different. For example, the late component in *a* and *c* is not evident in *b*.

257

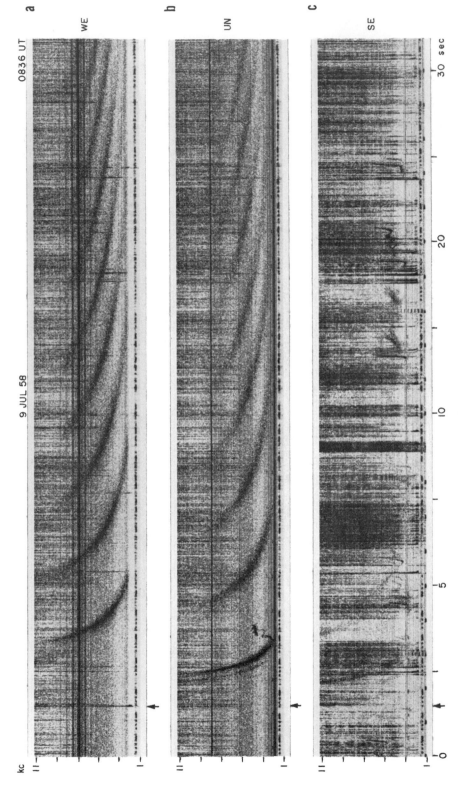

Fig. 7-47. Whistler-triggered emission. Although whistler train is perceptible at all stations, the triggered emission is seen only at one station (UN). Emissions observed at SE are not identifiable at other stations; MA record (not illustrated) shows no activity.

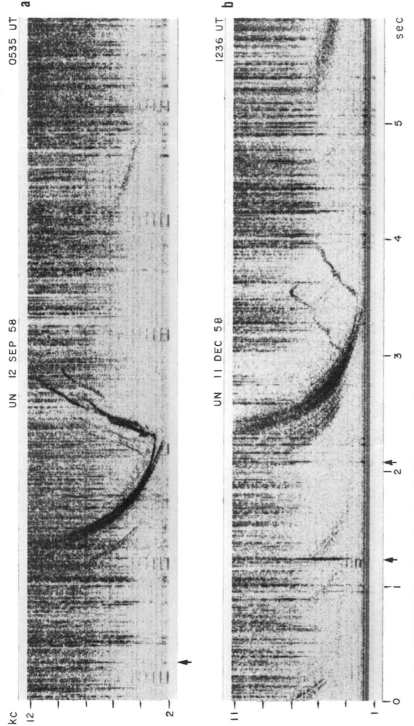

Fig. 7-48. Whistler-triggered hooks. Hook breaks away from lower portion of one-hop multipath whistler. *a*, One triggered hook beginning at 3.2 kc/s, and several associated risers. *b*, One triggered hook beginning at 2.6 kc/s together with a stepped riser beginning at 3.4 kc/s; a weak whistler, whose source is marked by second arrow, crosses both emissions at points of inflection, suggesting that whistler acts to change character of both emissions.

259

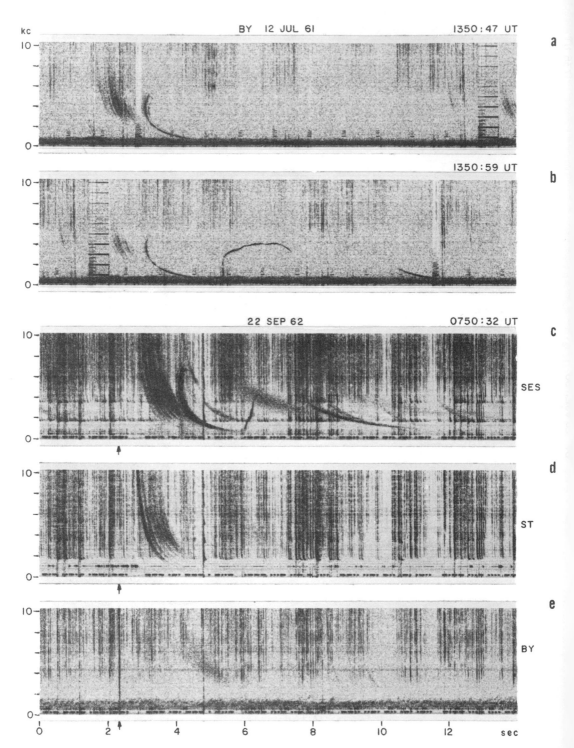

FIG. 7-49. Emissions triggered near tail of nose whistlers. *a, b,* Two similar, multipath whistlers with an unusual emission associated only with the weaker of the two whistlers. The whistler trace and the emission trace appear to join smoothly at their lower frequencies. *c, d, e,* Multipath whistler with prominent nose component at SES that appears to be associated with a riser. Nose component and riser are not evident at either ST or BY.

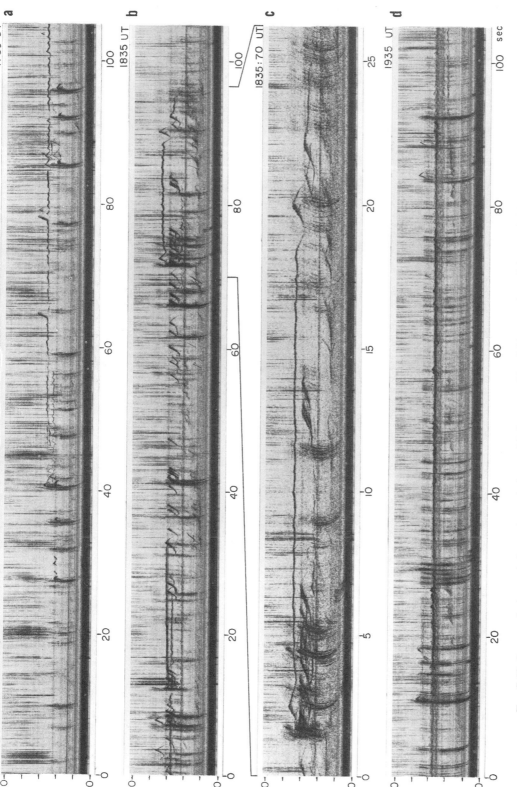

FIG. 7-50. Long-enduring emissions triggered above whistler nose. Fourfold expansion of time scale of indicated portion of *b* is shown in *c*; long enduring emission at 7 kc/s continues without significant interruption for 19 sec. Note characteristic upper cutoff of many emissions and whistlers. Most whistler traces exhibit nose frequencies between 3.7 kc/s and 4.2 kc/s; at 6.5 sec in *c*, traces with nose frequencies near 2 kc/s appear. Many emissions begin with a short rise in frequency.

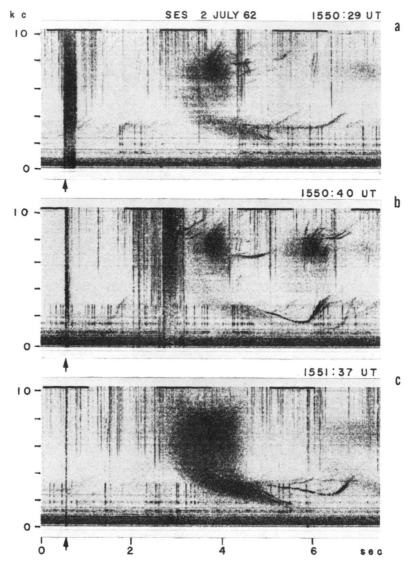

FIG. 7-51. Emissions triggered above and below whistler nose. Repeated observations show similar whistler components but different emission forms.

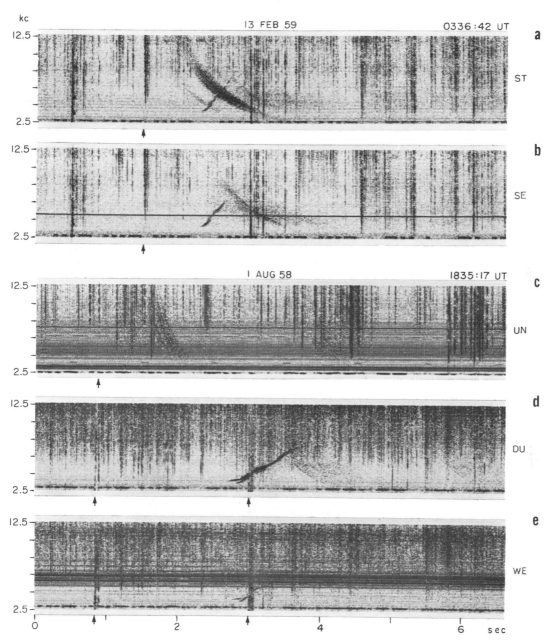

kc

13 FEB 59   0336:42 UT   **a**

12.5 —

2.5 —   ST

12.5 —   **b**

2.5 —   SE

1 AUG 58   1835:17 UT   **c**

12.5 —

2.5 —   UN

12.5 —   **d**

2.5 —   DU

12.5 —   **e**

2.5 —   WE

0   2   4   6   sec

FIG. 7-52. Precursors. *a, b,* Simultaneous recordings at ST and SE with similar precursor shapes; strong two-hop whistler components at ST cross emission, whereas strong components at SE arrive after emission. *c, d, e,* Long, intense precursor with branched structure; associated two-hop whistler is weak at DU and not detectable at WE; corresponding one-hop whistler is observed at UN.

263

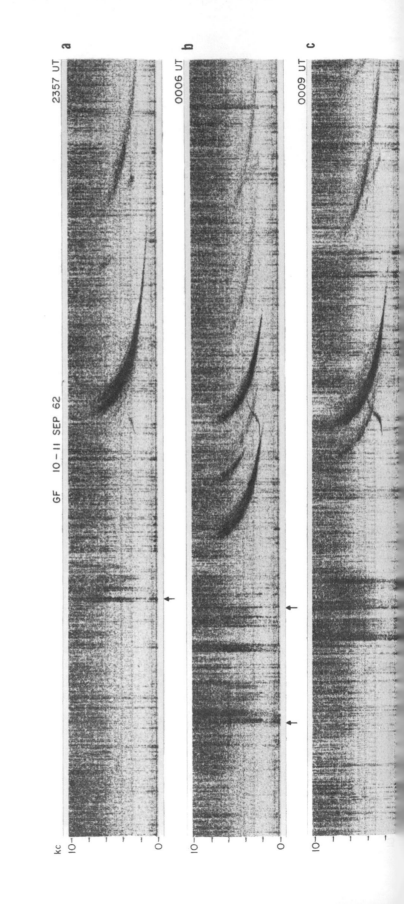

GF 10 – 11 SEP 62

a 2357 UT

b 0006 UT

c 0009 UT

kc 10—

0—

10—

0—

10—

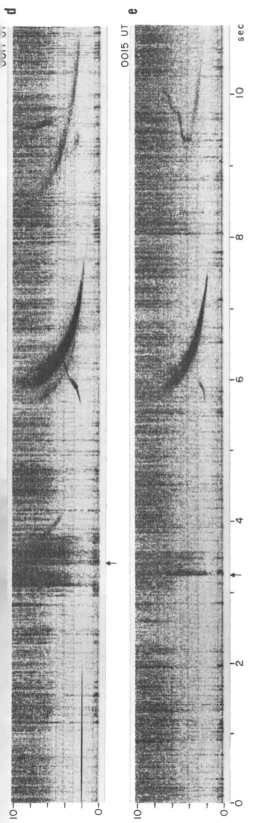

FIG. 7-53. Precursors. Repeated precursors show slight changes in form. Two-hop dispersed echo of precursor shows same echo delay as associated two-hop whistler. The precursor displays a maximum echo intensity at 2.9 kc/s and a two-hop period of 3.4 sec. Records have been aligned with respect to the precursor. Variation in time of causative impulse shows changes in position of precursor relative to associated whistler. Note irregular riser beginning in the four-hop whistler echo in *e*. (Constant tone at 2 kc/s at beginning of *d* is of instrumental origin.)

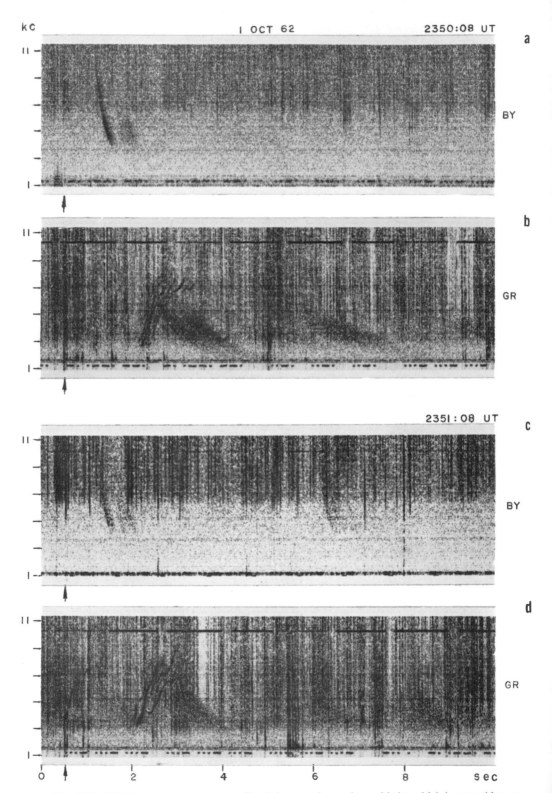

FIG. 7-54. Multicomponent precursor. Byrd shows early one-hop whistler which is not evident at GR. Two-hop components at GR are associated with the weaker one-hop components at BY.

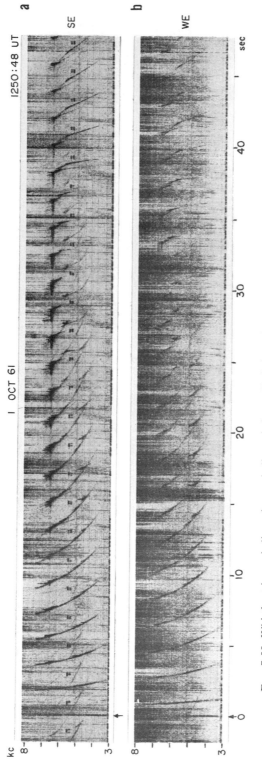

Fig. 7-55. Whistler-triggered dispersive periodic emissions. Emissions develop at frequencies between 6 and 7 kc/s. Echoing emission grows from the whistler-mode echo of the previous emission. This growth is especially prominent on the thirty-ninth whistler hop at WE and the fortieth hop at SE.

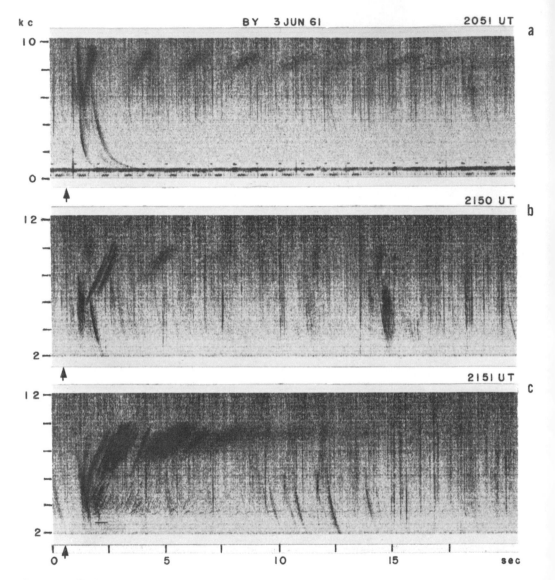

FIG. 7-56. Whistler-triggered dispersive periodic emissions. Periodic emissions show dispersion characteristic of frequencies above the nose; *a*, *b*, P(8.0 kc/s) = 2.2 sec. *c*, Multiple triggered emissions that echo with the same period as the emissions in *a* and *b*.

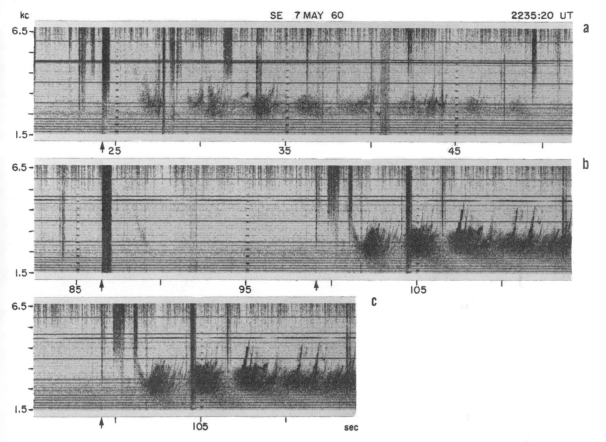

FIG. 7-57. Periodic non-dispersive emissions associated with atmospherics. *a*, Emissions follow atmospheric source. *b*, First source is followed by a weak whistler and no emission; second source is followed by a similar whistler and strong periodic emissions. The emissions appear to be associated with the whistler in *b*, and the similarity with *a* suggests that the triggering source in *a* is also a weak whistler. Last half of *b* is repeated in *c* to emphasize the similarity of the two whistlers and the two sets of emissions; P(2.9 kc/s) = 2.6 sec.

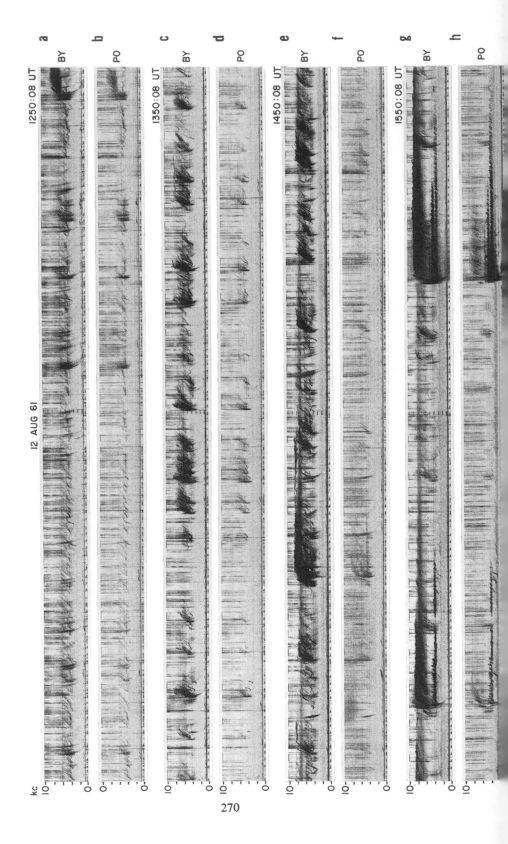

270

FIG. 7-58. Emissions, triggered and spontaneous. Shapes are identical at both BY and PO, but relative intensity shows marked variation. Midband events are observed at both stations. Events at frequencies greater than 7 kc/s may be intense at BY and undetectable at PO. Band between 2 and 3 kc/s, well defined on 1550 run, appears stronger at PO. Band below 1 kc/s appears stronger at BY. No gain changes were made during the preparation of this figure.

271

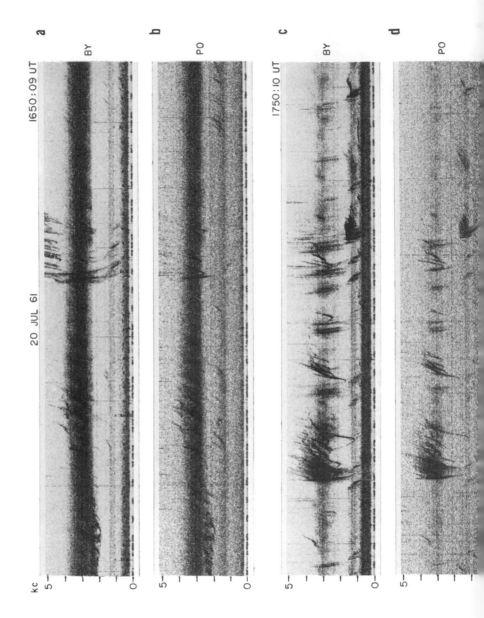

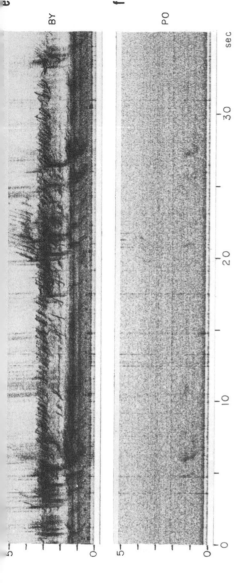

Fɪɢ. 7-59. Whistler-triggered emissions observed simultaneously at BY and PO. *a–d*, Records show virtually the same events except that the strong emission band below 1 kc/s at BY is absent at PO. *e, f*, Activity at BY has increased, whereas that at PO is almost completely absent. Station NPG inserted at bottom of records in *a–d*.

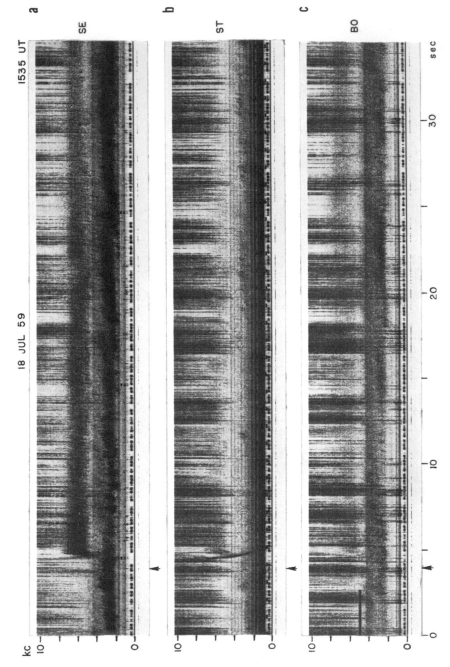

Fig. 7-60. Whistler-triggered chorus. Strong chorus band centered at 6 kc/s at SE is barely evident at ST and BO. Whistler is strongest at ST, weaker at SE, and barely detectable at BO. The 5-kc/s mark at beginning of BO record is of instrumental origin. The strong chorus in irregular band centered at about 3 kc/s at SE appears much weaker at BO and is barely evident at ST.

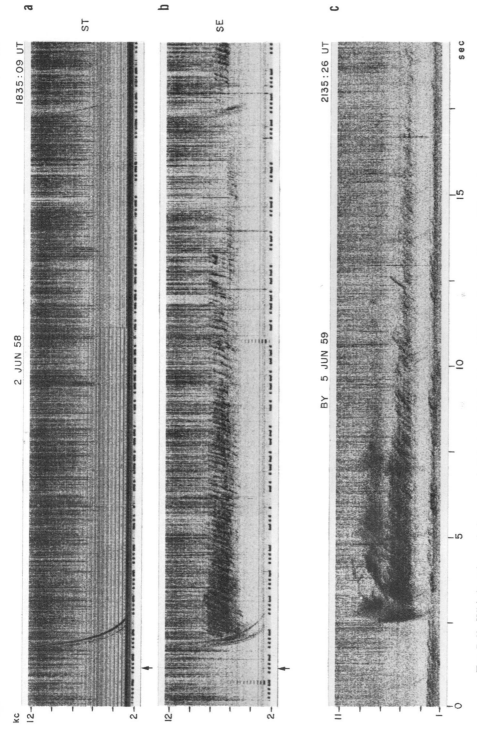

FIG. 7-61. Whistler-triggered chorus. *a, b,* Principal whistler trace at ST also clearly evident at SE; early traces at ST not apparent at SE; early traces at SE correspond to higher-latitude paths and are explained in terms of the knee whistler phenomenon (see Fig. 4-28); triggered chorus appears to be associated with the early high-latitude traces at SE. *c,* Slopes of chorus elements less than those in *b*: upper band appears above nose frequency (6.5 kc/s).

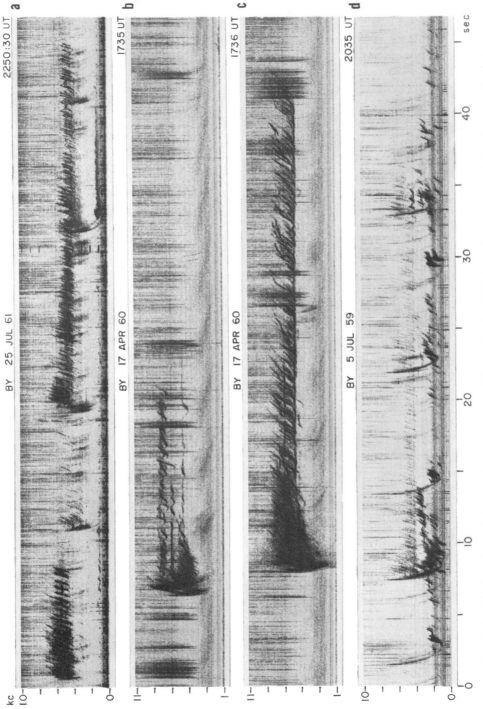

FIG. 7-62. Whistler-triggered chorus. Note occurrence of discrete bands. Whistlers echo below nose in *b* and *c* runs. In *d*, strong emissions are often associated with extremely weak whistlers.

276

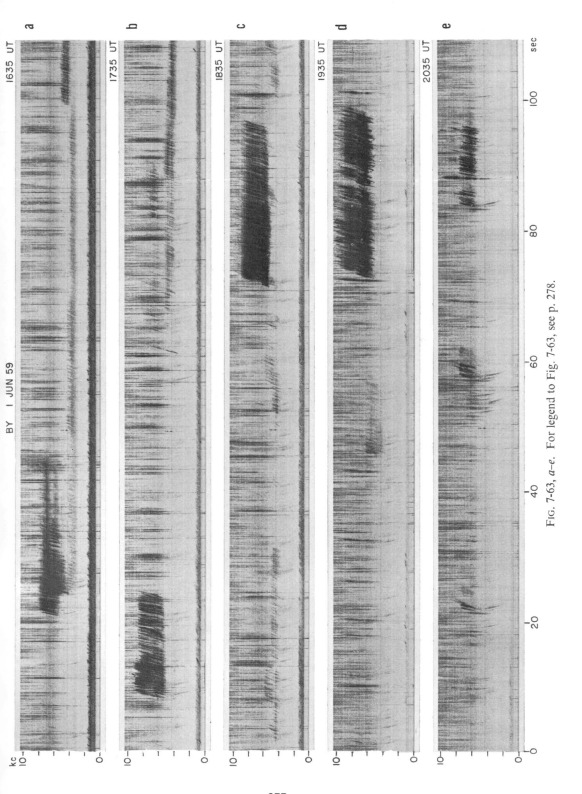

FIG. 7-63, *a-e*. For legend to Fig. 7-63, see p. 278.

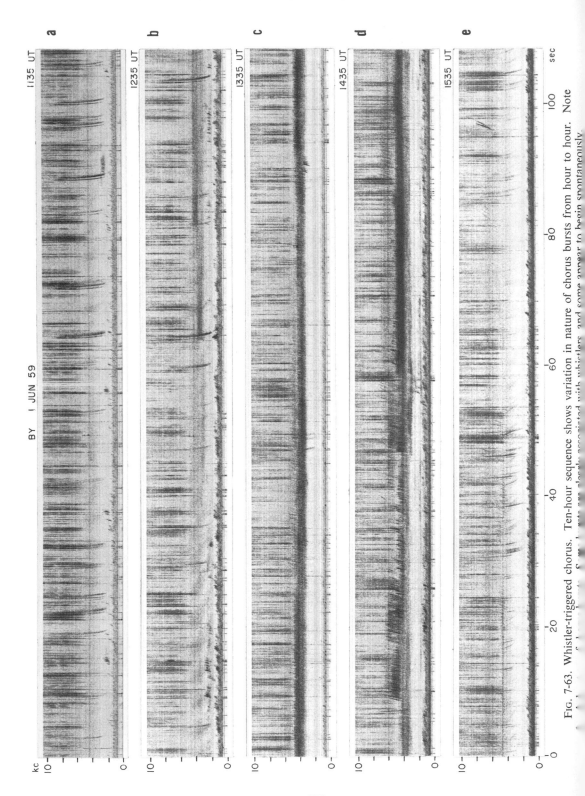

FIG. 7-63. Whistler-triggered chorus. Ten-hour sequence shows variation in nature of chorus bursts from hour to hour. Note that ... are closely associated with whistlers, and some appear to begin spontaneously.

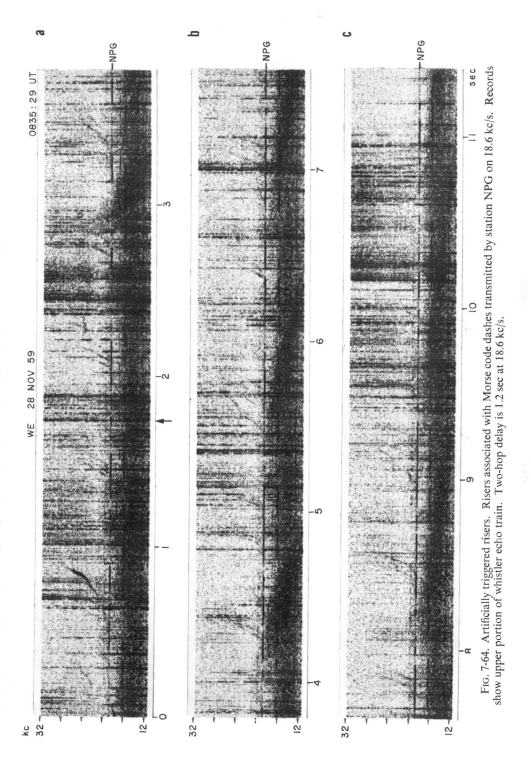

Fig. 7-64. Artificially triggered risers. Risers associated with Morse code dashes transmitted by station NPG on 18.6 kc/s. Records show upper portion of whistler echo train. Two-hop delay is 1.2 sec at 18.6 kc/s.

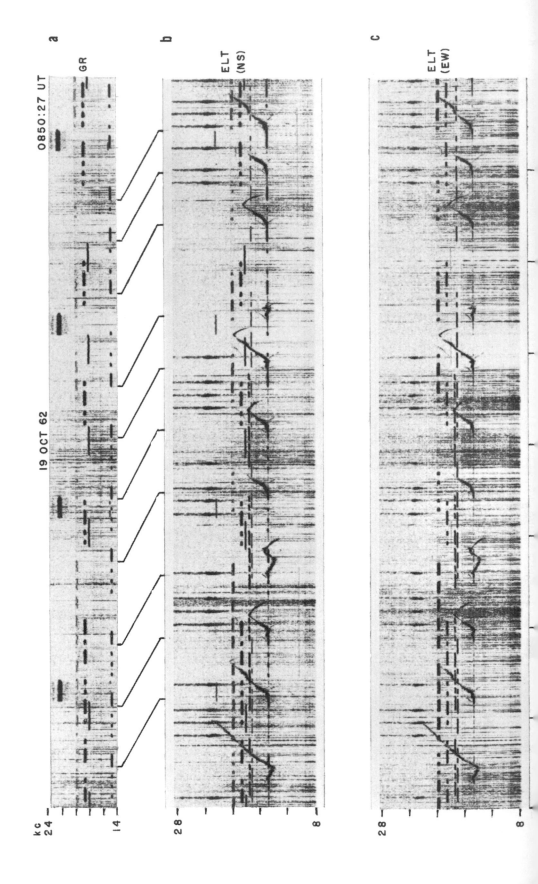

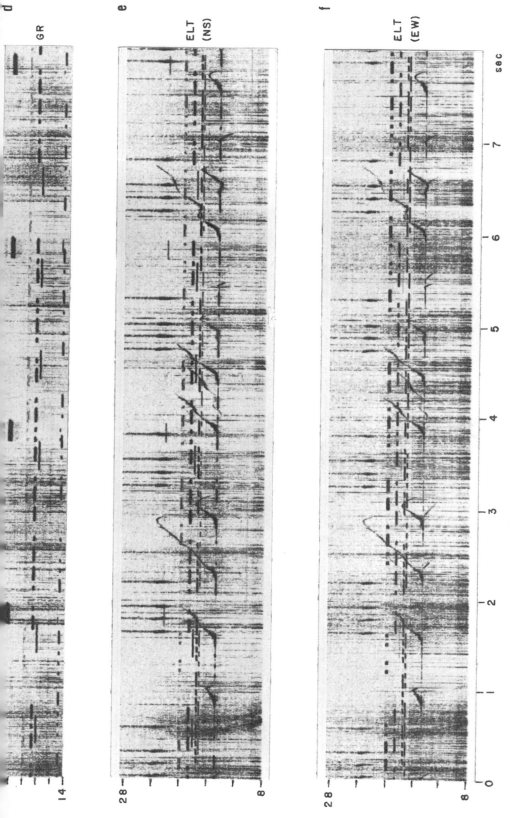

d
GR

e
ELT
(NS)

f
ELT
(EW)

Fig. 7-65, *a-f*. For legend to Fig. 7-65, see p. 283.

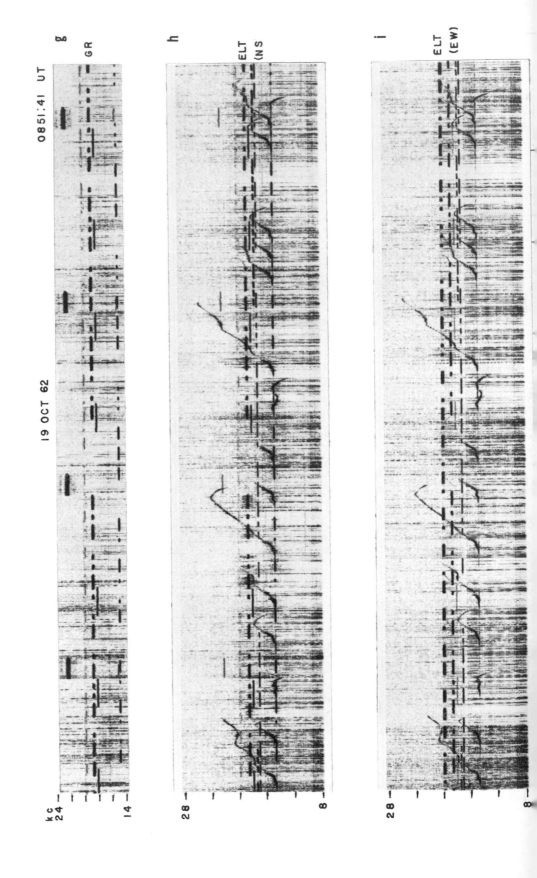

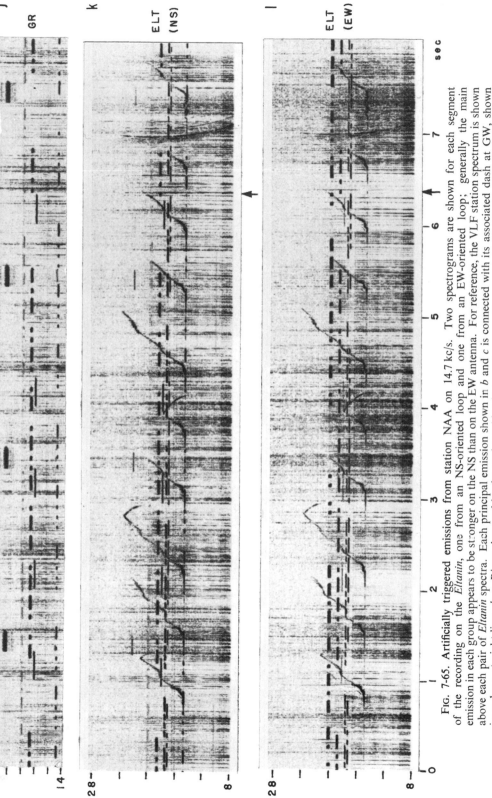

Fig. 7-65. Artificially triggered emissions from station NAA on 14.7 kc/s. Two spectrograms are shown for each segment of the recording on the *Eltanin*, one from an NS-oriented loop and one from an EW-oriented loop; generally the main emission in each group appears to be stronger on the NS than on the EW antenna. For reference, the VLF station spectrum is shown above each pair of *Eltanin* spectra. Each principal emission shown in *b* and *c* is connected with its associated dash at GW, shown in *a*, by a straight line. *b*, *c*, Risers, inverted hooks, and combination events; preceding nearly every main event by about 40 msec is a short, very weak riser; following several of the main events by about 100 msec is a weak, falling tone; short vertical traces with maximum strength at about 23 kc/s believed to originate on board ship. *e*, *f*, Falling tones, several of which appear stronger on EW loop than on NS loop; two nose whistlers appear between 0 and 1 sec. *h*, *i*, Maximum upper frequency limit (25 kc/s) of emissions. *k*, *l*, Well-defined nose whistler ($f_n = 20$ kc/s).

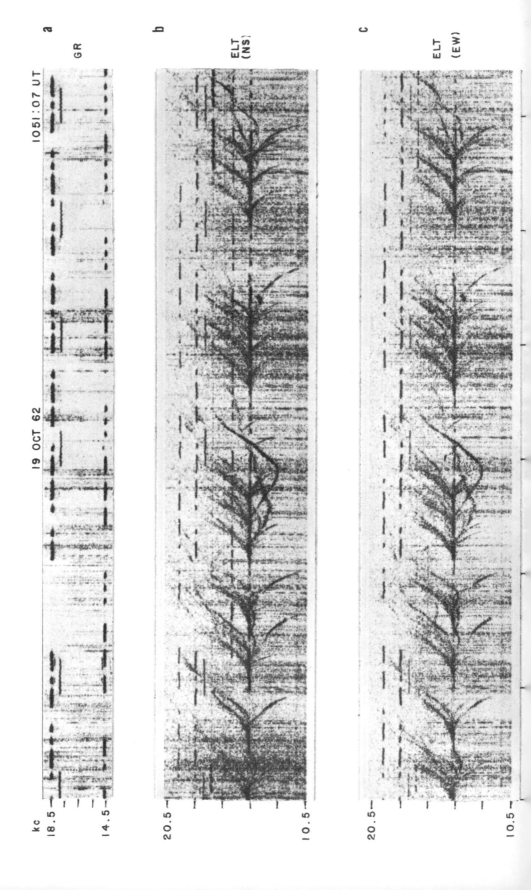

1051:07 UT

19 OCT 62

a GR

kc
18.5
14.5

b ELT (NS)

20.5
10.5

c ELT (EW)

20.5
10.5

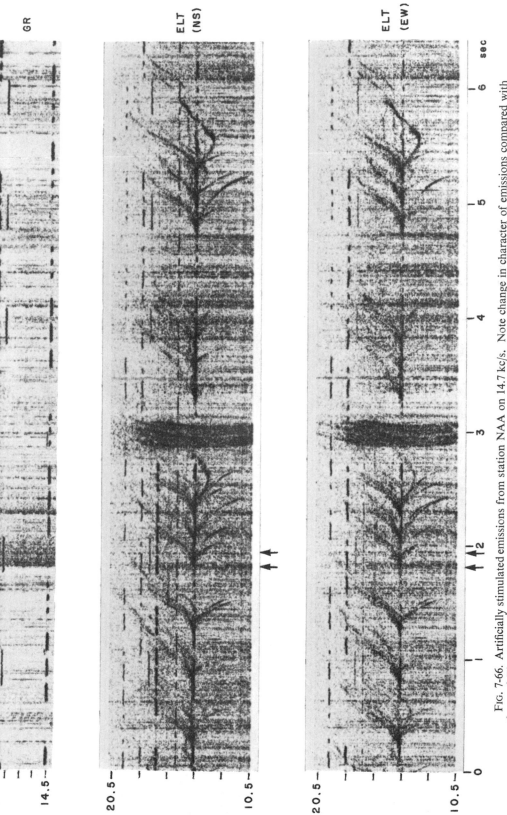

FIG. 7-66. Artificially stimulated emissions from station NAA on 14.7 kc/s. Note change in character of emissions compared with those of Fig. 7-65, observed two hours earlier; many more components, both rising and falling, associated with each parent dash; elements tend to be more diffuse. b, c, Several emissions decrease markedly in strength and then recover before disappearing. e, f, Minimum lower frequency limit (11 kc/s) of emissions; two multipath nose whistlers; average f_n is about 14 kc/s; t_n varies from 1.08 sec to 1.16 sec, allowing for source delay.

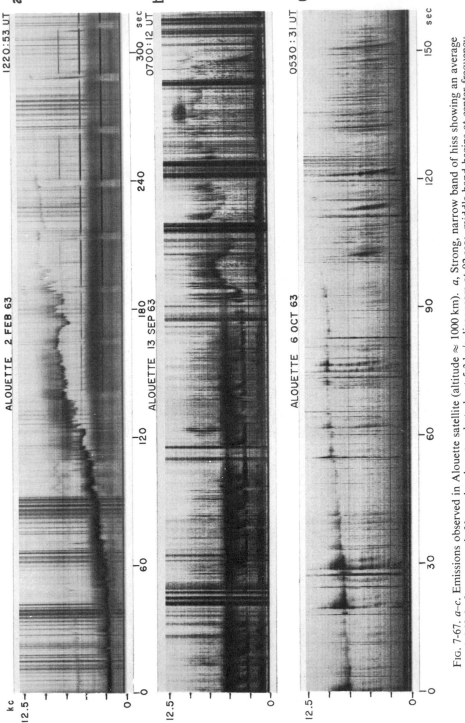

FIG. 7-67. *a–c*. Emissions observed in Alouette satellite (altitude ≈ 1000 km). *a*, Strong, narrow band of hiss showing an average upward drift in frequency. *b*, Upper band centered at about 5.3 kc/s disappears at 92 sec; middle band begins at center frequency of 2.6 kc/s and drifts slowly up to 3.1 kc/s at about 89 sec, after which the frequency shows relatively wide fluctuations; marked enhancements, apparently triggered by whistlers, occur in this band; lower band, at about 1 kc/s, shows evidence of discrete emissions and is relatively constant in frequency. *c*, Narrow band of hiss drifts upward in frequency from 7.9 kc/s at start of record (L = 3.2) to 10 kc/s at 92 sec (L = 2.7); noise is enhanced by whistlers.

286

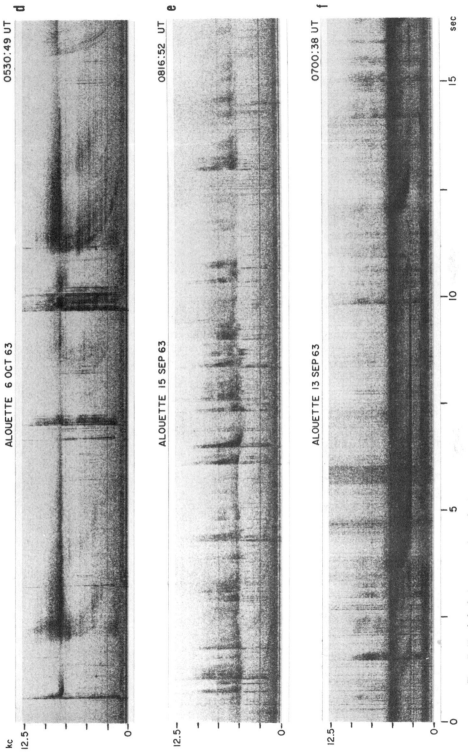

FIG. 7-67. *d–f. d*, An expansion of *c* between 18 sec and 34 sec to illustrate detail of emission bursts triggered by short and long fractional-hop whistlers. *e*, Emission bursts triggered by short fractional-hop whistlers. *f*, An expansion of *b* between 26 sec and 42 sec showing details of relationship between whistlers and enhancements of emission in middle band. Whistlers begin in upper band and terminate in middle band.

7.2 Emission Properties

Amplitude of VLF emissions.   At any given location the amplitude of VLF emissions varies widely with time and with frequency. At Byrd Station, for example, the amplitude of emissions at 5 kc/s varies from below the receiver noise level, which is about 10^{-18} wm^{-2}(c/s)$^{-1}$, to as high as 10^{-14} wm^{-2}(c/s)$^{-1}$. Noise levels as high as 10^{-13} wm^{-2}(c/s)$^{-1}$ have been observed at 750 cps. These values are similar to those reported by Dowden (1962a) from measurements made at Hobart, Tasmania.

The general nature of the integrated amplitude spectrum of VLF noise is readily defined with the aid of a narrow-band filter that is swept rapidly in frequency (Watts, 1957a,b). Illustrative records obtained by this method at Byrd Station are shown in Fig. 7-68. Each record consists of about sixty super-imposed one-second sweeps. Ordinates in watts per square meter per cycle per second may be obtained by comparison with the scale shown in Fig. 7-68*f*, which includes the effects of variation of filter bandwidth with frequency, and the effects of the frequency response of the system. At frequencies below about 400 cps, the main source of noise is atmospherics.

Spectra characteristic of different types of noise are shown in Fig. 7-68. Part *a* shows strong broad-band auroral hiss that extends above the upper limit of the analyzer at 20 kc/s and exhibits a lower cutoff at roughly 600 cps. An analysis of the tape recording from the nearest synoptic run showed that the strength of this hiss varied with a period of about five seconds. A relatively narrow band of steady hiss between 10 kc/s and 15 kc/s is shown in part *b*. Although it is not known if aurora was present simultaneously, this form of hiss is often associated with aurora. This record shows an additional band, centered at 700 cps, consisting of a mixture of chorus and hiss, sometimes called "roar." A pattern of chorus and hiss much broader in frequency is shown in part *c*, where the peak near 2 kc/s represents a strong band of periodic chorus. Part *d* shows chorus and hiss in a sharply defined double-peaked band between 1 and 2 kc/s. Three separate bands of emission of about the same intensity are shown in part *e*, with a narrow band of hiss at 400 cps, chorus (risers) at 800 cps, and hiss at 2 kc/s.

Occurrence in bands is a distinctive characteristic of the spectrum of VLF emissions and is apparent in many of the spectra shown in the Atlas. The simultaneous appearance of two or more bands is common, but these bands are seldom harmonically related and the emissions in the different bands generally exhibit different spectral details.

The diurnal variation of the amplitude of VLF emissions at Byrd Station for the month of October 1961, is shown in Fig. 7-69. The values shown are the averages of the maximum and minimum values in each hour scaled from continuous chart recordings made in narrow bands with a minimum-reading detector (Marks, 1962). At 750 cps, 2 kc/s, and 4 kc/s, the curves show a relatively broad diurnal peak at 1500 UT to 1700 UT, which consists mainly of chorus and other discrete forms. At 4 kc/s and 8 kc/s there is a secondary peak at 0300 UT to 0400 UT and the noise during this part of the day consists mainly of hiss associated with auroras. At 8 kc/s, relatively little chorus is

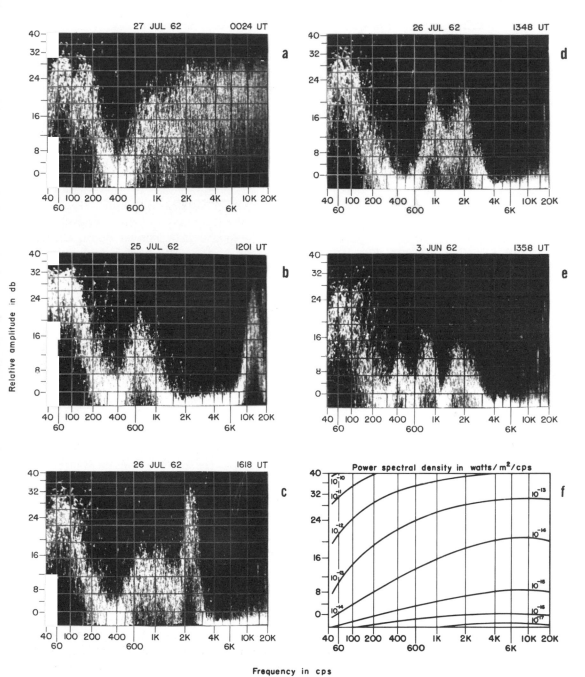

FIG. 7-68. Examples of integrated amplitude spectrum of VLF emissions. Ordinates give relative amplitude in db at output of panoramic analyzer. Conversion to power spectral density using curves of *f*. *a*, Auroral hiss from 600 cps to 20 kc/s. *b*, Auroral hiss from 8 kc/s to 20 kc/s; chorus and hiss peaking at 700 cps. *c*, Chorus and hiss between 500 cps and 2 kc/s; periodic chorus between 2 kc/s and 3 kc/s. *d*, Two bands of chorus and hiss peaking at 900 cps and 2 kc/s. *e*, Three bands of emissions; hiss at 400 cps, risers at 800 cps, hiss at 2 kc/s.

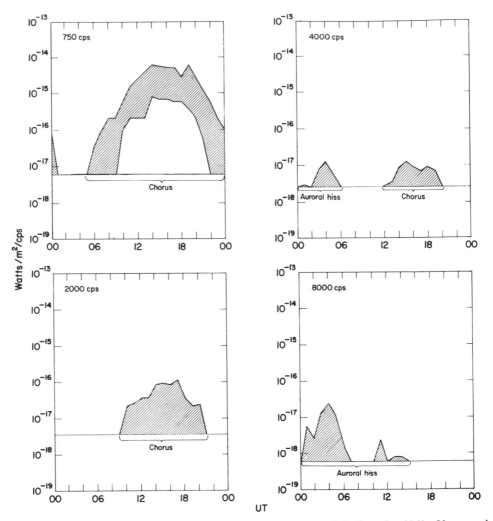

FIG. 7-69. Diurnal variation of VLF emission amplitude at Byrd Station, Oct 1961. Upper and lower curves show averages of maximum and minimum values, respectively, in each hour. Base line represents sensitivity threshold of recorder.

observed; the weak noise from 10 to 14 UT consists mostly of hiss. Other months show diurnal variations of similar shape.

Seasonal variations in the amplitude of VLF emissions are not well defined. An exception is a form of chorus found mainly at magnetic latitudes greater than 60° (Figs. 7-36 and 7-37a). This chorus, which consists of steady noise or discrete events, or both, and which typically occurs in a band below 1500 cps, has been called "polar chorus" (Ungstrup and Jackerott, 1963).* Its occurrence at Godhavn shows a pronounced peak around 0900 LMT (1235 UT) and a seasonal peak in local summer. At Kiruna, Sweden, a band of emissions that

---

* The first observations of this type of chorus were probably made by Burton (1930), who reported "a jumble of hollow rustling or roaring sounds" on a submarine cable in Newfoundland.

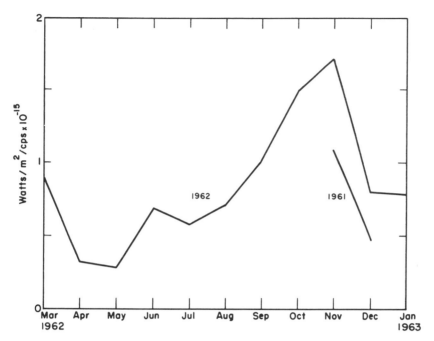

FIG. 7-70. Monthly average intensity of VLF emissions at 750 cps at Byrd Station.

peaked around 0800 LMT was found at 750 ± 150 cps (Aarons *et al.*, 1960; Gustafsson *et al.*, 1960; Egeland *et al.*, 1962). At Byrd Station the seasonal peak in 750 cps emissions also occurs during local summer, as is shown in Fig. 7-70. This figure represents the power that corresponds to the field strength which has been averaged over each hour and scaled from the same continuous chart recordings used in obtaining Fig. 7-69. It can be seen that the intensity at Byrd peaks in November and reaches a minimum in May, whereas at Godhavn, data for the period July 1957 to December 1961 show a peak in June and a minimum in January. The differences between these polar chorus data from Godhavn and Byrd Station may possibly be caused by statistical fluctuation.

Localized nature of emissions. Discrete emissions are often seen simultaneously at stations less than a few hundred kilometers apart (Allcock and Martin, 1956; Helliwell and Carpenter, 1961), but when the separation exceeds 1000 km, correlation is considerably reduced. The very strong hooks recorded at Seattle on 6 October 1959 (Fig. 7-8 of the Atlas), which were barely detectable at Stanford, 1100 km farther south, provide an example of the limited range of discrete events. Other examples of the localization of discrete emissions are shown in Figs. 7-49, 7-59, 7-60 and 7-61 of the Atlas. Occasionally the same emissions may be observed at widely separated stations, as illustrated in Figs. 7-45, 7-46, 7-58, and 7-59.

Although discrete emissions appear to be restricted in geographical coverage, it has been observed that the intensity of emissions integrated over a minute or more correlates well at stations spaced up to several thousand kilometers apart

(Pope, 1959b; Ellis *et al.*, 1959; Ellis, 1960a, 1961; Dowden, 1961b). This is not surprising in view of the positive correlation between the general level of emissions at middle latitudes and world-wide magnetic activity. These results suggest the possibility that the virtual sources of discrete emissions are relatively small and may lie within considerably larger regions of general emission activity.

Additional evidence on the local nature of emissions has been obtained by means of directional observations at 5 kc/s (Ellis, 1960a). In this study a number of noise bursts were located with a network of direction finders in southeastern Australia. Their apparent source positions ranged in latitude from 34° S to greater than 42° S. Their apparent geographical size was estimated from the depth of the null and ranged from 400 km to 1000 km. In this study the electric field of the received wave was assumed to be polarized in the plane of incidence. However, this assumption may not always be justified, and furthermore the presence of an abnormal component tends to reduce the depth of the null (Crary, 1961). If this effect is present, then the source would appear larger than its true size.

At conjugate stations the correlation in emission activity is generally high (Allcock, 1957; Lokken *et al.*, 1961). Examples are shown in Figs. 7-5, 7-10, 7-15, 7-17, 7-19, 7-22, 7-39, 7-40, 7-45, and 7-55 of the Atlas. However, it is clear from these records that the degree of correlation is related to the type of emission. Thus in Fig. 7-39, which shows emissions recorded simultaneously at Great Whale and Byrd Station, the periodic emission is present at both stations, but the chorus band below 1 kc/s is present only at Great Whale. Apparently this band was generated only at the northern end of the path and did not travel back to Byrd via the whistler mode. This difference suggests that the source of the periodic emission and that of the chorus band may be located in different regions of the ionosphere. A hiss band at 2.3 kc/s appears stronger at Byrd than at Great Whale, suggesting a source localized in the vicinity of Byrd.

Distribution of emissions. In view of the limited geographical extent of particular emissions, it is not surprising that long-term averages of emission occurrence show marked temporal and geographical variations. Most statistical studies of these variations have been limited to chorus. However, in one study (McInnes, 1961) it was found that all types of emissions recorded at Macquarie Island (61.1° S geomagnetic latitude) showed about the same diurnal variation, with a peak in occurrence shortly before local noon. On the other hand, some differences in seasonal distributions of the different types of noise were suggested by the data. Because of limitations in the comparability of aural data in different seasons, the seasonal variation has not been well defined.

Chorus is perhaps the best known and most distinctive general class of emission and is found most commonly in the frequency range 1 to 5 kc/s (Pope, 1963). The diurnal behavior of polar chorus at Byrd Station has been shown in Fig. 7-69 on the basis of the quantitative measurement of the intensity at 750 cps. Similar diurnal curves for Byrd Station are obtained from the aural data. From these diurnal variations in chorus activity, a time of maximum activity can be measured for each station. Allcock (1957), Pope (1957; 1959a; 1960), and Crouchley and Brice (1960), using aural data from stations between 40° and 65° geomagnetic latitude, found that the local time of diurnal maximum in chorus activity was a linear function of geomagnetic latitude. Later data from higher latitudes did not follow this simple relation (Ungstrup, 1962; Pope, 1963). It has been found instead that the diurnal behavior of chorus can be represented in a fairly systematic way by spiral lines of constant universal time of chorus maximum emanating from the geomagnetic poles (Ondoh, 1961; Pope, 1963). These authors have suggested that these lines might be related to the spirals of precipitation of charged particles from the sun (Størmer, 1955).

Relationship to magnetic activity. In the early work at middle latitudes, it was found that the occurrence of VLF emissions showed a positive correlation with magnetic activity (Storey, 1953; Allcock, 1957). At higher latitudes there is evidence for a negative correlation, at least during certain periods. In a study of chorus activity in the band 1 to 4 kc/s at College, Alaska (geomagnetic latitude 65° N), Pope (1959a, 1963) found that the correlation between chorus and magnetic activity was positive during the solstice periods but negative during equinox periods. He suggested that the negative correlation might result from ionospheric absorption, which is known to be correlated positively with magnetic activity. Support for this interpretation is found in Fig. 3-31, which shows that during a representative polar blackout situation the lower-ionosphere absorption at 3 kc/s increases by 49 db with respect to quiet night conditions and by 38 db with respect to day conditions. These increases greatly exceed the ratio of the diurnal maximum of the average noise intensity to set noise at 3 kc/s, which was estimated to be about 10 db. Crouchley and Brice (1960) report that at Macquarie Island, 61° S geomagnetic, a negative correlation exists between chorus and magnetic activity. They suggest that the region of maximum chorus activity moves toward the equator during disturbed periods. This trend was also reported by Helliwell and Carpenter (1961).

The relation between VLF emissions and magnetic activity at different latitudes has been further investigated by Yoshida and Hatanaka (1962a,b), who find that the curve of emission activity with K_p reaches a peak at a certain value of K_p that decreases with latitude. At middle-latitude stations, such as Boulder and Norwich, peak activity occurs at $K_p = 6$. At high-latitude stations, such as Knob Lake, they find the peak at K_p values of 1 to 3.

A direct comparison of emission activity with the magnetic records indicates a significant relation (Ellis, 1960c; Aarons *et al.*, 1960). Sudden increases in chorus strength have been related to the H-component of the magnetic field by Tokuda (1962). In 17 months of synoptic aural chorus data from College, Alaska, he identified 94 chorus increases, of which 89 were preceded by negative bays in the H-component. The maximum excursion of the bays tended on the whole to coincide with the beginning of the chorus increase, and the magnitudes of the magnetic bays were found to be negatively correlated with the time delay between the onset of the bays and the occurrence of maximum chorus peak.

Micropulsation activity has also been found to be correlated with VLF noise (Westcott *et al.*, 1960; Pope, 1963). From synoptic records from College, Alaska, Ondoh (1962a) finds that of 79 increases in chorus activity that occurred in relatively quiet geomagnetic conditions after magnetic bays, 52 were associated with pulsations of periods from 1 to 6 min, and 11 were associated with pulsations of about 30 sec.

From a comparison of 8 kc/s hiss recorded at Godhavn (October 1962 through January 1963) with magnetic disturbance as measured by A_p, T. S. Jørgenson (1964) finds a definite positive correlation in which the time of maximum hiss occurrence is delayed 1 to 3 days with respect to the time of maximum magnetic disturbance. A correlation was also found between hiss bursts and sporadic E observed at Narssarssuaq, with the time of maximum frequency of sporadic E occurring about 10 minutes after the associated peak in VLF hiss intensity.

Emission activity in the form of hiss above 5 kc/s tends to show a high correlation with magnetic micropulsations as a result of the common relationship to aurora discussed in the following section.

Relation of emissions to auroral activity.   In addition to the relation between VLF emissions and magnetic disturbance, there is also an association between VLF emissions and auroral phenomena. Statistical correlations have been established, both between sub-visual auroras and hiss (Duncan and Ellis, 1959), and between visual auroras and hiss (Martin *et al.*, 1960; Morozumi, 1962; Jørgensen and Ungstrup, 1962). Hiss that is associated with aurora usually appears at frequencies above 4 kc/s, but on occasion the low-frequency limit may fall as low as 600 cps, as in Fig. 7-68*a*. The upper frequency limit sometimes exceeds the upper cutoff frequency (32 kc/s) of the recorder, as in Fig. 7-1*a*. Increases in the intensity of atmospheric noise on 20 kc/s during auroral displays have been reported (Gherzi, 1960), and it is possible that the observed noise may have been hiss.

Details of the relation between VLF hiss and aurora were explored in a study carried out at the South Pole during the dark months of 1960 (Morozumi, 1962). It was found that VLF hiss does not seem to be characteristic of all auroras, but is closely associated with auroral arcs and bands. Hiss was associated with two kinds of arc and band auroras. The first is the display of arcs and bands without prominent development, and the second type consists of arcs and bands followed by breakups.

A comparison of all-sky photometer white light recordings and all-sky camera photographs with the hiss recordings showed that the peak in VLF hiss coincided with the development of homogeneous arcs and bands in the aurora (Morozumi, 1962). However, when the aurora broke up and arrived at the zenith, the total light intensity increased, but the VLF intensity decreased, possibly because of increased absorption of the VLF energy in the D region of the ionosphere.

Both hiss and the related bright band type of aurora at the South Pole show a well-defined diurnal maximum near UT midnight. In addition, a second, weaker peak in auroral activity occurs near UT noon. This second peak is associated with the less bright ray-type aurora, ionospheric absorption, and chorus. Detailed studies showed that when the ray type of aurora occurred near UT midnight, ionospheric absorption was high and hiss was usually absent.

Similar observations of hiss and aurora were made at Byrd Station by Helms and Turtle.* In addition, magnetic micropulsations and total magnetic field

---

* Personal communication.

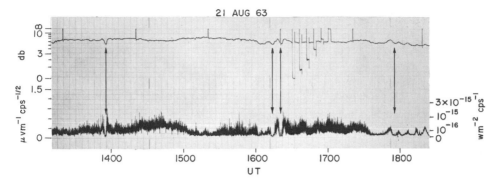

FIG. 7-71. Relation between absorption and chorus intensity at Byrd. Upper trace shows relative riometer absorption on 30 mc/s, while lower trace shows intensity of chorus at 1 kc/s. Arrows mark well-defined simultaneous minima in both chorus and absorption. (Riometer signal courtesy Central Radio Propagation Laboratory, Boulder, Colorado.)

were recorded. These workers found that aurora, hiss, and magnetic micro-pulsations all peak at about 0300 UT and show similar day-to-day variations in activity. The diurnal behavior of auroral hiss at Byrd Station is shown in parts c and d of Fig. 7-69. Simultaneous sudden commencements of these phenomena were found to occur mainly during the period 0000 to 0700 UT, which includes magnetic midnight (0615 UT).

Recent work at Byrd by Morozumi* has shown that during moderate distur-bances, absorption events, as measured by a riometer, are closely related to chorus increases observed in a narrow band near 1 kc/s. An example of this relationship is shown in Fig. 7-71, in which four events are marked. Each event consists of a marked decrease in absorption, lasting a few minutes, accompanied by a drop in chorus intensity nearly to set noise level. These one-to-one corre-lations occur mainly in the period 1300 to 1900 UT, which includes magnetic noon (1815 UT) and are believed to be closely related to the previously men-tioned second peak in auroral activity observed at the South Pole.

Sudden-commencement emissions. When a VLF emission begins suddenly it is called a sudden-commencement emission (Fig. 7-32b). Isolated discrete events are by their very nature sudden-commencement emissions. However, the so-called steady emission (hiss) and the chorus may also begin and end suddenly. Many sudden-commencement emissions appear to start spontaneously, but others may be initiated or triggered by whistlers or other emissions. These are called triggered emissions, or interactions.

The most common triggered emissions are risers and hooks. These emissions usually separate from the whistler trace at the middle or lower part of the whistler as illustrated in Figs. 7-46, 7-47, and elsewhere in the "triggered" section of the Atlas. The rising tone that on rare occasions is observed to precede a whistler is called a precursor. This case is discussed later in connection with periodic emissions. An examination of the small number of such events obtained

* Personal communication.

from the Stanford library of whistler tapes has shown that in every case the precursor was associated with a two-hop whistler (see Figs. 7-52, 7-53, and 7-54).

Most triggered risers and hooks apparently do not alter the shape of the parent whistler. However, in some cases there is a continuous, smooth transition from the whistler trace to the emission trace, as illustrated in Fig. 7-49b. In such a case it would appear, therefore, that the coupling between the whistler and the postulated emission-generating stream is sufficiently strong to distort the parent whistler. Discrete emissions may also be triggered by other discrete emissions. For example, a strong hook may trigger a second hook, as shown in Fig. 7-13d of the Atlas. Sometimes a relatively weak emission triggers a much stronger emission as shown by parts c and d of Fig. 7-28. Artificially stimulated emissions of the discrete type triggered by man-made signals are described in the next section.

Emissions of the chorus type are frequently observed to begin and end suddenly. These bursts of chorus may occur in different restricted-frequency bands and may last for 10 to 25 seconds, as illustrated in Fig. 7-32. Often the strength of these emissions is high, approaching 1 mv/m at Byrd Station. Although a burst may appear to begin spontaneously, it is more common to observe a whistler or another emission preceding the burst.

Although the growth of bands of emissions is often accompanied by a whistler or an emission, there is seldom any corresponding event associated with the disappearance of a band. Disappearance may occur suddenly, as illustrated by Fig. 7-63 of the Atlas.

In addition to spontaneous and triggered emission bands, similar bands of noise have been observed to be formed from a multitude of whistler echoes. On many occasions whistlers are followed by very long trains of echoes of roughly equal intensity. The effect of dispersion as these whistlers echo back and forth between the hemispheres is to flatten out and extend in time the lower-frequency components. When there are many whistlers producing echoes, the accumulation of echo traces will form a distinct and intense band of noise, usually in the 3 to 4 kc/s range. The development of noise from whistler echo trains is illustrated by Fig. 7-29c of the Atlas.

The seasonal and diurnal variations of sudden-commencement emission bursts may be related to the corresponding variations in the occurrence of the triggering signal, usually a whistler. For example, at Byrd Station these bursts are prevalent during the winter months and rare during the summer. However, few data on this relation are available. Although the diurnal variation of spontaneous emission bursts follows the diurnal variation of whistler activity, it is possible that the peak in occurrence of whistler-triggered emissions may occur two to three hours after the peak in whistler activity. It is observed, however, that whistlers occurring at any time of day may excite emissions.

Artificially stimulated emissions. Emissions of the type triggered by whistlers can also be artificially stimulated, or triggered, by Morse code transmissions from VLF stations. Risers, falling tones, and hooks, both of the single and of the multiple type, have been observed to be triggered in this manner. The observed transient forms are similar both to the natural events that are associated with whistlers and to those occurring spontaneously. Since only a few examples of this remarkable phenomenon have been found, each one will be described separately.

The first example of artificially stimulated VLF emissions is shown in spectral form in Fig. 7-64 of the Atlas. The emissions consist principally of rising tones, which begin at the frequency of station NPG on 18.6 kc/s. These emissions were recorded on the standard, two-minute IGY broad-band recordings made at Wellington, New Zealand. During the run a strong multihop whistler was recorded, from which the whistler delay at 18.6 kc/s was found to be 0.55 sec. From pen-chart recordings of the NPG dots and dashes, the delay of the corresponding whistler-mode echoes was found to be 0.55 sec, the same as that of the whistlers. The relation between the starting time of each riser and the starting time of all adjacent dots and dashes was examined statistically over a range of 1.6 sec both before and after the riser. These measurements were divided into two groups, one for the dash (150 msec in length) and the other for the dot (50 msec in length). The distribution of the delay times is shown on the histogram of Fig. 7-72. The histogram for the dashes shows a pronounced peak in the range 0.62 sec to 0.68 sec before the riser, whereas the short-pulse histogram shows no pronounced peaks. Instead a pronounced minimum is found in the same time interval. Thus it appears that only the dashes are associated with the risers and the delay from the leading edge of the dash to the beginning time of the associated riser averages 0.62 to 0.68 sec. The dots do not appear to produce a significant number of emissions.

To verify this conclusion, each dot and dash was examined with respect to what happened at 0.62 to 0.68 sec after its beginning. It was found that risers could be associated with only 6 per cent of the dots but were clearly associated with 97 per cent of the dashes, confirming the conclusion that the triggering mechanism required a signal longer than a dot and shorter than a dash. The statistical delay of risers with respect to the leading edge of dashes has been compared with the whistler delay for the path of propagation. This comparison shows that the riser began 70 msec to 130 msec after the arrival at Wellington of the leading edge of the whistler-mode echo from NPG. Thus the risers begin during the last half of each dash, after a time that is slightly greater than the duration of a Morse code dot. Consequently the observed time delay with respect to the leading edge of the whistler-mode dash is consistent with the low probability of triggering by dots.

Shortly after the discovery described above of emissions artificially stimulated by signals from NPG, similar phenomena were reported from the U.S.N.S. *Eltanin*, which was observing station NAA while cruising at about 50° S geomagnetic. Spectra of NAA and of the associated triggered emissions are shown in Figs. 7-65 and 7-66 of the Atlas. These records are unusually clear, and confirm the general characteristics deduced from the NPG-triggered emissions. It is obvious from the figures that only the dashes produced emissions.

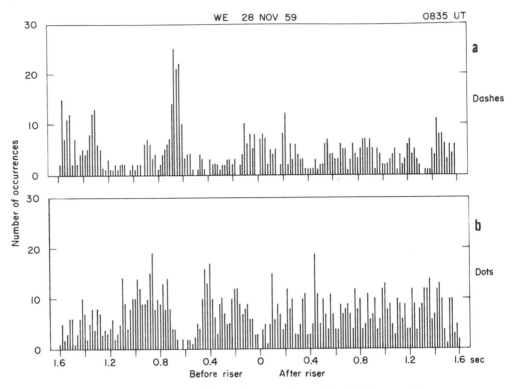

Fig. 7-72. Histogram of delays of risers triggered by NPG transmissions, recorded at WE 28 Nov 1959, at 0835 UT (see Fig. 7-64). Parts *a* and *b* show, respectively, the starting times of all dashes and dots within the time interval ±1.6 sec measured from the starting time of each riser in the 2 min run.

The emissions triggered by NAA include rising tones, falling tones, hooks, and combinations, as Fig. 7-65 shows. One variety consists of several risers triggered by a single dash. Another type consists of a series of hooks. Less often the emission is of the falling-tone type. Of particular interest is the tendency for the emissions to begin with a slight rise which is followed by a short fall and then a long rise. In some cases it appears that the first fall simply continues to the end of the emission, whereas in other cases it reverses and rises to a relatively high frequency. On occasion the long riser is followed by a falling tone.

In the second set of examples, recorded two hours later and illustrated by the spectra of Fig. 7-66 in the Atlas, both rising and falling tones were produced by the same dash. Several discrete emissions of both rising and falling types were associated with each transmitted dash, suggesting the possibility that each one may have been triggered on a separate path.

During the recording made between the two shown in Figs. 7-65 and 7-66, the only evidence of NAA-triggered emissions was a slight broadening of the trace on the spectrogram. However, during this period risers triggered by whistlers were observed in the range 2 to 7 kc/s, suggesting that the optimum frequency for the triggering of emissions may have dropped to a lower value in the intermediate hour.

A number of conclusions can be drawn from these observations of artificially stimulated emissions. First, it is clear that the triggering of discrete emissions requires a certain minimum signal duration. A 50-msec dot is insufficient, whereas almost every 150-msec dash produces an emission during a favorable period. This result suggests the presence of a nonlinear mechanism of interaction between waves and particle streams. Since every dash transmitted by the station produced a discrete emission with a fixed group delay, it can be concluded that the conditions required for triggering are omnipresent at least over the two-minute interval of a typical observation. It would appear that an electromagnetic wave is capable of organizing the charged particles in an existing stream in such a way that they radiate coherently at particular frequencies determined by the properties of the stream and of the medium. This point is discussed in more detail in Sec. 7.4.

Periodic emissions. Among the many remarkable types of VLF emissions is one that consists of short bursts of noise repeated at regular intervals of a few seconds. These events we shall call periodic VLF emissions. Examples have been reported by a number of investigators.

The first spectra of periodic emissions seen by the author were presented at a meeting of the U.S.A. National Committee of the URSI, by Dinger (1957b). Other examples have been published by Gallet (1959a), Pope and Campbell (1960), Lokken *et al.* (1961), and Brice (1962).

Periodic VLF emissions can be classified as either dispersive or non-dispersive. In the dispersive type the period between bursts varies in a systematic way with frequency. Often this variation is exactly the same as that found in associated echoing whistlers, from which it is deduced that each burst is the result of whistler-mode echoing of the previous burst. In non-dispersive periodic emissions, there is little or no observable systematic change in period with frequency. In all previous attempts to explain this type of periodic emission, the authors assume the *a priori* existence of a small bunch of charged particles that oscillates between mirror points in the earth's magnetic field. It is also assumed that the bunch radiates a noise burst each time it passes through a favorable region of the ionospheric plasma, so that the emission period is the same as the mirror period of the bunch. We shall refer to this explanation as the particle-bunch theory of non-dispersive periodic VLF emissions.

The dispersive type of periodic emission is illustrated in Fig. 7-55, which shows the spectra made from tapes recorded simultaneously at Seattle, Washington (54° N geomagnetic latitude), and Wellington, New Zealand (45° S geomagnetic latitude), on 1 October 1961, 1250 UT (Helliwell, 1963c). The period of observation was preceded by a sudden-commencement magnetic storm beginning at 2109 UT, 30 September, 1961. A magnetic K_p index of 8− was observed during the associated three-hour period. At $t = 0$ (Fig. 7-55) a strong atmospheric is seen at both Seattle and Wellington and is followed at each station by an echoing whistler. The echo train is of the two-hop, or "long" type at Seattle, and of the one-hop, or "short" type at Wellington. The travel times of the whistler and its echoes are in the ratios 1:2:3:4:5 and so forth, with the even-numbered ratios occurring in the Northern Hemisphere (SE) and the odd-numbered ratios in the Southern Hemisphere (WE). Several other whistler echo trains with similar characteristics were observed in the same two-minute run, but are not considered because the associated emissions were much weaker.

The same whistler echo trains and related noise bursts were observed at several other stations (spectra not shown), including Stanford, California; Logan, Utah; Lauder, New Zealand; and Byrd Station, Antarctica. Since the details of the spectral shapes recorded at these other stations are identical to those presented in Fig. 7-55 from Seattle and Wellington, only the latter two recordings are presented. It is concluded that the whistlers and associated noise traveled over the same magnetic field-line path and, after exiting from the ionosphere, reached the receivers by propagating in the earth–ionosphere waveguide. The one-hop travel time at 5 kc/s is 1.03 sec, corresponding to a dispersion of $D = t\sqrt{f} = 73$ sec$^{1/2}$, a value typical of normal observations at these stations (Carpenter, 1962b). Using the method of Smith and Carpenter (1961), we can estimate the path latitude from measurements of the variation of dispersion with frequency of the whistler. From the Stanford and Seattle records of this particular two-hop whistler, D. L. Carpenter* has estimated the path latitude to be 52° geomagnetic, which is also typical of these stations (Carpenter, 1962b).

The echoing of the whistler can be detected clearly up to about the 26th hop on the Seattle record. After the first one or two hops, an emission appears in the form of a slight, irregular broadening on the trailing edge of the whistler trace, mostly in the frequency range 6 to 7 kc/s and to a lesser extent in the range 4 to 5 kc/s. With each successive echo the intensity of the emission in the upper range increases and the echo of the original whistler becomes weaker. The shape of any given emission trace can be transformed approximately into that of its preceding (or following) neighbor by simply subtracting (or adding) at each frequency the appropriate two-hop group delay obtained from the echoing whistler. However, each emission trace shows components that were not present in the preceding echo, the cumulative effect being the production of a characteristic trace shape which differs from that of the echoing whistler.

On most of the emission elements, notably the 10th through the 44th hop, the trace appears to contain short segments of whistler traces. This suggests that a whistler that arrives in the generation region at the same time as the emission may be enhanced in the frequency range of the emission. Such coincident whistlers may in fact be an important source of energy in the growth of the emission.

The difference between the echoing emission and the echoing whistler is

---

* Personal communication.

TABLE 7-2

COMPARISON OF PERIODS OF WHISTLER AND ASSOCIATED EMISSION

Event	Whistler Hop Number		Average Echoing Period in sec	
	Begin	End	$f = 4.15$ kc	$f = 5.3$ kc
First falling tone	40	46	—	1.99 ± 0.02
Second falling tone	40	56	—	1.991 ± 0.01
	40	50	2.216 ± 0.01	—
Parent whistler	0*	24	—	1.987 ± 0.004
	0*	14	2.214 ± 0.01	—

* Zero hop number designates the impulsive atmospheric that causes the whistler.

especially obvious at and following the 16th hop, after which the emission appears to be stronger than the associated whistler echo. On the 39th hop at Wellington, a marked downward extension of the noise burst (a falling tone) appears for the first time and then echoes in the whistler mode to the end of the record. On the 40th hop at Seattle, a similar downward extension occurs, preceding the echo of the first falling tone at Wellington, and it too echoes in the whistler mode. Representative measurements of the echoing periods of these two falling-tone emissions and of the parent whistler were made at two frequencies, and the results are compared in Table 7-2. This comparison shows that the echoing periods of both of these falling tones are the same (within a relatively small experimental error) as those in the parent whistler at corresponding frequencies.

The non-dispersive type of periodic noise is illustrated in Fig. 7-17 which shows a series of emissions observed in simultaneous synoptic recordings taken at Byrd Station (70° S geomagnetic latitude) and Norwich, Vermont (55°.2 N geomagnetic latitude) on 21 January 1961, at 2350 UT (Helliwell, 1963c). The period of observation was magnetically quiet but was preceded by two days of magnetic disturbance, during which the K_p index reached a maximum value of 6. This particular event was found during a survey of emission activity at Byrd Station, after which the tapes from Knob Lake and Norwich were analyzed. The Knob Lake spectra are identical in every measurable respect to those for Norwich, but are less clear and hence are not shown. The spectra shown in Fig. 7-17 are an extension in time of previously published examples that covered only the period from 58 sec to 64 sec (Lokken et al., 1961).

Universal time on the Byrd records was defined by time signals from station NBA (Canal Zone) at 18.0 kc/s, which were included in the broad-band information recorded on the magnetic tape and were reinserted in the spectrum at 500 cps.

Time intervals on the Norwich records were determined by seconds ticks locally generated at a frequency of 8 kc/s and synchronized by a tuning-fork oscillator. The signals from NBA were not received at Norwich. The exact universal time of the Norwich ticks was determined by comparing certain atmospherics on the Norwich tape with the same atmospherics on the Knob Lake tape, which also contained the NBA time signals. It was deduced that the Norwich seconds tick preceded the NBA seconds tick by 0.10 sec $\pm$ 0.02 sec. Errors resulting from differences in the travel times of atmospherics and NBA time signals to the different stations were estimated to be less than 20 msec, and therefore were not considered in the correction.

In contrast to the echoing emission shown in Fig. 7-55, the train of emissions in Fig. 7-17 begins abruptly. The first burst (labeled A_0) appears at Byrd in the form of a rising tone, or riser, at approximately 57.6 sec. The second burst (labeled A_1) appears at Norwich about 0.82 sec later and is followed at the same interval by bursts (labeled A_2 through A_7) appearing alternately at Byrd and at Norwich. These bursts form a series, the elements of which are uniformly spaced in time and appear alternately at Byrd and at Norwich. Such a periodic series, called a "set," is designated by a capital letter with a subscript numeral to denote the number of periods following the first identified member of the set. The time of a burst is taken to be the "center of mass" on the record and is subject to an uncertainty of about ± 20 msec. Most of the bursts on Fig. 7-17 can readily be associated with a particular set. Eight of these sets are marked with the letters A through H. In several sets the first element appears to be triggered by a particular burst of another set. For example, the B set begins with a hook that is triggered by A_1, with a delay of about 0.45 sec. Likewise the first element of the D set follows C_7 with a delay of 0.43 sec, and the first element of the F set follows E_5 with a delay of 0.30 sec. It is supposed that for the other sets the triggering source, although too weak to be identified, is part of the structure of some previous set. Where two or more sets with the same period overlap in time, we have what might be called a "multiphase" periodic emission. For example, the elements G_0, D_{13}, and H_0, and their echoes, form a three-phase system in which each phase corresponds to a particular set.

The average delay between emissions in a particular set was taken to be the mean of the averages at the two stations. These values are given in Table 7-3, which shows for each set the first and last elements at each station and the corresponding average one-hop delay. The averages of sets B through H are nearly the same, and so a single over-all average (0.835 sec) is computed for them. For the A set, the average (0.817 sec) is distinctly different, and is therefore treated separately.

When the records of Fig. 7-17 were first examined it was thought that the A series began spontaneously, since there was no obvious triggering source. However, further analysis revealed that the first emission at Norwich (A_1) coincided in time and initial frequency with the 10th hop (labeled W_{10a}) of the first component of a multipath whistler, whose one-hop travel time at 5 kc/s is 0.850 sec. This value corresponds to a 5-kc/s dispersion D_5 of 60 $\text{sec}^{1/2}$. The second component (W_{a+b}) is delayed 0.26 sec with respect to the first (W_{2a}) and is

TABLE 7-3
MEASURED PERIODS OF PERIODIC EMISSIONS
21 JANUARY 1961, 2350 UT

Set	Station	Begin	End	Average one-hop period, sec
A	BY	A_0	A_6	0.813
	NO	A_1	A_7	0.821
			Average, set A	0.817
B	BY	B_1	B_{15}	0.833
	NO	B_0	B_{18}	0.834
C	BY	C_0	C_8	0.837
	NO	C_1	C_9	0.840
D	BY	D_1	D_{19}	0.836
	NO	D_0	D_{18}	0.835
E	BY	E_0	E_6	0.830
	NO	E_1	E_7	0.828
F	BY	F_1	F_3	0.840
	NO	F_0	F_4	0.826
G	BY	G_0	G_6	0.835
	NO	G_1	G_5	0.835
H	BY	H_0	H_4	0.835
	NO	H_1	H_3	0.840
			Average, sets B–H	0.835

believed to arise from successive one-hop traverses of two separate field-aligned paths. Echoing must have occurred only over the shorter of the two paths to account for the observed echo structure, which includes a weak one-hop whistler (labeled W_{1a}) at Byrd. As Fig. 7-17 shows, the whistler is relatively weak and the higher order echoes are seen only at Norwich and are restricted to a small band of frequencies centered at 5 kc/s. From the duration of the eighth-hop echo, the bandwidth of the higher order echoes is estimated to be about 300 cps. The first detectable emission in set A occurs at Byrd, at a time corresponding to the ninth hop of the whistler, even though the ninth hop is not detectable on the spectrograms. The absence of any evidence of this whistler echo train at Byrd (except the first hop) can be explained by the fact that Byrd is located at a much higher geomagnetic latitude than Norwich, and hence these signals can be expected to suffer more attenuation in traveling to the receiver, if we assume a middle-latitude exit point.

The reason that the emissions did not start until the ninth hop of the whistler may be related to the triggering signal duration requirement observed in the artificially stimulated emissions described above. There the critical duration lay between 50 and 150 msec. In the case of Fig. 7-17 the duration of the nine-hop echo is estimated from the bandwidth of 300 cps and the dispersion of 60 sec$^{1/2}$ to be 230 msec, and although larger than the above, it is not unreasonable since the whistler was relatively weak. Furthermore, the effective duration would be less if the width of the band that is sensitive to triggering were less than that of the triggering signal itself.

Support for the assumption of a middle-latitude path is found in the fact that the signals are stronger at Norwich than at either Knob Lake or Byrd. Furthermore, the 5-kc/s dispersion of this whistler is 60 sec$^{1/2}$, a value that can be expected at the latitude of Norwich during disturbed conditions (Carpenter, 1962a). Because of the difficulty of obtaining the variation in dispersion with frequency of this particular whistler, the estimated nose frequency (Smith and Carpenter, 1961) (and hence the path latitude) is not readily determined. However, the fact that there is no evidence for a nose in the observed traces gives additional support to the assumption of a middle-latitude path.

Successive noise bursts in a given set show some differences in spectral shape, but these differences are for the most part not simply related to whistler-mode dispersion. An exception is the C set, which shows some evidence of systematic dispersion of the whistler-mode type.

It is of interest to determine the frequency f_w at which the whistler one-hop delay equals the average one-hop delay of the emissions. We shall assume that the whistler dispersion value of 60 sec$^{1/2}$ computed at 5 kc/s applies to the new frequencies, since they fall very close to 5 kc/s. For the A set, with $T = 0.817$ sec, we have $f_w = D^2/T^2 = 5.40$ kc/s, which falls close to the lower edge of emission A_1. For the sets B through H, with $T = 0.835$ sec, we have $f_w = 5.17$ kc/s, which falls at or just above the lower edges of these emissions. In many cases the burst begins at its lowest frequency. It should be noted that the center of gravity of the A set is noticeably higher in frequency than those of most of the other sets. This is consistent with the smaller period of the A set, if we assume whistler-mode propagation at a frequency below the nose frequency.

Both the dispersive and the non-dispersive periodic emissions described above are closely related in period and phase to an associated whistler. The whistler appears to initiate or trigger the emissions in both cases, but the amount of energy released is markedly different. In the dispersive case (Fig. 7-55) the whistler is relatively strong and most individual emissions show only a small amount of noise added to the echo of the previous emission, leaving the characteristic whistler-mode dispersion of the echoes clearly defined.

In the non-dispersive case a weak whistler triggers a strong emission, which subsequently echoes and triggers another emission of rather similar appearance, and so on. Since each emission extends over an appreciably wider frequency range than the echoes of the whistler, it would appear that only over a small portion of the frequency spectrum of each emission does energy actually echo in the whistler mode. Each emission consists chiefly of new energy and contains relatively little echoing energy. Hence the evidence of whistler-mode dispersion is absent even though the time at which the emission is observed is determined by the whistler-mode echoing period. On the basis of this interpretation it would be natural to expect a virtually continuous variation in the relative amount of dispersed signal observable in periodic VLF ionospheric noise, ranging from zero up to that characteristic of pure whistler-mode propagation over the same path. Figures 7-55 and 7-17 probably represent the extremes of this range rather well. Other published examples of periodic noise are consistent with this new interpretation (Gallet, 1959a; Pope and Campbell, 1960).

It will be recalled that an association between emissions and whistlers was reported by Storey (1953), who observed that if a whistler occurred during a period of general riser activity, it would usually be followed by a riser. He cited spectrograms of such events that had been published by Potter (1951). Additional examples of whistlers followed by risers are shown in the "triggered" section of the Atlas. These spectra clearly suggest a cause-and-effect relationship in which the riser is initiated or triggered by the whistler. A logical extension of this idea is the suggestion that an emission may also be triggered by another emission propagating in the whistler mode. If this triggered emission echoes in the whistler mode at the appropriate frequency, then the triggering process is repeated, giving rise to a set of periodic emissions in which the period is equal to the whistler-mode group delay at the triggering frequency. Strong absorption of the whistler-mode echo of the emission over most of its frequency range, coupled with strong emission, gives non-dispersive periodic emissions (Fig. 7-17); on the other hand, weak absorption and weak emission give the dispersive type (Fig. 7-55).

For the particle-bunch theory of non-dispersive periodic emissions to be acceptable, the particle bunch would have to be related to the whistler-producing atmospheric, and the mirror period for the particle bunches would have to be the same as the whistler-mode echo period at the triggering frequency. Furthermore, the nearly identical periods for several sets of periodic emissions would require that the several corresponding particle bunches have almost exactly the same mirror period. Since these conditions appear most unlikely, the particle-bunch theory is ruled out as an explanation of non-dispersive periodic emissions.

The acceptance of the triggering hypothesis, on the other hand, leads to explanations of other emission phenomena not previously understood. Under conditions similar to those that yield non-dispersive periodic emissions (Fig. 7-17), a parent whistler might be undetectable because of absorption, so that only the triggered emissions would be observed (in fact, the observation of the Byrd emissions of Fig. 7-17 was originally placed in this category). This would explain reports of the association of emissions with atmospherics (Storey, 1953; Knudsen and Norinder, 1963; Norinder and Knudsen, 1963), which is illustrated in Fig. 7-57. It could also explain emissions that appear to begin spontaneously, having no apparent connection with any preceding event, but that are in fact triggered by an undetected one-hop whistler (or one of its echoes) whose source was in the opposite hemisphere (see Fig. 7-57). Likewise, in a hybrid whistler (Helliwell, 1959), if the one-hop component was not observed, but triggered a riser, the emission would appear to be associated with the two-hop component, and would precede it. Emissions of this type are referred to as precursors (Helliwell and Carpenter, 1961) and are illustrated in Figs. 7-52, 7-53, and 7-54.

This mechanism for the production of precursors, however, remains speculative because the existence of a sufficiently strong one-hop hybrid component has not been demonstrated. It may be necessary to look for a mechanism that depends entirely on the two-hop component. Conceivably this component on its first traverse of the path modifies the distribution of the generating stream through longitudinal resonance. The stream then becomes unstable in the transverse mode, radiating an emission backward along the path. If generation takes place at the top of the path, the emission would arrive at the point of origin of the whistler at about the same time that the whistler arrived at the other end. Subsequent reflection of the whistler back to the point of origin would result in a two-hop whistler that would arrive after the emission.

Four sets of non-dispersive periodic emissions observed in a two-minute recording period at Boulder were found by Gallet (1959a) to have the same period in each set (1.64 sec at 5.9 kc/s). This observation would be explained in the same way as Fig. 7-17 on the basis of the triggering hypothesis.

Further support for the triggering hypothesis is found in the measurements of the periodic emissions illustrated in the Atlas. Their dispersions vary from 52 to 182 $sec^{1/2}$, with an average value of 99 $sec^{1/2}$, based on 54 samples. Each sample consists of one dispersion measurement $\{[P(f)/2]\sqrt{f}\}$ from each record. Where two or more values were available from a single record, the one determined at the lowest frequency was chosen. These dispersions fall within the range expected for whistlers observed under comparable conditions. For the 70 measurements given in the Atlas legends, the emission period averages 3.36 sec and ranges from 1.46 sec to 6.75 sec. The frequencies at which these periods were measured range from 1.3 kc/s to 9.5 kc/s, with a median value of 4.1 kc/s. The ninety-percentile range is 1.6 kc/s to 7.3 kc/s.

Multiphase periodic emissions are a common occurrence. An example with three phases, a surprisingly common type, is shown in Fig. 7-19. The three sets appear in a limited frequency band near 3 kc/s and are identified by the letters A, B, and C in the expanded portion of the record from 61 to 81 sec. They exhibit the expected anti-phase conjugate-point relationship at SE and BY. The period is 2.94 sec, which is comparable to two-hop whistler-mode delays at this frequency. Because of the equal spacing and the similar appearance of the three sets, particularly on the Seattle record, it is relatively easy to draw the conclusion that the period is one-third of the actual period. The anti-phase conjugate relationship is preserved in this incorrect interpretation because the number of phases is odd. When the sets are equally spaced, the emissions are sometimes called symmetrical multiphase periodic emissions. They were first identified in the three-phase form by M. Trimpi in October 1962 from the records of Fig. 7-19.

The cause of the equal spacing between sets of emissions in Fig. 7-19 is not known, but it may be related to a "recovery" time in the medium. Let us suppose that the emitting region is temporarily disorganized after each burst, and hence any attempt by a wave packet to stimulate a new emission will be resisted. The net effect is to delay very slightly the generation of a burst with respect to the preceding burst (of a different set, of course). After many periods this tendency would produce roughly equal spacings, as observed.

On the basis of this recovery, or relaxation, time, the prevalence of symmetrical three-phase emissions compared with two-phase emissions can be explained (Brice, 1964b). Suppose that an element of the A phase becomes stronger than average; the next element (B phase) is then suppressed, which causes its successor (C phase) to increase. This increase, in turn, causes a decrease in the next element of the original A phase, so that the initial fluctuation tends to be damped out. This amounts to a kind of negative feedback. On the other hand, if only two phases are present, the feedback is positive, causing one phase to grow and the other to die away until only one is left. An example of this suppression effect can be seen in Fig. 7-21a, which shows a sequence of single-phase and multiphase emissions. At 8.3 minutes on this record, an element of a new phase appears just ahead of an element of the existing phase. These two phases are present over the next twelve periods, during which the new phase grows while the old phase decays until it disappears into the background noise. A clearer example of this phase transition appears in Fig. 7-22b, beginning at 116 sec and ending at 130 sec, three periods later.

Multiphase periodic emissions with different numbers of phases are shown in Figs. 7-16, 7-17, 7-19, 7-20, 7-22, and 7-23 of the Atlas. Of particular interest are those rare cases in which the number of phases is even and the phases are equally spaced. The conjugate-point records then show an in-phase relationship if the basic period is taken (incorrectly) to be the true period divided by the number of phases. Examples of multiphase emissions of this type, with two phases, are shown in Figs. 7-23a and b, and 7-26b of the Atlas.

Multiphase periodic emissions appear to account for a number of cases of chorus. A transition from a well-defined periodic emission to chorus is illustrated in Fig. 7-30. Chorus of the type illustrated by these spectra is readily interpreted as the superposition of several sets of periodic emissions, each with the same echoing period. If additional paths with different echoing periods were present, then the pattern would appear less regular.

Quasi-periodic emissions. In addition to the periodic emissions described above, there is another phenomenon, called quasi-periodic emissions, that appears in the same range of frequencies but that exhibits much longer and less regular periods. Quasi-periodic emissions are usually characterized by variations in the frequency and the amplitude of the envelope of emissions. Some examples are shown in Fig. 7-19 and Figs. 7-40 through 7-45, and include 14 separate cases whose periods average 29 sec and range from 7 sec to 64 sec. This phenomenon was described by the term "long period VLF pulsations" when it was first reported (Watts *et al.*, 1963). Often the quasi-periodic emissions consist simply of successive sets of drifting periodic emissions. In virtually every such case the frequency of each set increases with time.

Quasi-periodic emissions have not yet been satisfactorily explained. However, certain features of the record of Fig. 7-19a suggest a possible mechanism. Here the slopes of the emission elements vary synchronously with the envelope of the frequency and amplitude variations. The upper parts of the emission elements are most nearly vertical when their amplitude and upper cutoff frequency are maximum, after which the lower parts increase in duration due to dispersion. It is suggested that the increased duration of the lower parts provides better triggering, which in turn results in increased amplitude and cutoff frequency of the upper parts. The importance of the duration of the triggering signal was noted in connection with Fig. 7-17 and in the discussion of artificially stimulated emissions. Another quasi-periodic emission with rather similar properties is shown in Fig. 7-41b. However, many cases of quasi-periodic emissions can be found in which these features are not evident, and it is possible that other factors, such as fluctuations of the earth's field, may also be a cause of quasi-periodic variations in VLF emissions. More information on this phenomenon could be obtained with the aid of controlled VLF triggering signals.

Quasi-periodic emissions have periods comparable with those of micropulsations, and these two phenomena are often closely associated in time of occurrence. In fact there is evidence from Eights Station that occasionally they have the same period,* which suggests a cause-and-effect relationship. Possibly the micropulsation might modulate the pitch angle distribution of the particles in such a way as to vary the emission characteristics.

7.3   Satellite Observations of VLF Emissions

The effects of the lower ionosphere on the propagation of VLF emissions have largely been eliminated, and the study of these emissions has been greatly simplified, by using satellite-borne receivers. The first VLF observations in a satellite were made using the magnetometer in Vanguard III (Cain et al., 1961; Cain et al., 1962), but there were few VLF emissions recorded, primarily because of the relatively low inclination of the orbit. Very-low-frequency observations made at higher latitudes by the recent Alouette (Barrington and Belrose, 1963a,b; Barrington et al., 1963) and Injun III (Gurnett, 1963; Gurnett and O'Brien, 1964) satellites have already produced interesting results.

One of the most striking observations of both Alouette and Injun III is the appearance of chorus below 1 kc/s at virtually all latitudes, including the equator. On the ground such emissions are usually observed only at high latitudes. Their observation at all latitudes in the satellites indicates that the emission mechanism is effective over a wide range of the static magnetic intensity at the top of the line of force and that the absence of observations on the ground can be attributed to propagation factors in the ionosphere below the satellites. As pointed out in Chap. 3, propagation across the lower boundary of the ionosphere requires that the wave normal be nearly vertical, or the wave will be

---

* Michael Trimpi, personal communication.

reflected back into the ionosphere. However, at low latitudes such wave normals must necessarily make large angles with the earth's field, thereby causing absorption to become large. Thus, regardless of the wave-normal orientation, the attenuation across the lower boundary of the ionosphere should increase as the latitude is decreased.

In addition to emission bands whose frequencies are independent of position, the satellites often see an emission band with a well-defined lower frequency that increases with decreasing latitude of the satellite. An example of this variable-frequency noise as recorded at Stanford from the Alouette satellite is shown in Fig. 7-67. Observations during full sweeps of Alouette across the equator have shown that the variable-frequency band seen in the Northern Hemisphere is repeated at roughly corresponding L values in the Southern Hemisphere (Barrington et al., 1963). On any particular sweep the lower frequency of the band is approximately proportional to the strength of earth's magnetic field at the top of the field line passing through the satellite, suggesting that conditions at the top of the line of force control the emissions seen at the satellite.

Observation of similar emissions triggered by short, fractional-hop whistlers suggests that this noise may originate at or below the satellite (Barrington and Belrose, 1963b). Further study (Brice et al., 1964) has shown that this noise can be triggered or enhanced by both short and long fractional-hop whistlers, which places the region of generation close to the satellite. An example of these triggering phenomena is shown in Fig. 7-67 of the Atlas. It is suggested that this noise is related, not to ordinary VLF emissions as seen on the ground, but to an ion plasma oscillation, at the "lower hybrid" resonance, occurring close to the satellite (Brice and Smith, 1964).

Quantitative measurements of the intensity of the magnetic flux of VLF emissions have been made in the Injun III satellite in the range 200 cps to 7000 cps. In a number of passes of Injun III it was found that the emissions were mainly chorus and appeared principally in the 1- to 4-kc/s band. The noise showed a maximum rms flux density of about 8×10^{-3} gamma (8×10^{-12} weber/m²) at an L value of 5 and tended to disappear at L values above 9 or 10. It is difficult to obtain the corresponding power density because of uncertainty in the relation between the wave normal and the loop antenna and the refractive index of the medium. Also the body of the satellite may conceivably disturb the medium in some way. However, an order-of-magnitude estimate can be made from available data. Taking refractive index to be 20 at a mean altitude of 1000 km and a frequency of 2.5 kc/s, we find from Eq. (3.59) that the power density is 10^{-9} w/m². If we assume an average bandwidth of 1 kc/s, the power spectral density is then 10^{-12} w/m²/cps. This value is considerably larger than the power spectral densities measured on the ground (see Fig. 7-70), as might be expected. Attenuation factors include absorption, reflection loss at the ionosphere boundary, and divergence from the exit point to the receiver.

7.4 Emission Mechanisms

General survey. Although no detailed theory of VLF emissions has yet been developed, there is general agreement that the sources of these emissions must be situated within the ionosphere. Extra-terrestrial sources have not been considered because the magnetosphere is thought to be opaque to VLF energy from outside and because the noise is often closely related to whistlers. In current theories the electromagnetic energy of the emission is derived primarily from the kinetic energy of streams of charged particles trapped on the lines of force of the earth's magnetic field. Possible sources of power for the streams, and mechanisms for the conversion of this power, are considered by Sturrock (1962).

Conversion mechanisms that have been considered can be divided into two main categories depending on whether the longitudinal motion or the transverse motion of the charged particle is the controlling factor. Mechanisms depending on longitudinal motion include Čerenkov radiation and a kind of amplification somewhat analogous to that observed in a laboratory traveling-wave tube, which we shall call "TWT mechanism." The transverse motion of charged particles in the earth's magnetic field is very nearly circular and the associated radiation is of the cyclotron type.

A basic difficulty with known mechanisms of generation such as Čerenkov radiation and cyclotron radiation is that the calculated flux densities are too low to account directly for the observed intensities (Maeda and Kimura, 1962, 1963). Direct generation by the Čerenkov process was first suggested by Ellis (1957, 1959), but the calculated intensities were found to be too low. Other authors who have considered the Čerenkov process at very low frequencies are Gendrin (1960b), Ginzburg (1961a,b), McInnes (1961), Ondoh (1961, 1962a,b, 1963a,b,c), Sturrock (1962), and McKenzie (1963); authors who have considered this process in a general manner are Eidman (1958), Cohen (1961), Bekefi and Brown (1961), and Chamberlain (1961). Ungstrup* has proposed an extension of the Čerenkov mechanism in which primary auroral particles produce a large number of secondary electrons in the E region in the energy range 40 to 80 ev. These secondaries produce Čerenkov radiation below about 2.5 kc/s and are thought to be sufficiently bunched to produce the intensity levels seen in and above the auroral zones.

Cyclotron radiation from protons has been considered by various authors (MacArthur, 1959; Santirocco, 1960; Murcray and Pope, 1960a,b, 1961; Ginzburg, 1961a,b; Kimura, 1961; Maeda and Kimura, 1962, 1963; Ondoh, 1961; and Sturrock, 1962). Cyclotron radiation from electrons was first studied at very low frequencies by Eidman (1958) and later by Dowden (1962b,c,d,e,f,g,h, 1963a,b,c), whose work has been discussed by Brice (1962). It is important to note that in none of these papers has it been shown that the noise intensity from the cyclotron process would be adequate to explain the observations.

These difficulties have led to a search for more efficient conversion mechanisms. The first such proposal was the traveling-wave-tube mechanism in which a stream of electrons spiraling in the earth's magnetic field performs the function of the beam in the tube, and the low-velocity whistler-mode wave replaces the slow wave traveling on the helix of the tube (Gallet and Helliwell,

* Personal communication.

1959; Bell and Helliwell, 1960; Rydbeck and Askne, 1963). An alternative amplification mechanism has been proposed by Maeda and Kimura (1962, 1963) in which amplification takes place on a charged-particle beam carrying a slow cyclotron wave. In these theories the necessary condition for amplification is that the phase velocity of the wave be approximately equal to the longitudinal particle velocity in the streams. Since the phase velocity is frequency dependent, the amplification mechanism is frequency selective. Since the wave energy is supplied by the stream, the growth of the wave is accompanied by a slowing down of the beam. However, this effect would normally be small because the flux density in the stream is thought to be several orders of magnitude greater than that in the generated wave. This same requirement of approximate equivalence between longitudinal-stream velocity and wave phase velocity is characteristic of mechanisms based on Doppler-shifted cyclotron radiation from protons.

Resonance interaction conditions. In most theoretical treatments of whistler-mode propagation it is assumed that the wave normal is approximately aligned with the earth's magnetic field. This alignment appears to be necessary if one is to explain the transmission of whistler energy out of the ionosphere. However, the coupling of the electric field of the wave to the stream requires a longitudinal component of electric field, which in turn requires a non-zero angle between wave normal and the direction of the earth's field. A small angle, say 20 or 30 deg, can satisfy both requirements. For simplicity we assume that propagation is purely longitudinal, so that the condition for longitudinal resonance, or interaction between stream and wave is simply

$$v_s = v_p, \tag{7.1}$$

where v_s is the longitudinal component of particle velocity and v_p is the phase velocity of electromagnetic wave.

For longitudinal propagation the refractive index for the propagating mode (3.12) is given by

$$\mu_0^2 = 1 + \frac{f_0^2}{f(f_H - f)},$$

and therefore the phase velocity c/μ_0 is

$$v_p = c \left[\frac{f(f_H - f)}{f(f_H - f) + f_0^2} \right]^{1/2}, \tag{7.2}$$

where f is the wave frequency, f_H is the gyro-frequency, and f_0 the plasma frequency.

From (7.1) and (7.2), the frequencies of interaction are given by

$$f = \frac{f_H}{2} \left\{ 1 \pm \left[1 - \frac{4(v_s/c)^2 (f_0/f_H)^2}{1 - (v_s/c)^2} \right]^{1/2} \right\}. \tag{7.3}$$

If we restrict the discussion to cases in which the stream velocity is less than about 0.1 c, then $(v_s/c)^2 \ll 1$ and (7.3) can be written

$$f = \frac{f_H}{2} \left\{ 1 \pm \left[1 - (f_H/2P)^2 \right]^{1/2} \right\}, \tag{7.4}$$

where $P = f_0 v_s/c$ and is conveniently measured in kilocycles per second.

For interaction to occur, the solution to (7.4) must be real, and hence the condition for interaction is

$$f_H \geqq 2P. \qquad (7.5)$$

The maximum value of the wave frequency f is f_H, since the maximum real value of the radical in (7.4) is unity. The conditions for interaction are shown by the curves of Fig. 7-73, which is a plot of wave frequency f as a function of gyro-frequency f_H for different values of the parameter P. All curves are asymptotic to the line $f = f_H$.

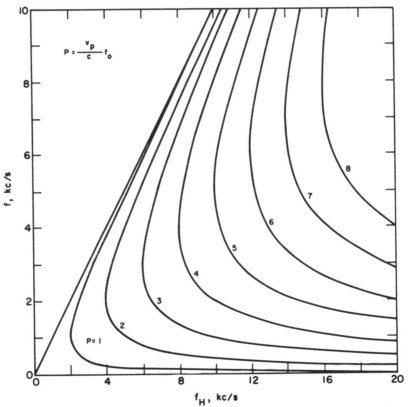

FIG. 7-73. Variation of wave frequency with local gyro-frequency for longitudinal resonance. Longitudinal wave propagation assumed.

As an example of the application of these curves, consider a stream of velocity 3000 km/s which is guided along an auroral line of force (near geomagnetic latitude 70°). The ambient plasma frequency is assumed to be constant and equal to 200 kc/s, and hence $P = 2$ kc/s. When the stream reaches the point $f_H = 2P$, interaction can begin at the wave frequency $f_H/2$, or 3 kc/s. The latitude of this point is found from the Appendix to be 29°. Beyond this point two frequencies can be amplified, and as f_H increases, the lower one approaches zero and the upper one approaches f_H, following the curve $P = 3$ in Fig. 7-73.

The stream velocity required for interaction is found from (7.4) and is given by

$$v_s = \frac{c}{f_0} \sqrt{f(f_H - f)} . \tag{7.6}$$

Values of the stream velocity for appropriate values of the medium parameters and of the wave frequency are given in Table 7-4. It is seen that the required stream velocity could vary between roughly 0.01 and 0.1 of the velocity of light. These velocities correspond to energies of 0.025 and 2.5 Kev, respectively.

TABLE 7-4

CALCULATED STREAM VELOCITIES FOR DIFFERENT PARAMETERS
OF INTERACTION REGION

Gyro-frequency, f_H (kc/s)	Distance from Surface	Minimum Geomagnetic Latitude	Plasma Frequency, kc	Wave Frequency, c		
				2 kc/s	5 kc/s	10 kc/s
1000	Regular layers	Middle latitudes	4000	0.011	0.018	0.025
			1000	0.044	0.071	0.1
100	~1.0 earth radii	44°	1000	0.014	0.022	0.030
			200	0.070	0.11	0.15
10	3.6 earth radii	61°	200	0.02	0.025	—
5	9.0 earth radii	65°	200	0.014	—	—

In terms of the TWT mechanism, the hiss is excited by a continuous stream of particles along which amplification occurs only over a restricted band of frequencies. The amount of gain at a given frequency depends upon, among other things, the corresponding interaction distance, which in turn depends on the variation of plasma frequency along the path.

Transient phenomena, of which chorus is an example, are less easily explained in terms of the TWT mechanism. It appears to be necessary to assume that TWT amplification is restricted to a discrete group of particles, either occurring naturally or formed temporarily by a strong whistler-mode wave as discussed earlier. As these bunches travel along the lines of force, amplification takes place in the region of the bunch. Each characteristic frequency is amplified for a length of time that depends upon the length and velocity of the bunch. As the bunch moves, the frequency generated varies with changes in the parameters of the medium. With this approach the shape of the hook was reproduced assuming a bunch of particles entering the F region from above (Gallet and Helliwell, 1959). In general the frequency–time curve observed on the ground will differ from the generated function because the group velocity and position of origin along the field line both vary with frequency.

In this mechanism it is clear that the duration of the discrete emission will be limited by the length of time the moving bunch spends in its trapped orbit before it is either absorbed in the lower ionosphere or mirrored in the earth's magnetic field (Brice, 1964d). The maximum duration will be at relatively low frequencies where $v_g = 2v_p$. If we assume that generation begins when the bunch starts up the line of force and that the frequency of generation and the longitudinal velocity of the bunch are constant, the emission begins at the opposite end of the line of force when the bunch reaches the top of the path. Hence the emission duration cannot exceed the time required for the bunch to travel over half the path. Consider the long-enduring emission of Fig. 7-50, which occurs at 6.5 kc/s and lasts 19 sec. If we take $f_{H_1} = 2f = 13$ kc/s, and $f_0 = 200$ kc/s, then $P = 6.5$ and $\phi_0 = 60.5°$; the corresponding particle velocity is then 0.0325 c and the half-length of the path is 29,000 km (see Appendix). The maximum possible duration of the emission is then about 3 sec, which is small compared with the observed value of 19 sec. It seems unlikely, therefore, that simple longitudinal resonance can account for this type of emission.

An alternative mechanism for explaining transient phenomena is based on the backward-directed, doppler-shifted cyclotron radiation from electrons spiraling in the earth's field. In this mechanism, waves and particles are in resonance when the spiraling electrons see a doppler-shifted wave frequency equal to their local gyro-frequency. If the longitudinal stream velocity is v_s and the oppositely directed wave velocity is v_p, then it is easily shown that transverse resonance occurs for non-relativistic electrons when

$$v_s = v_p(Y - 1), \qquad (7.7)$$

where $Y = f_H/f$.

Thus when the wave frequency is one-half the local gyro-frequency, condition (7.7) reduces to $v_s = v_p$, the same as the condition for longitudinal resonance except that the stream and wave are oppositely directed for transverse resonance. However, under more common conditions, Y is greater than 2, and the required stream velocity is relatively greater than for longitudinal resonance.

This mechanism has been applied to the problem of explaining various transient forms, such as hooks and periodic emissions, in a series of papers by Dowden (1962b,d,e, and g), but the agreement with experimental data has been questioned (Helliwell, 1962; Brice, 1962). Dowden (1963c) has suggested that departures of the experimental data from his theory can be explained in terms of unsymmetrical localized anomalies in the earth's magnetic field of the order of fifty gamma. In Dowden's theory the source is assumed to be a small bunch of particles that oscillates between mirror points in the earth's field, but this assumption was found to be incompatible with the phenomenon of whistler-triggered periodic emissions as discussed earlier. The hypothesis of wave-induced bunching deduced from these new observations (Helliwell, 1963c) is consistent with both the longitudinal and the transverse resonance mechanisms. However, the latter mechanism has the advantage that the radiation encounters new particles moving into the interaction region and so could modify their distribution in such a way as to produce more radiation. Another advantage stems from the fact that coupling in the transverse resonance is maximum for purely longitudinal propagation, whereas in the case of longitudinal resonance, coupling is zero. Mechanisms for "organizing" the transverse radiation from the particles have been proposed by Brice (1963) and by Hansen (1963). A non-convective instability in the transverse interaction was suggested by Brice (1963); the conditions for this instability were determined by Bell and Buneman (1964), an important step in establishing the validity of this mechanism. A fundamental advantage of the non-convective transverse instability is that the duration of the emission may be unlimited as long as particles continue to flow into the interaction region. This theory, therefore, provides an explanation for the long-enduring discrete emissions, as well as for the more common short emissions.

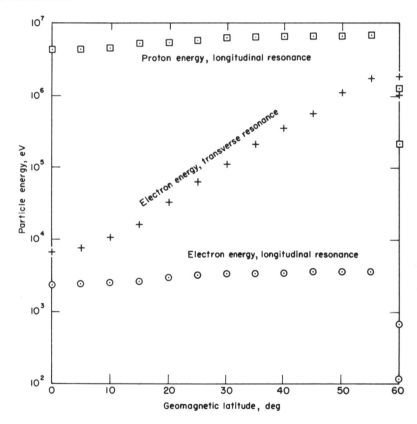

FIG. 7-74. Particle energies required for longitudinal and transverse resonance, based on model described in text.

An extension of the TWT mechanism for electrons has recently been proposed (Bell, 1964b) in which the energy for amplification of the wave is derived not from the longitudinal motions of the electrons but from their transverse motions. As in the ordinary TWT mechanism, propagation must be oblique and the approximate condition for resonance is (7.1) as before. However, the gyrating electrons encounter significant variations of the electric and magnetic fields of the wave when the gyro-radius is of the order of a wavelength in the medium. The result is that growth rates comparable with those calculated for the transverse resonance instability can be realized.

The proton and electron energies required for both longitudinal and transverse resonance are shown as functions of geomagnetic latitude for a typical set of conditions in Fig. 7-74 (Brice, 1964a,c). The calculations are based on a dipole line of force terminating at a geomagnetic latitude of 60° (L = 4), a wave frequency of 5 kc/s, and a total particle kinetic energy equal to three times its longitudinal energy. The plasma frequency is given by $f_0 = 1000 f_H^{1/2}$, except at 60°, where typical ionosphere critical frequencies of 3 Mc/s (upper points) and 7 Mc/s (lower points) are assumed. The curves for longitudinal resonance are based on (7.6). Below about 10^5 ev the curve for transverse resonance is given by (7.7), while above this energy relativistic corrections are required (Brice, 1964a). It is seen that for electrons in longitudinal resonance, the energy required is least, ranging from about 2.5 Kev to 3.5 Kev in the magnetosphere and from 100 ev to 700 ev in the ionosphere. For protons in longitudinal resonance, the required energies are relatively large, being greater than for electrons by the mass ratio of 1800. For electrons in transverse resonance, the required energy ranges from about 7 Kev in the equatorial plane to over 1 Mev at low altitudes. Since energetic electrons are generally more plentiful the lower the energy, more particles should be available for transverse resonance in the region of the equatorial plane than elsewhere. On the other hand, the energy for longitudinal resonance is relatively insensitive to position laong the field line, except for the relatively low values in the ionosphere.

Dipole Field: Charts and Expressions

At altitudes above several hundred kilometers, the earth's magnetic field can be approximated closely by a dipole located at the center of the earth. Many problems involving the geometry of the earth's field can be solved with the aid of a chart showing the dipole flux lines (Mlodnosky and Helliwell, 1962a,b). A scale model of the earth's dipole field is shown in Fig. 1. The magnetic moment is such that it produces a flux density of 0.314 gauss or 3.14×10^{-5} webers/m² at the geomagnetic equator. This corresponds to a magnetic field intensity of 0.314 oersteds or 25 ampere-turns per meter and an electron gyro-frequency of 880 kc/s. The radius of the earth is taken to be 6370 kilometers. Equations for a magnetic dipole flux line and for the field strength along that line are given by Alfvén (1950). The equation for arc length along a dipole flux line is given by Chapman and Sugiura (1956). These equations, with the list of symbols, are shown in Fig. 2.

Plots of the flux lines originating at every ten degrees of latitude are shown in Figs. 1 and 2 in hemispherical sectors of geomagnetic coordinates out to ten earth radii and one earth radius, respectively. Along the equatorial radial is shown a scale of the latitude at which a flux line at that distance passes through the earth's surface. Additional flux lines are readily sketched from the following simple table, where R_{eq} is the equatorial geocentric radial distance (also called the L value) of the desired line.

Latitude (deg)	Geocentric Radius
0	$1.00\, R_{eq}$
30	$0.75\, R_{eq}$
45	$0.50\, R_{eq}$
60	$0.25\, R_{eq}$

Scales of geocentric radial distance and altitude above the earth's surface are included in both figures. Semi-circles concentric with the earth's surface represent increments of one earth radius, and 500 km respectively, in Figs. 1 and 2.

Arc length is shown in the lower quadrant of Figs. 1 and 2 by the scales constructed along the lines of force with origins at the earth's surface.

In the upper quadrants of Figs. 1 and 2 are shown lines of constant electron gyro-frequency. Corresponding values of gyro-frequency for a singly charged ion are obtained simply by dividing the curve values by the number 1836 m_i, where m_i is the ratio of the molecular weight of the ion to the atomic weight of hydrogen.

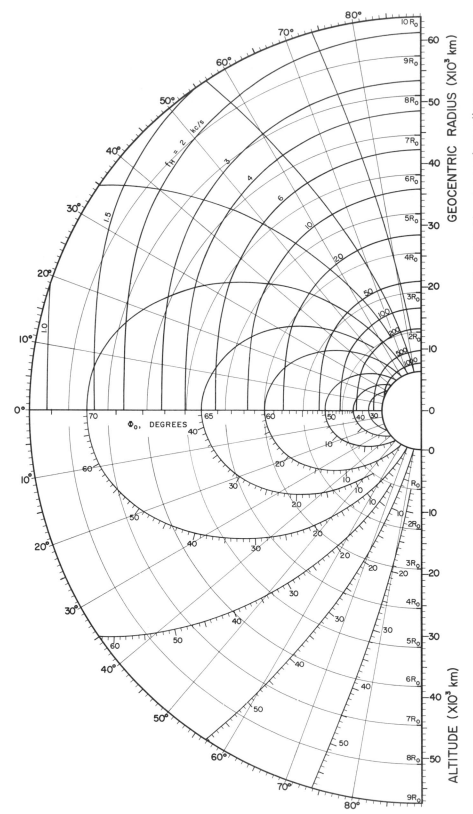

FIG. 1. Lines of force, arc lengths, and electron gyro-frequency of the earth's dipole magnetic field plotted in geomagnetic coordinates out to 10 earth radii.

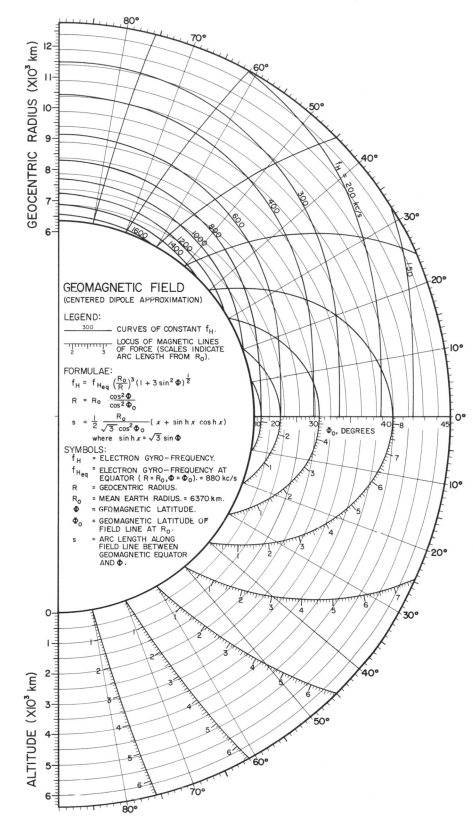

FIG. 2. Lines of force, arc lengths, and electron gyro-frequency of the earth's dipole magnetic field plotted in geomagnetic coordinates out to 1 earth radius.

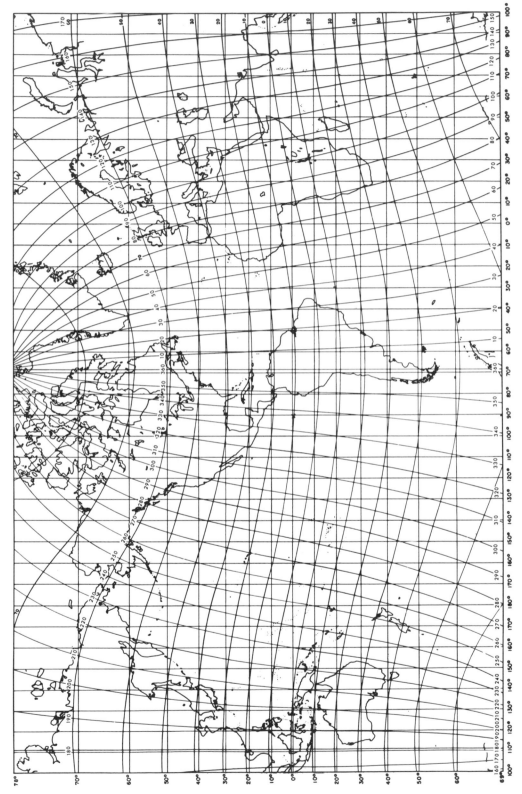

Fig. 3. Mercator projection of world with superimposed magnetic coordinate grid (curved lines), based on centered dipole approximation. (Francis S. Johnson, ed., *Satellite Environment Handbook* [Stanford, Calif.: Stanford University Press, 1961].)

The radius of curvature of a flux line is given by

$$R_c = \frac{R}{3} \cos^2 \phi \, \frac{(1 + 4 \tan^2 \phi)^{3/2}}{1 + \sin^2 \phi} \, ,$$

where ϕ is the geomagnetic latitude and R is the geocentric radius. In the geomagnetic equatorial plane, where $\phi = 0$ deg, the radius of curvature is simply $R_c = R/3$.

The relation of dipole field coordinates and geographical coordinates is shown on the Mercator projection of Fig. 3 (Johnson, 1961).

Bibliography

A page number in italics at the end of an entry refers to the page in this volume on which that entry is cited.

AARONS, J., 1956. Low frequency electromagnetic radiation 10–900 cycles per second. *J. Geophys. Res.*, **61**(4), 647–61.

———, 1960. Natural background noise at very low frequencies. Chap. 8 in *The Radio Noise Spectrum*, Donald H. Menzel, ed., Cambridge, Mass.: Harvard Univ. Press.

AARONS, J., G. GUSTAFSSON, and A. EGELAND, 1960. Correlation of audio-frequency electromagnetic radiation with auroral zone micropulsations. *Nature*, **185**(4707), 148–51. *Pp. 291, 293.*

ADACHI, S., and Y. MUSHIAKE, 1962. On VLF emissions in the exosphere. *IRE Trans. Ant. & Prop.*, **AP-10**(6), 785–87.

The Air Almanac, 1960, 1961. Wash., D.C.: Department of the Navy, U.S. Naval Observatory. *P. 165.*

AKHIEZER, A. I., V. G. BAR'YAKHTAR and S. V. PELETMINSKII, 1963. Effect of radiation processes on transport phenomena in a plasma in a strong magnetic field. *Soviet Phys. JETP*, **16**(5), 1231–35.

ALFVÉN, HANNES, 1950. *Cosmical Electrodynamics*. Oxford: Oxford Univ. Press. *Pp. 188, 317.*

ALLCOCK, G. McK., 1957. A study of the audio-frequency radio phenomenon known as "dawn chorus." *Australian J. Phys.*, **10**(2), 286–98. *Pp. 21, 292, 293.*

———, 1959. The electron density distribution in the outer ionosphere derived from whistler data. *J. Atmos. Terrest. Phys.*, **14**(3/4), 185–99. *P. 183.*

———, 1960a. IGY whistler results. URSI XIIIth Gen. Assembly, Commission IV, Doc. AG 60/IV/9, London. *P. 165.*

———, 1960b. Propagation of whistlers to polar latitudes. *Nature*, **188**(4752), 732–33. *Pp. 132, 199. P. 183.*

———, 1964. An evaluation of the current-jet hypothesis of whistler generation. *J. Geophys. Res.*, **69**(11), 2299–2303.

ALLCOCK, G. McK., R. A. HELLIWELL, C. K. BRANIGAN, J. C. MOUNTJOY, 1963. Whistler and other very low frequency phenomena associated with the high-altitude nuclear explosion on July 9, 1962. *J. Geophys. Res.*, **68**(3), 735–40. An abridged version, 1962, appeared in *New Zealand J. Geol. and Geophys.*, **5**(6), 975–77. *P. 135.*

ALLCOCK, G. McK., and L. H. MARTIN, 1956. Simultaneous occurrence of "dawn chorus" at places 600 km apart. *Nature*, **178**, 937–38. *Pp. 20, 291.*

ALLCOCK, G. McK., and M. G. MORGAN, 1958. Solar activity and whistler dispersion. *J. Geophys. Res.*, **63**(3), 573–76. *P. 150.*

ALLCOCK, G. McK., and M. F. RODGERS, 1961. Geomagnetic activity and the reception of whistlers in polar regions. *J. Geophys. Res.*, **66**(11), 3953–55. *P. 150.*

AL'PERT, YA. L., 1960. *Rasprostvanenie Radiovoln i Ionosfera*. Moscow: Acad. Sci. Press U.S.S.R. Also published in English, 1963, as *Radio Wave Propagation and the Ionosphere*, New York: Consultants Bureau.

ALTMAN, C., and H. CORY, 1962a. The transmission of audio-frequency electromagnetic waves through the terrestrial ionosphere in the magnetoionic mode. *J. Geophys. Res.*, **67**(10), 4086–90. *P. 61.*

———, 1962b. Absorption of audio-frequency electro-magnetic waves traversing the ionosphere in the magneto-ionic mode. *Bull. Res. Coun. Israel*, **11c**, 1–18. *P. 61.*

ANGERAMI, J. J., and J. O. THOMAS, 1963. The distribution of ions and electrons in the earth's exosphere. Tech. Rept. No. 4, NASA Grant NsG 30–60 Tech. Rept. No. 3412–3, AF-AFOSR-62-370, Radioscience Lab., Stanford Electronics Labs., Stanford Univ., Stanford, Calif.

ATAEV, O. M., 1959. Determination of the number of collisions in the ionosphere. *Radiotekh. i Elektron.*, 4(9), 1439–43. *P. 63.*

BANDYOPADHYAY, P., 1957. Models of the lower ionosphere as may be inferred from absorption results. *Indian J. Phys.*, 31(6), 297–308. *P. 63.*

BARKHAUSEN, H., 1919. Zwei mit Hilfe der neuen Verstärker entdeckte Erscheinungen. *Physik. Z.*, 20(1919), 401–3. *P. 11.*

——, 1930. Whistling tones from the earth. *Proc. IRE*, 18(7), 1155–59. *P. 14.*

BARRINGTON, R. E., 1959, Whistler propagation in the presence of ion streams. Paper presented at IRE-URSI Sym., May 4–7, 1959, Wash., D.C., Abstr. in *IRE Trans. Ant. & Prop.*, AP-7(3), 287.

——, 1960. The interaction of the whistler mode with the space charge modes of an electron stream. (Proc. Sym. Phys. Proc. in Sun-Earth Environment, July 20–21, 1959), DRTE No. 1025, Defence Res. Telecommunications Estab., Ottawa, Canada, 223–30.

——, 1962. Electron and positive ion densities of the exosphere deduced from whistlers. *NATO Conference Series, Electron Density Profiles in the Ionosphere and Exosphere*, 2, New York: Macmillan, 381–90.

BARRINGTON, R. E., and J. S. BELROSE, 1963a. Preliminary results from the very-low-frequency receiver aboard Canada's Alouette satellite. *Nature*, 198(4881), 651–56. *P. 308.*

——, 1963b. Alouette observations of whistlers and ionospheric noise. Paper presented at 1963 Spring URSI Meeting, Washington, D.C. *Pp. 62, 308, 309.*

BARRINGTON, R. E., J. S. BELROSE, and D. A. KEELEY, 1963. VLF noise bands observed by the Alouette I satellite. *J. Geophys. Res.*, 00(24), 6539–41. *Pp. 308, 309.*

BARRINGTON, R. E., and T. NISHIZAKE, 1960a. Whistler dispersion and exospheric hydrogen ions. *J. Geophys. Res.*, 65(9), 2581–82.

——, 1960b. The hydrogen ion effect in whistler dispersion. *Can. J. Phys.*, 38(12), 1642–52.

BARRINGTON, R. E., and W. E. THOMPSON, 1962. Whistlers and magnetic activity. *Can. J. Phys.*, 40(6), 775–81.

BARRINGTON, R. E., and E. THRANE, 1962. The determination of D-Region electron densities from observations of cross-modulations. *J. Atmos. Terrest. Phys.*, 24(1), 31–42. *Pp. 63, 72.*

BEGHIN, C., 1964. Ensembles d'enregistrement et d'analyse des sifflements atmospheriques GRI/NT/24, Groupe de Recherches Ionosphériques, St. Maur-des-Fossés, France.

BEKEFI, G., and S. C. BROWN, 1961. Emissions of radio-frequency waves from plasmas. *Am. J. Phys.*, 29(7), 404–28. *P. 310.*

BEKEFI, G., J. L. HIRSHFIELD, and S. C. BROWN, 1961. Cyclotron emission from plasmas with non-Maxwellian distributions. *Phys. Rev.*, 122(4), 1037–42.

BELL, T. F., 1964a. Time reversal of the geocyclotron mechanism. *J. Geophys. Res.*, 69(1), 177–79. *P. 204.*

——, 1964b. Traveling wave amplification of whistler-mode signals by means of a gyrating electron stream. (In preparation.) *P. 315.*

——, 1964c. Wave-particle gyroresonance interactions in the earth's outer ionosphere. Rept. No. SEL-64-063, prepared under Air Force Office of Scientific Research Contract AF49(638)-1060 and grant AF-AFOSR-62-370, Radioscience Lab., Stanford Electronics Labs., Stanford Univ., Stanford, Calif.

BELL, T. F., and O. BUNEMAN, 1964. Plasma instability in the whistler mode caused by a gyrating electron stream. *Phys. Rev.* 133 (5A), A1300–A1302. *P. 315.*

BELL, T. F., and R. A. HELLIWELL, 1960. Traveling-wave amplification in the ionosphere. (Proc. Sym. Phys. Proc. in Sun-Earth Environment, July 20–21, 1959), DRTE No. 1025, Defence Res. Telecommunications Estab., Ottawa, Canada, 215–22. *P. 311.*

BELL, T. F., R. A. HELLIWELL, R. F. MLODNOSKY, and R. L. SMITH, 1963. Geocyclotron feasibility study. Air Force Special Weapons Center, Air Force Systems Command, AFSWC-TDR-63-35, Final Rep. Contract No. AF 29(601)-4506. *P. 204.*

BELL, T., R. SMITH, and N. BRICE, 1963. Comments on "The magneto-ionic theory for a drifting plasma." *IEEE Trans. Ant. & Prop.*, **AP-11**(2), 194–95.

BELROSE, J. S., and R. E. BARRINGTON, 1964. VLF noise bands observed by the Alouette I satellite. National Bureau of Standards Technical Note 211, Vol. 1, 85–100.

BENEDIKTOV, E. A., and V. YA. EIDMAN, 1961. On the incoherent radio emission of fast moving charged particles in the earth's magnetic field. *I.V.U.Z.*, *Radiofiz.*, **4**(2), 253–58.

BENEDIKTOV, E. A., V. O. RAPOPORT, and V. YA. EIDMAN, 1962. Radiation of plasma waves in the ionosphere. *Geomag. and Aeron.* **2**(4), 591–93.

BENOIT, R., 1956. Low frequency radio wave noise of the earth's magnetic field. *Compt. rend.*, **242**, 2534.

BOOKER, H. G., 1962. Guidance of radio and hydromagnetic waves in the magnetosphere. *J. Geophys. Res.*, **67**(11), 4135–62. *P. 51.*

BOOKER, H. G., and R. B. DYCE, 1963. Dispersion of waves in a cold magneto-plasma from hydrodynamic whistler frequencies. Stanford Res. Inst., Menlo Park, Calif.

BOURDEAU, R. E., E. C. WHIPPLE, JR., J. L. DONLEY, and S. J. BAUER, 1962. Experimental evidence for the presence of helium ions based on Explorer VIII satellite data. *J. Geophys. Res.*, **67**(2), 467–75. *P. 191.*

BOWHILL, S. A., 1956. The fading of radio waves of frequencies between 16 and 2400 kc/s. *J. Atmos. Terrest. Phys.*, **8**(3), 129–45. *P. 169.*

BOYER, J. M., 1961. A radio wave mechanism to account for the known distribution of Van Allen belts about the earth. *Nature*, **190**(4776), 597–99.

BRANDSTATTER, J. J., 1959a. A survey of some promising methods for the study of ray propagation in a general medium. Paper presented at IRE-URSI Sym. May 4–7, 1959, Wash., D.C. Abstr. in *IRE Trans. Ant. & Prop.*, **AP-7**(3), 287.

———, 1959b. The theory of propagation of rays in an inhomogeneous and anisotropic medium. Final Ltd. Rept. Pt. I, P. O. S-112, Air Force Contract No. AF 18(603)-126, Stanford Res. Inst. Project 2241.

———, 1963. An introduction to waves, rays and radiation in plasma media. New York: McGraw-Hill, p. 360. *P. 35.*

BRICE, N. M., 1960. Traveling wave amplification of whistlers. *J. Geophys. Res.*, **65**(11), 3840–42.

———, 1962. Discussion of paper by R. L. Dowden, "Doppler-shifted cyclotron radiation from electrons: A theory of very low frequency emissions from the exosphere." *J. Geophys. Res.*, **67**(12), 4897–99. *Pp. 299, 310, 314.*

———, 1963. An explanation of triggered VLF emissions. *J. Geophys. Res.*, **68**(15), 4626–28. *P. 315.*

———, 1964a. Discrete very low frequency emissions from the upper atmosphere. Rept. No. SEL 64-088, Radioscience Lab., Stanford Electronics Lab., Stanford Univ. Stanford, Calif. *P. 316.*

———, 1964b. Multiphase periodic very low frequency emissions. *Radio Sci.* (in press). *P. 307.*

———, 1964c. Fundamentals of VLF emission generation mechanisms. *J. Geophys. Res.* (in press). *P. 316.*

———, 1964d. Maximum duration of discrete VLF emissions. *J. Geophys. Res.* (in press). *P. 314.*

———, 1964e. A qualitative explanation of the diurnal variation of chorus. *J. Geophys. Res.* (in press).

BRICE, N. M., and R. L. SMITH, 1963. Comments on a paper by H. Unz, "On the origin of very low frequency emissions." *J. Atmos. Terrest. Phys.*, **25**(3), 185.

———, 1964. Observation of a VLF plasma resonance by Alouette I. *Nature*, **282** (in press).

BRICE, N. M., R. L. SMITH, J. S. BELROSE, and R. E. BARRINGTON, 1964. Triggered very low frequency emissions observed by the Alouette I satellite. *Nature*, **282** (in press). *P. 309.*

BRICE, N. M., and E. UNGSTRUP, 1963. Use of "local mean auroral time" for very-low-frequency emissions. *Nature*, **198**(4883), 874.

BRIGGS, B. H., 1951. The determination of the collision frequency of electrons in the ionosphere from observation of the reflection coefficient of the abnormal E-layer. *J. Atmos. Terrest. Phys.*, **1**(5/6), 345–48. *P. 63.*

BROWN, H. E., and G. C. CAIRNS, 1962. Very low frequency noise at Brisbane. *Nature*, **194**(4832), 962.

BUDDEN, K. G., 1959. Effect of small irregularities on the constitutive relations for the ionosphere. *J. Res. NBS*, **63D**(2), 135–49. *P. 176.*

———, 1961. *Radio Waves in the Ionosphere.* Cambridge, Eng.: Cambridge Univ. Press. *Pp. 52, 74.*

BURTON, E. T., 1930. Submarine cable interference. *Nature*, **126**(3167), 55. *Pp. 14, 290.*

BURTON, E. T., and E. M. BOARDMAN, 1933a. Effects of solar eclipse on audio frequency atmospherics. *Nature*, **131**, 81–82. *P. 14.*

———, 1933b. Audio-frequency atmospherics. *Proc. IRE*, **21**(10), 1476–94. Also published in *Bell Syst. Tech. J.*, **12**, 498–516. *P. 14.*

CAHILL, L. J., and P. G. AMAZEEN, 1963. The boundary of the geomagnetic field. *J. Geophys. Res.*, **68**(7), 1835–44. *P. 201.*

CAIN, J. C., I. R. SHAPIRO, J. D. STOLARIK, and J. P. HEPPNER, 1961. A note on whistlers observed above the ionosphere. *J. Geophys. Res.*, **66**(9), 2677–80. *Pp. 134, 308.*

CAIN, J. C., I. R. SHAPIRO, and J. D. STOLARIK, 1962. Whistler signals observed with the Vanguard III satellite. *J. Phys. Soc. Japan*, **17** (Suppl. A-II, Intl. Conf. on Cosmic Rays and the Earth Storm, Part II), 84–87. *Pp. 134, 308.*

CALVERT, W., T. E. VANZANDT, R. W. KNECHT, and G. B. GOE, 1963. Evidence for field-aligned ionization irregularities between 400 and 1000 km above the earth's surface. In *Proceedings of the International Conference on the Ionosphere, 1962*, Dorking, Eng.: Bartholomew Press. *P. 135.*

CAPON, J., and M. R. WEISS, 1961. Use of a coherent memory filter in spectral measurements of atmospheric whistlers. *Proc. IRE*, **49**(11), 1707.

CARPENTER, D. L., 1959. Identification of whistler sources on visual records and a method of routine whistler analysis. Tech. Rept. No. 5, Air Force Contract No. AF 18(603)-126, Radioscience Lab., Stanford Electronics Labs., Stanford Univ., Stanford, Calif. *P. 122.*

———, 1962a. New experimental evidence of the effect of magnetic storms on the magnetosphere. *J. Geophys. Res.*, **67**(1), 135–45. *Pp. 123, 183, 304.*

———, 1962b. Electron-density variations in the magnetosphere deduced from whistler data. Tech. Rept. No. 11, Air Force Contract No. AF 18(603)-126 and National Science Foundation Grant NSF G17037, Radioscience Lab., Stanford Electronics Labs., Stanford Univ., Stanford, Calif. Also in *J. Geophys. Res.*, **67**(9), 3345–60. *Pp. 183, 197, 198, 200, 300.*

———, 1962c. The magnetosphere during magnetic storms; a whistler analysis. Tech. Rept. No. 12, Air Force Contract No. AF 18(603)-126 and National Science Foundation Grant NSF G17037, Radioscience Lab., Stanford Electronics Labs., Stanford Univ., Stanford, Calif. *Pp. 192, 195, 197, 201.*

———, 1963a. Whistler evidence of a "knee" in the magnetospheric ionization density profile. *J. Geophys. Res.*, **68**(6), 1675–82. *Pp. 123, 202.*

———, 1963b. Whistler measurements of electron density and magnetic field strength in the remote magnetosphere. *J. Geophys. Res.*, **68**(12), 3727–30.

———, 1964a. Whistlers. U.S. Nat'l. Comm. Rept. to URSI XIVth Gen. Assembly, Tokyo, Sept. 1963, Commission IV, Magnetospheric Radio, *Radio Sci.* **68D**(5), 609–15.

———, 1964b. Whistler measurements of the equatorial profile of magnetospheric electron density. *Proc. of Commission IV on Radio Noise of Terrestrial Origin during XIVth Gen. Assembly of URSI, Tokyo*, 1963, New York: American Elsevier (in press).

CARPENTER, D. L., and G. B. CARPENTER, 1962. Data summary: whistler-mode propagation. SEL-62-001, Radioscience Lab., Stanford Electronics Labs., Stanford Univ., Stanford,

Calif., prepared under National Science Foundation Grant NSF G17037, U.S. Navy Contract No. Nonr 225(27), and Air Force Contract No. AF 18(603)–126.

CARPENTER, D. L., and G. B. CARPENTER, 1963. Whistler-mode propagation data No. 2. Tech. Rept. No. 1113–1, SEL-63-006, Radioscience Lab., Stanford Electronics Labs., Stanford Univ., Stanford, Calif.

CARPENTER, D. L., and R. L. SMITH, 1964. Whistler measurements of electron density in the magnetosphere. *Rev. Geophys.*, **2**(3), 415–41.

CARPENTER, G. B., 1963. An FM technique for observation of VLF whistler-mode propagation. Tech. Rept. No. 3, Nonr-225(27), Tech. Rept. No. 3412-2, AF-AFOSR-62-370, Radioscience Lab., Stanford Electronics Labs., Stanford Univ., Stanford, Calif.

CARPENTER, G. B., and L. COLIN, 1963. On a remarkable correlation between whistler-mode propagation and HF northscatter. *J. Geophys. Res.*, **68**(20), 5649–58. *P. 169.*

CARTWRIGHT, D. G., 1960. Direction-finding on diffuse sources of electromagnetic radiation. *Australian J. Phys.*, **13**, 712–17.

———, 1964. Rocket observations of very low frequency radio noise at night. *Planet. Space Sci.*, **12**(1), 11–16.

CHAMBERLAIN, J. W., 1961. *Physics of the Aurora and Airglow*, New York: Academic Press. *P. 310.*

CHAPMAN, S., and M. SUGIURA, 1956. Arc lengths along the lines of force of a magnetic dipole. *J. Geophys. Res.*, **61**(3), 485–88. *P. 317.*

CLARENCE, N. D., and P. A. O'BRIEN, 1961. Dispersions of multiple-stroke whistlers. *Nature*, **190**(4781), 1096–97. *P. 133.*

CLEMMOW, P. C., 1962. Wave amplification in a plasma stream in a medium of high refractive index. *Proc. Phys. Soc. (London)*, **80**, 1322–32.

COHEN, M. H., 1961. Radiation in a plasma: I. Čerenkov effect. *Phys. Rev.*, **123**(3), 711–21. *P. 310.*

COLE, K. D., 1959. Electro-hydromagnetic waves in a fully ionized gas—I. *Planet. Space Sci.*, **1**, 319–24.

———, 1961. Electro-hydromagnetic waves in a fully ionized gas—II. *Planet. Space Sci.*, **5**, 292–98.

CONSOLI, T., G. ICHTCHENKO, and M. WEILL, 1963a. Chauffage et effets thermiques dans la propagation d'ondes polarisées circulairement à droite. Classification des effets observables. *Compt. rend.*, **256**, 626–29.

———, 1963b. Vérification expérimentale des phénomènes liés à la propagation d'ondes polarisées circulairement à droite dans un plasma chaud. *Compt. rend.*, **256**, 903–6.

———, 1963c. Vérification expérimentale du chauffage du plasma par propagation d'ondes polarisées circulairement à droite. *Compt. rend.*, **256**, 1090–92.

CORCUFF, Y., 1960. Choix d'un paramètre caractérisant les sifflements radioélectriques. *Ann. géophys.*, **16**(1), 128–39.

———, 1961. Variation de la dispersion des sifflements radioélectriques au cours des orages magnétiques. *Ann. géophys.*, **17**(4), 374–79.

———, 1962. La dispersion des sifflements radioélectriques au cours des orages magnétiques; ses variations nocturne, annuelle et semi-annuelle en périodes calmes. *Ann. géophys.* **18**(4), 334–40.

———, 1963. Occurrence et dispersion des sifflements radioélectriques enregistrés à Poitiers (juin 1957 à décembre 1958). Paris: Centre National de la Recherche Scientifique, série V, fas. 8.

CORCUFF, Y., and F. FISSON, 1963. La variation d'occurrence des sifflements et des bruits ionosphériques au moment du lever solaire dans l'ionosphère. *Ann. géophys.*, **19**(3), 244–49.

CORCUFF, Y., and JEAN-PIERRE LEGRAND, 1961. Corrélations entre le bruit radioélectrique basse fréquence et les orages magnétiques et cosmiques. *Ann. géophys.*, **17**(3), 338–40.

———, 1962. Correlations between the very low frequency emissions and the magnetic and cosmic ray storms." *J. Phys. Soc. Japan*, **17**(Suppl. A-II), 76–78.

CORNWALL, J. M., 1964. Scattering of energetic trapped electrons by very low frequency waves. *J. Geophys. Res.*, **69**(7), 1251–58.

CRARY, J. H., 1961. The effect of the earth–ionosphere waveguide on whistlers. Tech. Rept. No. 9, Air Force Contract No. AF 18(603)-126, Radioscience Lab., Stanford Electronics Labs., Stanford Univ., Stanford, Calif. *Pp. 75, 77, 129, 130, 131.*

———, 1964. Geometrical optics convergence coefficient for the whistler case. *Radio Sci.*, **68D**(2), 211–14 *P. 292.*

CRARY, J. H., R. A. HELLIWELL, and R. F. CHASE, 1956. Stanford-Seattle whistler observations. *J. Geophys. Res.*, **61**(1), 35–44. *P. 20.*

CROMBIE, D. D., 1955. Measurement of the arrival angle of whistlers. *J. Geophys. Res.*, **60**(3), 364–65. *P. 129.*

CROMBIE, D. D., F. A. MCNEILL, and G. McK. ALLCOCK, 1962. Variations in phase path of man-made one-hop whistler-mode signals at 18.6 kc/s Sci. Rept. No. 2, Dominion Phys. Lab., Lower Hutt, N.Z. Also in *J. Geophys. Res.*, **68**(23), 6229–35.

CROUCHLEY, J., 1961. A study of whistling atmospherics: part I. Occurrence. *Australian J. Phys.*, **14**(1), 22–39.

———, 1964a. A study of whistling atmospherics, IV. Comparison of observations at widely spaced stations. *Australian J. Phys.*, **17**(1), 75–87.

✓——, 1964b. A study of whistling atmospherics, V. Dispersion. *Australian J. Phys.*, **17**(1), 88–105.

CROUCHLEY, J., and N. M. BRICE, 1960. A study of "chorus" observed at Australian stations. *Planet. Space Sci.*, **2**(4), 238–45. *Pp. 292, 293.*

CROUCHLEY, J., and K. J. DUFF, 1962. A study of whistling atmospherics: Part III. Observations at closely spaced stations. *Australian J. Phys.*, **15**(4), 470–81.

CROUCHLEY, J., and R. J. FINN, 1961. A study of whistling atmospherics: Part II. Diffuseness. *Australian J. Phys.*, **14**(1), 40–56. *P. 129.*

CURTIS, H. W., 1958. The nature of lightning discharges which initiate whistlers. *Recent Advances in Atmospheric Electricity*, New York: Pergamon.

DELLIS, A. N., and J. M. WEAVER, 1964. Whistler-mode propagation in a laboratory plasma. *Proc. Phys. Soc.*, **83**, 473–89.

DELLOUE, J., 1957. Sur la direction d'arrivée et de la polarisation des atmosphériques siffleurs. *Compt. rend.*, **244**(6), 797–99. *P. 130.*

———, 1960a. La détermination de la direction d'arrivée et de la polarisation des atmosphériques siffleurs, première partie. *J. phys. radium*, **6**(6), 514–26. *P. 130.*

———, 1960b. La détermination de la direction d'arrivée et de la polarisation des atmosphériques siffleurs, deuxième partie. *J. phys. radium*, **21**(7), 587–99. *P. 130.*

DELLOUE, J., and M. GARNIER, 1963. Sur l'émergence des sifflements radioélectriques hors de l'ionosphère. *Compt. rend.*, **257**(6), 1327–30.

DELLOUE, J., M. GARNIER, F. GLANGEAUD, and P. BILDSTEIN, 1963. La polarisation des sifflements radioélectriques en relation avec leur direction d'arrivée. *Compt. rend.*, **257**(5), 1131–34.

DINGER, H. E., 1956. Whistling atmospherics. NRL Rept. 4825, Wash., D.C.: Naval Res. Lab. *Pp. 20, 204.*

———, 1957a. Sifflements atmosphériques exceptionnels. *Onde Elect.*, **37**(362), 526–34.

———, 1957b. Periodicity in dawn chorus. Paper presented at IRE-URSI Sym., May 22–25, 1957, Wash., D.C., Abstr. in *IRE Trans. Ant. & Prop.*, **AP-5**(3), 325. *P. 299.*

———, 1958. Report on URSI Commission IV—Radio noise of terrestrial origin. *Proc. IRE*, **46**, 1366–72.

✓——, 1960. A four-year summary of whistler activity at Washington, D.C. *J. Geophys. Res.*, **65**(2), 571.

DINGER, H. E., and W. E. GARNER, 1963. Whistler observations in connection with nuclear explosions. *J. Geophys. Res.*, **68**(20), 5641–48. *P. 135.*

DOWDEN, R. L., 1959. Low frequency (100 kc/s) radio noise from the aurora. *Nature*, **184** (4689), 803.

———, 1960. Geomagnetic noise at 230 kc/s. *Nature*, **187**, (4738), 677–78.

DOWDEN, R. L., 1961a. A theoretical model of electron density distribution along a geomagnetic line of force in the exosphere. *J. Atmos. Terrest. Phys.*, **20**(2/3), 122–30. *P. 188.*

———, 1961b. Simultaneous observations of VLF noise ("hiss") at Hobart and Macquarie Island. *J. Geophys. Res.*, **66**(5), 1587–88. *P. 292.*

———, 1962a. Wide-band bursts of VLF radio noise (hiss) at Hobart. *Australian J. Phys.*, **15**(1), 114–19. *P. 288.*

———, 1962b. Doppler-shifted cyclotron radiation from electrons: A theory of very low frequency emissions from the exosphere. *J. Geophys. Res.*, **67**(5), 1745–50. *Pp. 310, 314.*

———, 1962c. Theory of generation of exospheric very-low-frequency noise (hiss). *J. Geophys. Res.*, **67**(6), 2223–30. *P. 310.*

———, 1962d. Very-low-frequency discrete emissions received at conjugate points. *Nature*, **195**(4836), 64–65. *Pp. 310, 314.*

———, 1962e. Author's reply to preceding discussion. *J. Geophys. Res.*, **67**(12), 4900–4902. *Pp. 310, 314.*

———, 1962f. "Scale frequency" of the exosphere. *Nature*, **195**(4845), 984–85. *P. 310.*

———, 1962g. Cyclotron theory of very-low-frequency discrete emissions. *Nature*, **195**(4846), 1085–86. *Pp. 310, 314.*

———, 1962h. Method of measurement of electron energies and other data from spectrograms of VLF emissions. *Australian J. Phys.*, **15**(4), 490–503. *P. 310.*

———, 1963a. Doppler shifted cyclotron generation of exospheric very-low-frequency noise ("hiss"). *Planet. Space Sci.*, **11**(4), 361–69. *P. 310.*

———, 1963b. Very low frequency emissions from the exosphere. Ionospheric Prediction Service Research Rept., University of Tasmania, Hobart, Tasmania. *P. 310.*

———, 1963c. Effect of magnetic anomalies on very low frequency discrete emissions. *Australian J. Phys.*, **16**, 588–92. *Pp. 310, 314.*

DOWDEN, R. L., and G. T. GOLDSTONE, 1959. "Whistler-mode" echoes remote from the conjugate point. *Nature*, **183**(4658), 385–86.

DUNCAN, R. A., and G. R. ELLIS, 1959. Simultaneous occurrence of sub-visual aurorae and radio noise bursts on 4.6 kc/s. *Nature*, **183**(4675), 1618–19. *P. 294.*

DUNGEY, J. W., 1954. Electrodynamics of the outer atmosphere. Scientific Rept. No. 69, Air Force Contract No. AF 19(122)-44, Ionospheric Research Lab., Penn. State Univ. *Pp. 21, 188.*

———, 1963a. Resonant effect of plasma waves on charged particles in a magnetic field. *J. Fluid Mech.* **15**(1), 74–82.

✓——, 1963b. Loss of Van Allen electrons due to whistlers. *Planet. Space Sci.*, **11**(6), 591–95. *P. 204.*

ECKERSLEY, T. L., 1925. Note on musical atmospheric disturbances. *Phil. Mag.*, **49**(5), 1250–59. *P. 12.*

———, 1926. Electrical constitution of the upper atmosphere. *Nature*, **117**(2954), 821. *P. 13.*

———, 1928. Letter to the Editor. *Nature*, **122**(3081), 768. *P. 13.*

———, 1929. An investigation of short waves. *J. Inst. Elec. Engrs.*, **67**, 992–1032. *P. 13.*

———, 1931. 1929–1930 developments in the study of radio wave propagation. *Marconi Rev.*, **5**(31), 1–8. *P. 14.*

———, 1935. Musical atmospherics. *Nature*, **135**, 104–5. *P. 16.*

EGELAND, A., S. OLSEN, and G. GUSTAFSSON, 1962. Noise emissions in the audio-frequency range. Final Rept., Air Force Contract No. AF 61(514)-1314, Electronics Res. Directorate of the Air Force Cambridge Research Lab., Office of Aerospace Research, U.S. Air Force through its European Office. *P. 291.*

———, 1963. Audio and sub-audio-frequency electromagnetic radiation at high latitude. Final Rept., Air Force Contract No. AF 61(052)-600, Electronics Res. Directorate of the Air Force Cambridge Research Lab., Office of Aerospace Research, U.S. Air Force through its European Office.

EIDMAN, V. YA., 1958. The radiation from an electron moving in a magnetoactive plasma. *J. Exptl. Theoret. Phys. (USSR)*, **34**, 131–38. Also in *Soviet Phys. JETP*, **34**(7) No. 1, 91–95. *P. 310.*

ELLIS, G. R. A., 1956. On the propagation of whistling atmospherics. *J. Atmos. Terrest. Phys.*, **8**, 338–44. *P. 20.*

———, 1957. Low frequency radio emission from aurorae. *J. Atmos. Terrest. Phys.*, **10**, 302–6. *Pp. 21, 310.*

———, 1959. Low frequency electromagnetic radiation associated with magnetic disturbances. *Planet. Space Sci.*, **1**(4), 253–58. *P. 310.*

———, 1960a. Directional observations of 5 kc/s radiation from the earth's outer atmosphere. *J. Geophys. Res.*, **65**(3), 839–43. *P. 292.*

———, 1960b. Observations of atmospheric radio noise. *Nature*, **186**(4720), 229.

———, 1960c. Geomagnetic disturbances and 5 kilocycles per second electromagnetic radiation. *J. Geophys. Res.*, **65**(6), 1705–10. *P. 293.*

———, 1960d. A receiver for observation of VLF noise from the outer atmosphere. *Proc. IRE*, **48**, 1650–51.

———, 1961. Spaced observations of the low-frequency radiation from the earth's upper atmosphere. *J. Geophys. Res.*, **66**(1), 19–23. *P. 292.*

———, 1962. Cyclotron radiation from Jupiter. *Australian J. Phys.*, **15**(3), 344–53.

———, 1963. The radio emissions from Jupiter and the density of Jovian exosphere. *Australian J. Phys.*, **16**(1), 74–81.

———, 1964. On external radio emission from the earth's outer atmosphere. *Australian J. Phys.*, **17**(1), 63–74.

ELLIS, G. R. A., and C. A. CARTWRIGHT, 1959. Directional observations of radio noise from the outer atmosphere. *Nature*, **184**(4695), 1307–8. *P. 292.*

ELLIS, G. R. A., D. G. CARTWRIGHT, and J. R. V. GROVES, 1959. Spaced observations of radio noise from the outer atmosphere. *Nature*, **184**(4696), 1391–92.

ENTZIAN, G., and C. POPP. 1959. Lokalisierung von Initialsferics langer Whistler. *Z. Meteorologie*, **13**, 193–94.

ESHLEMAN, V. R., P. B. GALLAGHER, and R. C. BARTHLE, 1960. Radar methods of measuring the cislunar electron density. *J. Geophys. Res.*, **65**(10), 3079–86. *P. 191.*

EVANS, J. V., 1957. The electron content of the ionosphere. *J. Atmos. Terrest. Phys.*, **11**(4), 259–71. *P. 187.*

FAUCHER, J. A., 1962. On an integral equation in the theory of dispersion curves of whistlers. *Can. J. Phys.*, **40**(6), 794–96.

FEJER, J. A., and R. W. VICE, 1959. An investigation of the ionospheric D region. *J. Atmos. Terrest. Phys.*, **16**(3/4), 291–306. *P. 63.*

FRIEDMAN, H., 1959. Rocket observations of the ionosphere. *Proc. IRE*, **47**(2), 272–80. *P. 63.*

FUCHS, J., 1938. Discussion. *A report to the National Academy of Sciences—National Research Council*, Wash., D.C., Natl. Acad. of Sci.—Natl. Res. Coun., Pub. 581, 105. *P. 11.*

GALEEV, A. A., and L. I. RUDAKOV, 1964. Nonlinear theory of the drift instability of an inhomogeneous plasma in a magnetic field. *Soviet Phys. JETP*, **18**(2), 444–49.

GALLET, R. M., 1959a. The very low frequency emissions generated in the earth's exosphere. *Proc. IRE*, **47**(2), 211–31. *Pp. 188, 204, 205, 299, 305, 306.*

———, 1959b. Propagation and production of electromagnetic waves in a plasma. *Nuovo Cimento*, Supplement **13**(1), 234–56.

———, 1963a. Whistlers. In *Geophysics—The Earth's Environment*. New York: Gordon and Breach.

———, 1963b. The VLF emissions generated in the earth's exosphere. NATO Advanced Study Inst., Bad Homburg, Germany, July 22–Aug. 2, 1963 (in press).

———, 1964. Summary of research on VLF and ELF emissions. U.S. Nat'l. Comm. Rept. to URSI XIVth Gen. Assembly, Tokyo, Sept. 1963, Commission IV, Magnetospheric Radio, *Radio Sci.* **68D**(5), 615–18.

GALLET, R. M., and R. A. HELLIWELL, 1959. Origin of "very low frequency" emissions. *J. Res. NBS*, **63D**(1), 21–27. *Pp. 310, 313.*

GALLET, R. M., J. M. RICHARDSON, B. WIEDER, G. D. WARD, and G. N. HARDING, 1960.

Microwave whistler mode propagation in a dense laboratory plasma. *Phys. Rev. Lett.*, **4**(7), 347–49.

GALLET, R. M., and W. F. UTLAUT, 1961. Evidence on the laminar nature of the exosphere obtained by means of guided high-frequency wave propagation. *Phys. Rev. Lett.*, **6**(11), 591–94. Also published as Further evidence on fibrous nature of exosphere from guided HF wave propagation, Natl. Bureau of Standards Rept. No. 6747. *P. 51.*

GARRIOTT, O. K., 1958. A note on whistler propagation in regions of very low electron density. *J. Geophys. Res.*, **63**(4), 862–65. *P. 30.*

——, 1960. The determination of ionosphere electron density content and distribution from satellite observations: Part 2. Results of the Analysis. *J. Geophys. Res.*, **65**(4). 1151–57. *P. 191.*

GENDRIN, R., 1960a. Guidage des sifflements radioélectriques par le champ magnétique terrestre. *Compt. rend.*, **251**, 1085–87. *Pp. 42, 43.*

——, 1960b. Génération des bruits très basse fréquence dans l'exosphère par effet Čerenkov. *Compt. rend.*, **251**(10), 1122–23. *P. 310.*

——, 1961. Le guidage des whistlers par le champ magnétique, *Planet. Space Sci.*, **5**(4). 274–82. *Pp. 42, 43.*

——, 1962. Whistler studies of the lower exosphere. *NATO Conference Series, Electron Density Profiles in the Ionosphere and Exosphere*, **2**, 391–403.

GERSHMAN, B. N., 1958. The problem of the propagation of whistler atmospherics in the upper atmosphere. *I.V.U.Z. Radiofiz.*, **1**(5/6), 49–59.

GERSHMAN, B. N., and YU. S. KOROBKOV, 1958. Theory of the propagation of whistler atmospherics. *I.V.U.Z., Radiofiz.*, **1**(2).

GERSHMAN, V. I., and V. YU. TRAKHTENGERTS, 1961. The influence of ions on the propagation of whistlers. *Geomag. and Aeron.*, **1**(5), 595–601.

——, 1962. On the possibility of utilizing the data on the dispersions of whistlers for estimating the concentrations in the solar corpuscular fluxes. *Geomag. and Aeron.* **2**(4), 544–48.

GERSHMAN, B. N., and V. A. UGAROV, 1961. Propagation and generation of low frequency electromagnetic waves in the upper atmosphere. *Sov. Phys. Usp.*, **3**(5), 743–64.

GHERZI, E., 1960. Atmospherics on 20 kc/s at the time of local aurorae. *Nature*, **187**(4733), 225–26. *P. 294.*

GINZBURG, M. A., 1961a. A new mechanism producing short-period variations of the geomagnetic field. *Bull. Acad. Sci. U.S.S.R.*, Geophysics Series, Irving Emin, transl., (11), 1096–1102. *P. 310.*

——, 1961b. Electromagnetic radiation from solar corpuscular streams. *Phys. Rev. Lett.*, **7**(11), 399–401. *P. 310.*

——, 1962. The radio emission of solar corpuscular streams in the earth's atmosphere. *Geomag. and Aeron.*, **2**(4), 535–43.

——, 1963. Low-frequency waves in multicomponent plasma. *Geomag. and Aeron.*, **3**(4), 610–14.

GLASSTONE, S., ed., 1962. *The Effects of Nuclear Weapons*. Rev. ed., U.S. Dept. of Defense—U.S. Atomic Energy Commission, Wash., D.C.: Superintendent of Documents. *P. 135.*

GLIDDON, J. E. C., 1963. The distribution of ions in the exosphere. *J. Atmos. Terrest. Phys.*, **25**, 175–77.

GOLDEN, R. M., R. S. MACMILLAN, R. NATHAN, and W. V. T. RUSCH, 1956. A calculation of the radiation fields of whistling atmospherics. Tech. Rept. No. 1, AFOSR-TN-57-10, ASTIA Doc. AD115 042, Dept. of Elec. Engr. Calif. Inst. Technol., Pasadena, Calif.

GRIERSON, J. K., 1957. A technique for the rapid analysis of whistlers. *Proc. IRE*, **45**(6), 806–11. *P. 22.*

GURNETT, D. A., 1963. Very low frequency electromagnetic emissions observed with the ONR/SUI satellite Injun III. Dept. of Phys. and Astron., State Univ. of Iowa, Iowa City, Iowa. *P. 308.*

GURNETT, D. A., and B. J. O'BRIEN, 1964. High-latitude geophysical studies with satellite

Injun 3. Part 5, Very-low-frequency electromagnetic radiation. *J. Geophys. Res.*, **69**(1), 65–89. *P. 308.*

GUSTAFSSON, G., A. EGELAND, and G. AARONS, 1960. Audio-frequency electromagnetic radiation in the auroral zone. *J. Geophys. Res.* **65**(9), 2749–58. *P. 291.*

GUSTAFSSON, G., A. EGELAND, W. BARRON, and J. AARONS, 1963. Band emissions at gyro-frequencies of ionospheric ions and hiss frequencies. AGARDOGRAPH 74, New York: Pergamon 175–89.

HANSEN, S. F., 1963. A mechanism for the production of certain types of very-low-frequency emissions. *J. Geophys. Res.*, **68**(21), 5925–36. *P. 315.*

HARRIS, I., and R. JASTROW, 1959. An interim atmosphere derived from rocket and satellite data. *Planet. Space Sci.*, **1**(1), 20–26. *P. 191.*

HEADING, J., 1961. Analytical considerations of windows for low frequency radio waves. *J. Atmos. Terrest. Phys.*, **20**(1), 31–39.

HELLIWELL, R. A., 1956. Low frequency propagation studies: Part I. Whistlers and related phenomena Final Rept. Air Force Contract No. AF 19(604)-795, AFCRC-TR-56-189, ASTIA AD 110184, Stanford Electronics Labs., Stanford Univ., Stanford, Calif. *P. 19.*

———, 1958. Whistlers and VLF emissions. *Geophys. and the IGY* (Geophysics Monograph No. 2), AGU, Wash., D.C.

———, 1959. Whistler paths and electron densities in the outer ionosphere. (Proc. of the Symposium on Physical Processes in the Sun-Earth Environment), DRTE No. 1025, Telecommunications Estab., Defence Res. 165–75. *Pp. 133, 305.*

———, 1960a. Whistler-mode propagation. Chap. 6 in *The Radio Noise Spectrum*, Donald H. Menzel, ed. Cambridge, Mass.: Harvard Univ. Press.

———, 1960b. Summary of Research on whistlers and related phenomena. *J. Res. NBS*, **64D**(6), 642–44.

———, 1961a. Exospheric electron density variations deduced from whistlers: *Ann. geophys.*, **17**(1), 76–81.

———, 1961b. Whistlers: Radio probes for exploring the outer atmosphere. *New Scient.*, **II**, 458–60.

———, 1962. Very-low-frequency discrete emissions received at conjugate points. *Nature*, **195**(4836), 64–65. *P. 314.*

———, 1963a. Coupling between the ionosphere and the earth–ionosphere waveguide at very low frequencies. In *Proceedings of the International Conference on the Ionosphere, London, July* 1962, Dorking: Eng., Bartholomew Press.

———, 1963b. Whistlers. In *Propagation and Instabilities in Plasmas*, Walter I. Futterman, ed., Stanford, Calif.: Stanford Univ. Press, 25–36.

———, 1963c. Whistler-triggered periodic VLF emissions. *J. Geophys. Res.*, **68**(19), 5387–95. *Pp. 299, 301, 314.*

———, 1964. Whistlers and VLF emissions. *Research in Geophysics*, Vol. 1, *Sun, Upper Atmosphere, and Space*, Cambridge, Mass.: MIT Press (in press).

HELLIWELL, R. A., and T. F. BELL, 1960. A new mechanism for accelerating electrons in the outer ionosphere. *J. Geophys. Res.*, **65**(6), 1839–42. *Pp. 179, 204.*

HELLIWELL, R. A., T. F. BELL, and R. L. SMITH, 1957. A new whistler dispersion theory. Paper presented at IRE-URSI. *Symp.* Apr. 30–May 3, 1956, Wash., D.C., Abstr. in *IRE Trans. Ant. & Prop.*, **AP-5**(1), 163.

HELLIWELL, R. A., and D. L. CARPENTER, 1961. Whistlers-West IGY-IGC synoptic program. Final Rept. National Science Foundation Grants IGY 6.10/20 and G-8839, Radio-science Lab., Stanford Electronics Labs., Stanford Univ., Stanford, Calif. *Pp. vi, 291, 293, 306.*

———, 1962. Whistlers-West—Results from the IGY/IGC-59 synoptic program. *IGY Bull.*, *NAS* (57), 1–9.

———, 1963. Whistlers excited by nuclear explosions. *J. Geophys. Res.*, **68**(15), 4409–20. *P. 135.*

HELLIWELL, R. A., J. H. CRARY, J. P. KATSUFRAKIS, and M. L. TRIMPI, 1961. The Stanford University real-time spectrum analyzer. Tech. Rept. No. 10, Air Force Contract No.

AF 18(603)-126, Radioscience Lab., Stanford Electronics Labs., Stanford Univ., Stanford, Calif. *P. 87.*

HELLIWELL, R. A., J. H. CRARY, J. H. POPE, and R. L. SMITH, 1956. The "nose" whistler—a new high latitude phenomenon. *J. Geophys. Res.,* **61**(1), 139–42. *P. 20.*

HELLIWELL, R. A., and E. GEHRELS, 1958. Observations of magneto-ionic duct propagation using man-made signals of very low frequency. *Proc. IRE,* **46**(4), 785–87. *Pp. 153, 169.*

HELLIWELL, R. A., A. G. JEAN, and W. L. TAYLOR, 1958. Some properties of lightning impulses which produce whistlers. *Proc. IRE,* **46**(10), 1760–62. *P. 121.*

HELLIWELL, R. A., J. KATSUFRAKIS, and G. CARPENTER, 1962. Whistler-mode propagation studies using Navy VLF transmitters. Office of Naval Research Contract Nonr 225(27), SEL 62–035, Radioscience Lab., Stanford Electronics Lab., Stanford Univ., Stanford, Calif. *Pp. 71, 145, 153.*

HELLIWELL, R. A., J. KATSUFRAKIS, M. TRIMPI, and N. BRICE, 1964. Artificially-stimulated VLF radiation from the ionosphere. *J. Geophys. Res.,* **69**(11), 2391–94.

HELLIWELL, R. A., and L. H. MARTIN, 1961. Studies of geomagnetic latitude control of VLF and ELF phenomena in the Antarctic (VLF air-lifted traverse). Final Rept., National Science Foundation Grant 13532, Radioscience Lab., Stanford Electronics Labs., Stanford Univ., Stanford, Calif.

HELLIWELL, R. A., and M. G. MORGAN, 1956. IGY whistler observations. *Science,* **123**(3201), 788.

———, 1959. Atmospheric whistlers. *Proc. IRE,* **47**(2), 200–208.

———, 1960. The production of whistlers by lightning strokes. *Proc. IRE,* **48**(1), 117.

HINES, C. O., 1957. Heavy-ion effects in audio-frequency radio propagation. *J. Atmos. Terrest. Phys.,* **11**(1), 36–42. *Pp. 21, 82.*

HINES, C. O., W. C. HOFFMAN, and H. WEIL, 1959. Transverse whistler propagation. Rept. No. 2894-1-F, AF19(604)-5553, Univ. of Michigan Research Inst., Ann Arbor, Mich.

HODARA, H., 1962. Some remarks on "Penetration of the ionosphere by very-low-frequency radio signals." *Proc. IRE,* **50**(9), 2000.

HOFFMAN, W. C., 1959. The current-jet hypothesis of whistler generation. *Planet. Space Sci.,* **2**(1), 72–73.

———, 1960a. The current-jet hypothesis of whistler generation. *J. Geophys. Res.,* **65**(7), 2047–54. *P. 133.*

———, 1960b. Conditions for the persistence of purely longitudinal or purely transverse propagation. *J. Atmos. Terrest. Phys.,* **18**(1), 1–7.

HORNER, F., ed., 1962. *Radio Noise of Terrestrial Origin* (Proceedings of Commission IV, 13th General Assembly of URSI, London, 1960), New York; Am. Elsevier.

ICHIMIYA, T., K. TAKAYAMA, I. DOTE, Y. AONO, K. HIRAO, S. MIYAZAKI, T. SUGIYAMA, and T. MURAOKA, 1961. Measurement of positive ion density in the ionosphere by sounding rocket. *Nature,* **190**, 156–58. *P. 63.*

ISTED, G. A., and G. MILLINGTON, 1957. The "dawn chorus" in radio observation. *Nature,* **180**, 716. *P. 205.*

IWAI, A., and J. OUTSU, 1956. On an investigation of whistling atmospherics in Japan. *Proc. Res. Inst. Atmos., Nagoya Univ.,* **4**, 29–47.

———, 1958a. On an investigation of the field intensity of whistling atmospherics. *Proc. Res. Inst. Atmos., Nagoya Univ.,* **5**, 50–52.

———, 1958b. On the characteristic phenomena for short whistlers observed at Toyokawa in winter. *Proc. Res. Inst. Atmos., Nagoya Univ.,* **5**, 53–63. *Pp. 124, 125, 199.*

———, 1962. Observing method for whistlers and its results. *J. Inst. Elec. Comm. Eng.,* Japan, **45**(4), 556–63.

JACKEROTT, I. M., T. STOCKFLET, and J. TAAGHOLT, 1964. Observations of whistlers and VLF-emissions at Godhavn and Narssarssuaq, Greenland, and at Tromsø, Norway, in 1962. Rept. No. 18, Ionosphere Laboratory, Royal Technical University of Denmark.

JACKEROTT, I. M., J. TAAGHOLT, and E. UNGSTRUP, 1963. Whistlers and VLF emissions from Saltholm, Denmark, 1960–1961. Rept. No. 15. Air Force Contract No. AF 61(052)–652, Ionosphere Lab., Royal Tech. Univ. Denmark.

JASTROW, R., 1962. The magnetosphere. *Trans. N.Y. Acad. Sci.*, Ser. II, **24**(6), 690–703.

JIŘÍČEK, F., 1962. On the types and dispersions of whistlers as observed in Czechoslovakia. *Studia Geophys. et Geodaet.*, **6**(1), 98–101.

JOHNSON, F. S., 1959. Telluric origin of the whistler medium. *Nature*, **184**(4701), 1787–88. *P. 188.*

——, 1960. The exosphere and upper F region. *J. Geophys. Res.*, **65**(9), 2571–75. *P. 188.*

JOHNSON, F. S., ed., 1961. *Satellite Environment Handbook*, Stanford, Calif.: Stanford Univ. Press.

——, 1962. Physics of the distribution of ionized particles in the exosphere. *NATO Conference Series, Electron Density Profiles in the Ionosphere and Exosphere*, **2**, 404–13. *P. 321.*

JONES, D. L., R. GALLET, J. M. WATTS, and D. N. FRAZER, 1963. An atlas of whistlers and VLF emissions—A survey of VLF spectra from Boulder, Colorado. Tech. Note 166, Natl. Bureau of Standards, Central Radio Propagation Lab., Boulder, Colo. *P. 204.*

JØRGENSON, T. S., 1964. Some observations of V.L.F.-hiss and correlated phenomena. *J. Atmos. Terrest. Phys.*, **26**(5), 626–28. *P. 294.*

JØRGENSEN, T. S., and E. UNGSTRUP, 1962. Direct observation of correlation between aurorae and hiss in Greenland. *Nature*, **194**(4827), 462–63. *P. 294.*

KANE, J. A., 1959. Arctic measurements of electron collision frequencies in the D region of the ionosphere. *J. Geophys. Res.*, **64**(2), 133–39. *P. 63.*

KANTOR, G., 1963. The whistler-hydromagnetic extension of magneto-ionic theory. Upper Atmosphere Physics Lab., Project 4603, Air Force Cambridge Research Lab., Office of Aerospace Research, AFCRL-63-929.

KIMPARA, A., 1959. Diurnal and seasonal variations in whistler records in Japan. *Proc. Res. Inst. Atmos., Nagoya Univ.*, **6**, 38–43.

——, 1960a. On some remarkable characteristics of whistling atmospherics. *Rept. Iono. Space Res., Japan*, **14**(2), 160–79. Also in *Proc. Res. Inst. Atmos., Nagoya Univ.*, **7**, 40–57. *P. 150.*

——, 1960b. Correlation of occurrence of whistlers with geomagnetic activities. *Nature*, **186**(4720), 230.

——, 1960c. Sur une corrélation entre les atmosphériques siffleurs et les perturbations géomagnétiques. *Compt. rend.*, **250**(14), 2596–97.

——, 1962a. Sur une corrélation entre les sifflements radioélectriques et l'activité solaire. *Compt. rend.*, **254**(7), 1321–22.

——, 1962b. Whistlers and solar activity. *Nature*, **193**(4816), 666–67.

——, 1962c. Dispersion of whistlers. *Nature*, **193**(4816), 667–68. *P. 199.*

——, 1962d. Some characteristics of the dispersion of whistlers. *Proc. Res. Inst. Atmos., Nagoya Univ.*, **9**, 5–17. Also published in *Rept. Iono. Space Res., Japan*, **16**(1, pt. 1), 27–36, and *Compt. rend.*, **254**(8), 1467–69.

——, 1962e. Occurrence of whistlers and solar activity. *Proc. Res. Inst. Atmos., Nagoya Univ.*, **9**, 43–44. Also published in *Rept. Iono. Space Res., Japan*, **16**(1, pt. 1), 69–70.

KIMURA, I., 1961. Amplification of the VLF electromagnetic wave by a proton beam through the exosphere. An origin of the VLF emissions. *Rept. Iono. Space Res., Japan*, **15**(2), 171–91. *P. 310.*

KLINKER, L., and G. ENTZIAN, 1960. Bemerkungen zu den jahres- und tageszeitlichen Variationen im Gang der Whistlerhäufigkeit. *Z. Meteorologie*, **14**(7–9), 207–12.

——, 1962. Jahreszeitliche Phasenunterschiede im Whistler-Tagesgang. *Tagungs. Geomag. Aeron.*, **29**, 178–82.

KLINKER, L., K. H. SCHMELOVSKY, and R. KNUTH, 1960a. Jahreszeitliche Variationen der mittleren Elektronenkonzentration zwischen 400 und 1200 Km Höhe. *Naturwiss.* **47**(9), 197–98.

KLINKER, L., K. H. SCHMELOVSKY, and R. KNUTH, 1960b. Die Elektronenkonzentration der äusseren Ionosphäre: winterliche Verhältnisse and jahreszeitliche Variationen. *Gerlands Beitr. Geofys.*, **69**(6), 328–50.

KNOX, C. F., and M. J. RYCROFT, 1964. Observations of background electromagnetic noise in east Greenland. *Nature*, **201**(4920), 693–94.

KNUDSEN, E., and H. NORINDER, 1963. Different types of musical atmospherics and their relations to lightning discharges. *Arkiv Geofys.*, **4**(1), 83–101. *P. 305.*

KOLOMENSKY, A. A., 1956. Radiation emitted by an electron moving uniformly in a plasma in the presence of a magnetic field. *Dokl. Akad. Nauk SSSR*, **106**, 982.

KOSTER, J. R., and L. R. O. STOREY, 1955. An attempt to observe whistling atmospherics near the magnetic equator. *Nature*, **175**(4444), 36–37. *P. 148.*

LAASPERE, T., M. G. MORGAN, and W. C. JOHNSON, 1963. Some results of five years of whistler observations from Labrador to Antarctica. *Proc. IEEE*, **51**(4), 554–68. *Pp. 150, 168.*

——, 1964. Chorus, hiss and other audio-frequency emissions at stations of the 'Whistlers-East' network. Hanover, N.H.: Dartmouth College, Thayer School of Eng. Also in IEEE (in press).

LEIPHART, J. P., R. W. ZEEK, L. S. BEARCE, and E. TOTH, 1962. Penetration of the ionosphere by very-low-frequency radio signals—interim results of the Lofti I experiment. *Proc. IRE*, **50**(1), 6–17. *P. 175.*

LIEMOHN, H. B., 1962. Dispersion of waves in hot plasmas. Geo-Astrophysics Lab. Rept. No. D1-82-0174, Boeing Scientific Res. Labs., Seattle, Wash.

——, 1963, Thermal cutoffs of the whistler mode of propagation. Geo-Astrophysics Lab. Rept. No. Dl-82-0229, Boeing Scientific Research Labs., Seattle, Wash.

LIEMOHN, H. B., and F. L. SCARF, 1962a. Exospheric electron temperatures from nose whistler attenuation. *J. Geophys. Res.*, **67**(5), 1785–89. *Pp. 127, 179.*

——, 1962b. Whistler attenuation by electrons with an $E^{-2.5}$ distribution. *J. Geophys. Res.*, **67**(11), 4163–67. *Pp. 127, 179.*

——, 1963. Whistler determination of electron energy and density distributions in the magnetosphere. Geo-Astrophys. Lab. Rept. No. D1-82-0245, Boeing Sci. Res. Lab., Seattle, Wash.

——, 1964. Whistler determination of electron energy and density distributions in the magnetosphere. *J. Geophys. Res.*, **69**(5), 883–904.

LIKHTER, YA. I., 1961. Research on atmospherics in the U.S.S.R. in 1957–1959. *Geomag. and Aeron.*, **1**(2), 200–203.

LIPPMANN, B. A., 1960. Bomb-excited whistlers. *Proc. IRE.*, **48**(10), 1778–79.

LOCKWOOD, G. E. K., and L. E. PETRIE, 1963. Low latitude field-aligned ionization observed by the Alouette topside sounder. *Planet. Space Sci.*, **11**(3), 327–30.

LOKKEN, J. E., J. A. SHAND, and C. S. WRIGHT, 1962. A note on the classification of geomagnetic signals below 30 cycles per second. *Can. J. Phys.*, **40**(8), 1000–1009.

LOKKEN, J. E., J. A. SHAND, S. C. WRIGHT, L. H. MARTIN, N. M. BRICE, and R. A. HELLIWELL, 1961. Stanford-Pacific Naval Laboratory conjugate point experiment. *Nature*, **192**(4800), 319–20. *Pp. 292, 299, 301.*

MACARTHUR, J. W., 1959. Theory of the origin of the very-low-frequency radio emissions from the earth's exosphere. *Phys. Rev. Lett.*, **2**(12), 491–92. *P. 310.*

MAEDA, K., 1962. Whistlers and VLF emissions in connection with the earth storms. *J. Phys. Soc. Japan*, **17**(Suppl. A-II), 95–103.

MAEDA, K., and I. KIMURA, 1956. A theoretical investigation of the propagation path of the whistling atmospherics. *Rept. Iono. Space Res., Japan*, **10**(3), 105–23.

——, 1959. Calculation of the propagation path of whistling atmospherics. *J. Atmos. Terrest. Phys.*, **15**, 62–65. *P. 55.*

——, 1962. Amplification of the VLF electromagnetic wave by a proton beam through the exosphere. *J. Phys. Soc. Japan*, **17**(Suppl. A-II), 92–95. *Pp. 310, 311.*

——, 1963. Origin and mechanism of VLF emissions. In *Space Science Research III*, New York: Wiley. *Pp. 310, 311.*

MAEDA, K., I. KIMURA, and T. TAKAKURA, 1963. Observation of low frequency radio waves in the ionosphere. *Rept. Iono. Space Res., Japan*, **17**(4), 259–72.

MAEDA, K., and H. OYA, 1963. Penetration of VLF radio waves through the ionosphere. *J. Geomag. and Geoelec.*, **14**(3), 151–71.

MARKS, K., 1962. Instruction manual for automatic whistler and hiss recorders at Byrd and South Pole Stations, Antarctica. SEL 62-076, Int. Memo. 1108-1, Radioscience Lab., Stanford Electronics Labs., Stanford Univ., Stanford, Calif. *P. 288.*

MARTIN, L. H., 1958. Whistlers in the Antarctic. *Nature*, **181**(4626), 1796–97. *P. 132.*

——, 1960. Observations of "whistlers" and "chorus" at the South Pole. *Nature*, **187**(4742), 1018–19. *P. 168.*

MARTIN, L. H., R. A. HELLIWELL, and K. E. MARKS, 1960. Association between aurorae and very-low-frequency hiss observed at Byrd Station, Antarctica. *Nature*, **187**(4739), 751–53. *P. 294.*

MARTYN, D. F., 1959. The normal F region of the ionosphere. *Proc. IRE*, **47**(2), 147–55. *P. 63.*

MATTERN, G., 1959. Über die Whistler-Beobachtungen des Taunus-Observatoriums. *Z. Geophys.*, **25**, 265–71.

McINNES, B. A., 1961. A study of ionospherics at Macquarie Island. *Australian J. Phys.*, **14**(2), 218–33. *Pp. 292, 310.*

McKENZIE, J. F., 1963. Čerenkov radiation in a magnetoionic medium (with application to the generation of low-frequency electromagnetic radiation in the exosphere by the passage of charged corpuscular streams). *Phil. Trans. Roy. Soc. (London)*, **A255**, 585–606. *P. 310.*

MENDONÇA, F. DE, and O. K. GARRIOTT, 1962. Ionospheric electron content calculated by a hybrid faraday-doppler technique. *J. Atmos. Terrest. Phys.*, **24**, 317–21.

MENZEL, D. H., and W. W. SALISBURY, 1948. Audio-frequency radio waves from the sun. *Nature*, **161**(4081), 91.

MENZEL, D. H. and E. K. SMITH, JR., eds., 1964. *Conference on non-linear processes in the ionosphere, December 16–17, 1963*, NBS Tech. Note No. 211, Vols. 1–6.

MITRA, A. P., 1957. Night-time ionization in the lower ionosphere: II. Distribution of electrons and positive and negative ions. *J. Atmos. Terrest. Phys.*, **10**, 153–62. *P. 63.*

MLODNOSKY, R. F., D. L. CARPENTER, and R. A. HELLIWELL, 1962. Non-thermal noise measurements near planets. In *La Physique des Planètes* (Les Congrès et Colloques de l'Université de Liège, Vol. 24), *Mémoires de la Société Royal des Sciences de Liège*, 5ième Sér., **7**(1).

MLODNOSKY, R. F., and R. A. HELLIWELL, 1962a. Graphic data on the earth's main magnetic field in space. *J. Geophys. Res.*, **67**(6), 2207–14. *Pp. 69, 317.*

——, 1962b. Corrigendum. *J. Geophys. Res.*, **67**(11), 4524. *Pp. 69, 317.*

MOOK, C. P., 1959. A preliminary meteorological study of the origin of whistlers. *J. Geophys. Res.*, **64**(7), 745–48.

MORGAN, M. G., 1957. Whistlers and dawn chorus. *Ann. IGY 1957–1958*, **3**, 315–36.

——, 1958a. Correlation of whistlers and lightning flashes by direct aural and visual observations. *Nature*, **18**(4631), 332–33.

——, 1958b. *Whistler studies at Dartmouth College.* (Monograph No. 2, Am. Geophys. Union) Wash., D.C.: American Geophysical Union, 31–34.

——, 1959. Whistlers. *J. Atmos. Terrest. Phys.*, **15**(1/2), 54–57.

——, 1960a. An island as a natural very-low-frequency transmitting antenna. *IRE Trans. Ant. and Prop.*, **AP-8**(5), 528–30.

——, 1960b. Summary of research on whistlers and related phenomena, Dartmouth College. *J. Res. NBS*, **64D**(6), 644–46.

MORGAN, M. G., and G. McK. ALLCOCK, 1956. Observations of whistling atmospherics at geomagnetically conjugate points. *Nature*, **177**(4497), 30–31. *P. 19.*

MORGAN, M. G., H. W. CURTIS, and W. C. JOHNSON, 1959. Path combinations in whistler echoes. *Proc. IRE*, **47**(2), 328–29. *P. 132.*

MORGAN, M. G., and H. E. DINGER, 1956. Observations of whistling atmospherics at geomagnetically conjugate points. *Nature*, **177**(4497), 29–30. *P. 19.*

MOROZUMI, H., 1962. A study of the aurora Australis in connection with association between VLFE hiss and auroral arcs and bands observed at the South Geographical Pole 1960. SUI 62–14, State Univ. of Iowa, Iowa City, Iowa. *P. 294.*

——, 1963. Semi-diurnal auroral peak and VLF emissions observed at the South Pole, 1960. *Trans. AGU*, **44**(3), 798–806.

MRAZEK, J., 1960. On the occurrence of atmospheric whistlers over Central Europe in 1958. *Studia Geophys. et Geodaet.*, **4**(3), 298–302.

——, 1962. Zur Frage der Ausbreitung von sehr langen elektromagnetischen Wellen in der Magnetosphäre. *Studia Geophys. et Geodaet.*, **6**(4), 385–90.

MULLALY, R. F., 1962a. Ray paths in inhomogeneous anisotropic media. *Australian J. Phys.*, **15**(1), 96–105.

——, 1962b. The ray paths of whistling atmospherics—differential geometry. *Australian J. Phys.*, **15**(1), 106–13.

MURCRAY, W. B., and J. H. POPE, 1960a. Doppler-shifted cyclotron frequency radiation from protons in the exosphere. *Phys. Rev. Lett.*, **4**(1), 5–6. *P. 310.*

——, 1960b. Radiation from protons of auroral energy in the vicinity of the earth. *J. Geophys. Res.*, **65**(11), 3569–74. *P. 310.*

——, 1961. Energy fluxes from the cyclotron radiation model of VLF radio emission. *Proc. IRE*, **49**(4), 811–12. *P. 310.*

National Bureau of Standards, 1953–1961. CRPL-F Series, Natl. Bureau of Standards, Central Radio Propagation Lab., Boulder, Colo. *P. 69.*

NERTNEY, R. J., 1953. The lower E and D region of the ionosphere as deduced from long radio wave measurements. *J. Atmos. Terrest. Phys.*, **3**, 92–107. *P. 63.*

NICOLET, MARCEL, 1959. Collision frequency of electrons in the terrestrial atmosphere. *Phys. Fluids*, **2**(2), 95–99. *P. 63.*

NICOLET, M., and A. C. AIKIN, 1960. The formation of the D region of the ionosphere. *J. Geophys. Res.*, **65**(5), 1469–83. *P. 63.*

NORINDER, H., 1960. Some comments on the penetration of whistlers through ionospheric layers. *Planet. Space Sci.*, **2**, 261–62.

NORINDER, H., and E. KNUDSEN, 1959. The relation between lightning discharges and whistlers. *Planet. Space Sci.*, **1**, 173–83. *Pp. 121, 141.*

——, 1960a. Lightning discharges as a source of whistlers. *Arkiv Geofys.*, **3**(2–3), 255–88.

——, 1960b. Multiple lightning discharges followed by whistlers. *Arkiv Geofys.*, **3**, 289–98.

——, 1961a. Recent results in the investigation of the relation between lightning discharges and whistlers. *Planet. Space Sci.*, **5**(1), 46–49.

——, 1961b. The dispersion of whistlers compared with the geomagnetic latitudes of their sources. Res. Note, *Planet. Space Sci.*, **5**, 326–28.

——, 1961c. Occurrence of different kinds of whistler activity. *Arkiv Geofys.*, **3**(4), 347–66.

——, 1963. Comments on distinct types of musical atmospherics in their relation to thunderstorm activity. *Planet. Space Sci.*, **11**(5), 579. *P. 305.*

NORTHOVER, F. H., 1959a. The propagation of electromagnetic waves in ionized gases with special reference to whistlers. *J. Atmos. Terrest. Phys.*, **17**(1/2), 158–78.

——, 1959b. The propagation of electromagnetic waves in ionized gases. *IRE Trans. Ant. & Prop.*, **AP-7** (Supplement), S340–60.

OBAYASHI, T., 1958. Geomagnetic pulsations and the earth's outer atmosphere. *Ann. Géophys.*, **14**(4), 464–74.

——, 1959. Geophysical effects associated with the high-altitude nuclear explosion. Part III. Ionospheric radio propagation disturbances. *J. Geomag. Geoelec.*, **11**(2), 51–53. *P. 51.*

OBAYASHI, T., S. FUJII, and T. KIDOKORO, 1959. An experimental proof of the mode theory of VLF ionospheric propagation. *J. Geomag. Geoelec.*, **10**(2), 47–55.

O'BRIEN, B. J., 1964. High-latitude geophysical studies with Satellite Injun 3. 3. Precipitation of electrons into the atmosphere. *J. Geophys. Res.*, **69**(1), 13–43 (Jan. 1).

O'BRIEN, B. J., and H. TAYLOR, 1964. High-latitude geophysical studies with Satellite Injun 3. 4. Auroras and their excitation. *J. Geophys. Res.*, **69**(1), 45–63 (Jan. 1).

ONDOH, T., 1961. On the origin of VLF noise in the earth's exosphere. *J. Geomag. Geoelec.*, **12**(2), 77–83. *Pp. 293, 310.*

ONDOH, T., 1962a. VLF emissions and geomagnetic disturbances at the auroral zone: Part II. Chorus increases and geomagnetic pulsations at the auroral zone. *J. Geomag. Geoelec.*, **14**(2), 86–98. *See also* Tokuda (1962), Part I. *Pp. 293, 310.*

———, 1962b. A possibility of the generation of VLF emissions in the outer earth's exosphere. *Planet. Space Sci.*, **9**, 69–70. *P. 310.*

———, 1963a. Ionospheric absorption of cosmic radio noise and chorus at the auroral zone. *J. Geomag. Geoelec.*, **14**(3), 133–43. *P. 310.*

———, 1963b. Some relations of the chorus activity to the cosmic noise absorption, auroral activity, and K-index at the auroral zone. *J. Geomag. Geoelec.*, **14**(3), 172–74. *P. 310.*

———, 1963c. A note on the VLF emissions in the outer exosphere. *J. Geomag. Geoelec.*, **14**(3), 175–176. *P. 310.*

———, 1963d. The ionospheric absorption of the VLF emissions at the auroral zone. *J. Geomag. Geoelec.*, **15**(2), 90–108.

ONDOH, T., and S. HASHIZUME, 1960. The effect of proton gyration in the outer atmosphere represented on the dispersion curve of whistler. *J. Geomag. Geoelec.*, **12**(1), 32–37.

OUTSU, J., 1960. Numerical study of tweeks based on waveguide mode theory. *Proc. Res. Inst. Atmos., Nagoya Univ.*, **7**, 58–71.

OUTSU, J., and A. IWAI, 1959a. Investigation of the presence of ionized hydrogen in the outer atmosphere using whistler dispersions. *Proc. Res. Inst. Atmos., Nagoya Univ.*, **6**, 44–55.

———, 1959b. Ionization in the outer atmosphere inferred from whistling atmospherics. *J. Geomag. Geoelec.*, **10**(4), 135–42.

———, 1961. SEA and hiss associated with great bursts of solar radio emission in November 1960: Part III—Hiss. *Proc. Res. Inst. Atmos., Nagoya Univ.*, **8**, 13–16.

———, 1962a. VLF phenomena in lower latitudes during magnetically high active periods. *J. Phys. Soc. Japan*, **17**(Suppl. A-II), 1962 Intl. Conf. Cosmic Rays and the Earth Storm, Part II, 88–91.

———, 1962b. Some correlations between occurrence rate and dispersions of whistlers at lower latitudes and magnetic K-index. *Proc. Res. Inst. Atmos., Nagoya Univ.*, **9**, 19–24.

OUTSU, J., A. IWAI, and Y. TANAKA, 1963. Annual variations of whistler occurrence rate in middle and low latitudes since July, 1957. *Bull. Res. Inst. Atmos., Nagoya Univ.*, **13**, 11–24.

OWREN, L., 1959. Deduction of the electron density in the exosphere from nose whistler observations. Chap. II in Arctic propagation studies at tropospheric and ionospheric modes of propagation. Final Rept., Air Force Contract No. AF 19(604)-1859, AFCRC-TR-59-366, Geophys. Inst., Univ. of Alaska, College, Alaska.

PAETZOLD, H. K., 1959. Die Erforschung der terrestrichen Exosphäre. *Z. angew. Phys.*, **11**(6), 234–43. *P. 198.*

PAKHOMOV, V. I., and K. N. STEPANOV, 1963. Radiation of low frequency waves by ions and electrons in a magneto-active plasma. *Phys. Soviet JETP*, **16**(6), 1522–30.

PARKER, E. N., 1961. Transresonant electron acceleration. *J. Geophys. Res.*, **66**(9), 2673–76. *P. 204.*

PATTERSON, T. N. L., 1961. Whistler dispersions for a model of the ionic distribution in the exosphere. *Planet. Space Sci.*, **8**(2), 71–76.

PEDERSEN, P. O., 1929. Wireless echoes of long delay. *Proc. IRE*, **17**(10), 1750–85. *P. 51.*

PIERCE, E. T. 1962. Very-low-frequency atmospherics due to lightning flashes. Prepared under Air Force Contract No. AF 33(657)-7009 by Stanford Research Institute, Menlo Park, Calif. *P. 121.*

POEVERLEIN, H., 1948. Strahlwege von Radiowellen in der Ionosphäre. *Sitz. Bayerischen Akad. Wiss.* 1948, (1), 175–201. *Pp. 35, 37.*

————, 1961. Resonance of the space between earth and ionosphere. *J. Res. NBS*, **65D**(5), 465–74. *P. 125.*

POPE, J. H., 1957. Diurnal variation in the occurrence of "dawn chorus." *Nature*, **180**, 433. *Pp. 21, 292.*

POPE, J. H., 1959a. An investigation of whistlers and chorus at high latitudes. Sci. Rept. No. 4. Air Force Contract No. AF 19(604)-1859, pp. 1–38. Geophys. Inst., Univ. of Alaska, College, Alaska. *Pp. 292, 293.*

————, 1959b. Whistlers and chorus observations. Arctic propagation, AFCRC-TR-59-366, pp. 51–67. Final Rept., Air Force Contract No. AF 19(604)-1859, Geophys. Inst., Univ. of Alaska, College, Alaska. *P. 292.*

————, 1960. Effect of latitude on the diurnal maximum of "dawn chorus." *Nature*, **185**(4706), 87–88. *P. 292.*

————, 1961a. An estimate of electron densities in the exosphere by means of nose whistlers. *J. Geophys. Res.*, **66**(1), 67–75. *P. 184.*

————, 1961b. Some comments on obtaining electron densities in the exosphere using nose whistlers. *J. Geophys. Res.*, **66**(8), 2580–81.

————, 1962. A correction to the exospheric electron density estimate using the nose whistlers of March 19, 1959. *J. Geophys. Res.*, **67**(1), 412.

————, 1963. A high-latitude investigation of the natural very-low-frequency electromagnetic radiation known as chorus. *J. Geophys. Res.*, **68**(1), 83–99. *Pp. 205, 292, 293.*

POPE, J. H., and W. H. CAMPBELL, 1960. Observations of a unique VLF emission. *J. Geophys. Res.*, **65**(8), 2543–44. *Pp. 299, 305.*

POTTER, R. K., 1951. Analysis of audio-frequency atmospherics. *Proc. IRE*, **39**(9), 1067–69. *Pp. 16, 305.*

PRAUS, O., 1963. On the relation between VLF emission and other geophysical phenomena as observed at Mirny Station, Antarctica. *Studia Geophys. et Geodaet.*, **7**(3), 240.

PREECE, W. H., 1894. Earth Currents. *Nature*, **49**(1276), 554. *P. 11.*

RAMANATHAN, K. R., R. V. BHONSLE, and S. S. DEGAONKAR, 1961. Effect of electron-ion collisions in the F region of the ionosphere on the absorption of cosmic radio noise at 25 mc/s at Ahmedabad. *J. Geophys. Res.*, **66**(9), 2763–71. *P. 63.*

RAO, M. S. V., and H. G. BOOKER, 1963. Guiding of electromagnetic waves along a magnetic field in a plasma. *J. Geophys. Res.*, **68**(2), 387–94.

RATCLIFFE, J. A., 1959. *The Magneto-Ionic Theory and Its Applications to the Ionosphere.* Cambridge, Eng.: Cambridge Univ. Press. *Pp. 16, 23, 27, 61.*

————, 1960. *Physics of the Upper Atmosphere*, New York: Academic Press. *P. 63.*

RAWER, K., and K. SUCHY, 1961. Whistlers excited by sound waves. *Proc. IRE*, **49**(5), pt. 1, 968–69.

RENARD, C., 1961a. Aspects des bruits radioélectriques naturels de très basses fréquences enregistrés aux Kerguelen. *Terres Australes et Antarctiques françaises*, **(14)**, 3–27.

————, 1961b. Variation diurnes et cycliques de l'intensité des bruits radioélectriques naturels de très basses frequénces. *Compt. rend.*, **252**(9), 1365–67.

————, 1961c. Sur une méthode permettant de connaître la ligne de force magnétique empruntée par un sifflement. *Compt. rend.*, **252**, 3096–98.

————, 1962. Essais d'un intégrateur de bruits de très basses fréquences. *Terres Australes et Antarctiques françaises*, **18**(*Suppl.*), 1–16.

RIVAULT, R., 1953. Atmospherics. *Onde Elect.*, **33**, 165–72.

————, 1955. Perturbations radioélectriques d'origine terrestre. *Onde Elect.*, **35**(339), 593–97.

————, 1957. Characteristiques des sifflements observés au cours d'une année. *Onde Elect.*, **37**(362), 539–40. *P. 21.*

————, 1958. Perturbations radioélectriques d'origine terrestre. *Onde Elect.*, **38**(376), 527–32.

————, 1961. Perturbations radioélectriques d'origine terrestre. *Onde Elect.*, **41**(411), 547–52.

RIVAULT, R., and Y. CORCUFF, 1960. Recherche du point conjugué magnétique de Poitiers, variation nocturne de la dispersion des sifflements. *Ann. géophys.*, **16**(4), 550–54. *P. 199.*

RORDEN, L. H., R. A. HELLIWELL, and R. L. SMITH, 1963. An interpretation of LOFTI-I VLF observations (AGARDOGRAPH 74). New York: Pergamon. *P. 175.*

RYBNER, J. and E. UNGSTRUP, 1959. Research on relationships between natural atmospheric radio phenomena and geomagnetic field. Final Rept. Contract AF61(514)-1309, Science Foundation, Denmark.

RYDBECK, O. E. H., and J. ASKNE, 1963. Whistler-mode and ionized stream interactions. AFCRL-63-482, Ionosphere Res. Lab., Penn. State Univ., Univ. Park, Pa. Also in *Wave Interaction and Dynamic Nonlinear Phenomena in Plasmas*, Engineering Proceedings P-42, Penn. State Univ. *P. 311.*

SANTIROCCO, R. A., 1960. Energy fluxes from the cyclotron radiation model of VLF radio emission. *Proc. IRE*, **48**(9), 1650. *P. 310.*

SCARF, F. L., 1962. Landau damping and the attenuation of whistlers. *Phys. Fluids*, **5**(1), 6–13. *P. 179.*

SCHLAPP, D. M., 1959. Some measurements of collision frequency of electrons in the F region of the ionosphere. *J. Atmos. Terrest. Phys.*, **16**(3/4), 340–43. *P. 63.*

———, 1960. An attempt to measure the collision frequency of electrons in the F region of the ionosphere. *J. Atmos. Terrest. Phys.*, **17**(3), 246–53. *P. 63.*

SCHMELOVSKY, K. H., 1960. The electron density distribution derived from whistler data and faraday-fading observations. *J. Atmos. Terrest. Phys.*, **19**, 68–71.

SCHNEIDER, J., 1959. Stimulated emission of radiation by relativistic electrons in a magnetic field. *Phys. Rev. Lett.*, **2**(12), 504–5.

SCHOUTE-VANNECK, C. A., and M. S. MUIR, 1963. The electron density distribution in the magnetosphere derived from whistling atmospheric data. *J. Geophys. Res.*, **68**(22), 6079–82.

SHAMMATT, F. H., 1959. Atmospheric whistlers and the electron density in the ionosphere. Elec. Engr. Res. Lab., Rept. No. 6-30, AFCRC-TN-59-790 Air Force Contract No. AF 19(604)-5504, Univ. of Texas, Austin, Texas.

SHIMAZAKI, T., 1959. A statistical study of world-wide occurrence probability of spread-F *J. Radio Res.*, **6**(28), 669–704. *P. 144.*

SINGLETON, D. G., 1961. Spread-F and the latitude variation of occurrence of whistlers. *Nature*, **189**(4760), 215–16.

SMITH, E. J., P. J. COLEMAN, JR., D. L. JUDGE, and C. P. SONETT, 1960. Characteristics of the extraterrestrial current system: Explorer VI and Pioneer V. *J. Geophys. Res.*, **65**(6), 1858–61. *P. 181.*

SMITH, R. L., 1960a. The use of nose whistlers in the study of the outer ionosphere. Tech. Rept. No. 6, AFOSR-TN-60-861, Radioscience Lab., Stanford Electronics Labs., Stanford Univ., Stanford, Calif. *Pp. 35, 180, 184, 186, 188, 189, 191, 197.*

———, 1960b. Guiding of whistlers in a homogeneous medium. *J. Res. NBS-D, Radio Propagation*, **64D**(5), 505–8. *Pp. 35, 43, 50, 177.*

———, 1961a. Propagation characteristics of whistlers trapped in field-aligned columns of enhanced ionization. *J. Geophys. Res.*, **66**(11), 3699–3707. *Pp. 43, 50, 126, 177, 180, 184, 186, 188.*

———, 1961b. Properties of the outer ionosphere deduced from nose whistlers. *J. Geophys. Res.*, **66**(11), 3709–16. *P. 189.*

SMITH, R. L., and D. L. CARPENTER, 1961. Extension of nose whistler analysis, *J. Geophys. Res.*, **66**(8), 2582–86. *Pp. 191, 195, 300, 304.*

SMITH, R. L., J. H. CRARY, and W. T. KREISS, 1958. IGY instruction manual for automatic whistler recorders. Prepared under National Science Foundation Grant Y-6-10/20, Radioscience Lab., Stanford Electronics Labs., Stanford Univ., Stanford, Calif.

SMITH, R. L., and R. A. HELLIWELL, 1960. Electron densities to 5 earth radii deduced from nose whistlers. *J. Geophys. Res.*, **65**(9), 2583.

SMITH, R. L., R. A. HELLIWELL, and I. YABROFF, 1960. A theory of trapping of whistlers in field-aligned columns of enhanced ionization. *J. Geophys. Res.*, **65**(3), 815–23. *Pp. 43, 49.*

SPREITER, J. R., and B. R. BRIGGS, 1962. Analysis of the effect of a ring current on whistlers. *J. Geophys. Res.*, **67**(10), 3779–90.

STIX, T. H., 1962. *The Theory of Plasma Waves*, New York: McGraw-Hill. *Pp. 127.*

STOREY, L. R. O., 1953. An investigation of whistling atmospherics. *Phil. Trans. Roy. Soc. (London)*, A, **246**, 113–41. *Pp. 16, 36, 129, 144, 149, 177, 179, 182, 188, 293, 305.*

———, 1956a. Whistlers. *Sci. American*, **194**(1), 34–37.

———, 1956b. A method to detect the presence of ionized hydrogen in the outer atmosphere. *Can. J. Phys.*, **34**, 1153–63. *Pp. 20, 82.*

———, 1957a. Tables of functions for use in interpreting the dispersion curves of whistlers. RPL Project Rept. No. 23-4-2, Defence Res. Telecommunications Estab., Ottawa, Canada. *Pp. 21, 184.*

———, 1957b. A method for interpreting the dispersion curves of whistlers. *Can. J. Phys.*. **35**, 1107–22. *Pp. 21, 184.*

———, 1958. Protons outside the earth's atmosphere. *Ann. géophys.*, **14**(2), 144–53.

———, 1959. A method for measuring local electron density from an artificial satellite. *J. Res. NBS*, **63D**(3), 325–40.

———, 1962. Whistler theory. In *Monograph on Radio Noise of Terrestrial Origin*, F. Horner, ed., New York: American Elsevier.

———, 1963. Whistler propagation. *AGARD, Advances in Upper Atmosphere Research*, New York: Pergamon, pp. 231–44.

STØRMER, C., 1928. Short wave echoes and the aurora borealis. *Nature*, **122**(3079), 681. *Pp. 13, 51, 293.*

———, 1955. *The Polar Aurora*, Oxford: Clarendon Press.

STURROCK, P., 1962. Generation of radio noise in the vicinity of earth. *J. Res. NBS*, **66D**(2), 153–57. *P. 310.*

SWIFT, D. W., 1962a. The effect of positive ion collisions on whistler propagation. *J. Geophys. Res.*, **67**(3), 1175–77. *P. 68.*

———, 1962b. Very-low-frequency radio propagation in the ionosphere. *J. Res. NBS*, **66D**(6), 663–80.

TAYLOR, W. L., 1955. Description of recording equipment to be used in the study of whistling atmospherics. NBS Report 3559, Natl. Bureau of Standards, Central Radio Propagation Lab., Boulder, Colo.

TEPLEY, LEE R., 1961. Observations of hydromagnetic emissions. *J. Geophys. Res.*, **66**(6), 1651–58.

TEPLEY, L. R., and R. C. WENTWORTH, 1962. Hydromagnetic emissions, X-ray bursts and electron bunches: 1. experimental results. *J. Geophys. Res.*, **67**(9), 3317–33.

TERMAN, F. E., 1955. *Electronic and Radio Engineering*, New York: McGraw-Hill. 4th ed. *P. 155.*

TIDMAN, D. A., and R. K. JAGGI, 1962. Landau damping of transverse waves in the exosphere by fast-particle fluxes. *J. Geophys. Res.*, **67**(6), 2215–30.

TOKUDA, H., 1962. VLF emissions and geomagnetic disturbances at the auroral zone: Part I. Chorus bursts and preceding geomagnetic disturbances. *J. Geomag. and Geoelec.*, **14**(1), 33–40. *See also* Ondoh (1962), Part II. *P. 293.*

TOKUDA, H., 1964. Whistlers of exceptionally small dispersion observed at Kyoto. *J. Atmos. Terrest. Phys.*, **26**(1), 137–39.

TRAKHTENGERTS, V. YU., 1963. The mechanism of generation of very low frequency electromagnetic radiation in the earth's outer radiation belt. *Geomag. and Aeron.*, **3**(3), 365–71.

TWISS, R. Q., and J. A. ROBERTS, 1958. Electromagnetic radiation from electrons rotating in an ionized medium under the influence of a uniform magnetic field. *Australian J. Phys.*, **11**(3), 424–46.

UNGSTRUP, E., 1959. Observations of whistlers and very low frequency phenomena at Godhavn, Greenland. *Nature*, **184**, 806. *P. 132.*

————, 1962. Observations of VLF radio noise at Godhavn, Greenland. Rept. No. 12, Ionosphere Lab., Royal Tech. Univ. of Denmark. *P. 293.*

————, 1964a. Association between VLF emissions and flickering aurora. Tech. Rept. No. SEL 64-050, prepared under Air Force Office of Scientific Research Grant 62-370, Radioscience Lab., Stanford Electronics Labs., Stanford Univ., Stanford, Calif.

————, 1964b. Propagation of VLF radio waves across the auroral zone. Tech. Rept. No. SEL 64-051, prepared under National Science Foundation Grant GA-56, Radioscience Lab., Stanford Electronics Labs., Stanford Univ., Stanford, Calif.

UNGSTRUP, E., and I. M. JACKEROTT, 1963. Observations of chorus below 1500 cycles per second at Godhavn, Greenland, from July 1957 to December 1961. *J. Geophys. Res.,* **68**(8), 2141–46. *P. 290.*

UNZ, H., 1962a. On the origin of "very-low-frequency emissions." *J. Atmos. Terrest. Phys.,* **24**, 685–89.

————, 1962b. The magneto-ionic theory for drifting plasma. *IRE Trans. Ant. & Prop.* **AP-10**(4), 459–64.

————, 1962c. On the theory of hybrid whistlers. *J. Atmos. Terrest. Phys.,* **24**, 765–70.

URSI, 1963, *U.R.S.I. Golden Jubilee Memorial,* Brussels: International Scientific Radio Union. *P. 11.*

VESTINE, E. H., 1959. Note on conjugate points of geomagnetic field lines for some selected auroral and whistler stations of the IGY. *J. Geophys. Res.,* **64**(10), 1411–14. *Pp. 144, 165.*

VOGE, J., 1961. Propagation guidée le long d'un feuillet atmosphérique ou (plus particulièrement) exosphérique. Première partie, *Extrait des Ann. télécom.,* **16**(11–12), 288–94.

————, 1962. Propagation guidée le long d'un feuillet atmosphérique ou (plus particulièrement) exosphérique. Deuxième partie, *Extrait des Ann. télécom.,* **17**(1–2), 34–43.

WAIT, J. R., 1962. *Electromagnetic Waves in Stratified Media.* New York: Pergamon. *P. 144.*

WATTS, J. M., 1957a. An observation of audio-frequency electromagnetic noise during a period of solar disturbance. *J. Geophys. Res.,* **62**(2), 199–206. *Pp. 22, 288.*

————, 1957b. Audio frequency electromagnetic hiss recorded at Boulder in 1956. *Geophys. Pura e Appl.,* **37**, 169–73. *Pp. 22, 288.*

————, 1959. Direction findings on whistlers. *J. Geophys. Res.,* **64**(11), 2029–30. *P. 130.*

WATTS, J. M., J. A. KOCH, and R. M. GALLET, 1963. Observations and results from the "hiss recorder," an instrument to continuously observe the VLF emissions. *J. Res. NBS.,* **67D**(5), 569–79. *P. 307.*

WENTWORTH, R. C., and L. R. TEPLEY, 1962. Hydromagnetic emissions, X-ray bursts and electron bunches: 2. Theoretical interpretation. *J. Geophys. Res.,* **67**(9), 3335–43. [See part 1 under Tepley and Wentworth, 1962.]

WESCOTT, E. M., J. H. POPE, D. O. DYER, W. H. CAMPBELL, 1960. Rare hiss, earth currents and micropulsations on November 27, 1959. *Nature,* **185**(4708), 231. *P. 293.*

WHITSON, A. L., and E. T. PIERCE, 1963. Sudden ionospheric disturbances and the propagation of very-low-frequency radio waves: Part II. Whistler tape analysis and instrument development. Final Rept. Air Force Contract No. AF 49(638)-1081, Stanford Research Institute, Menlo Park, Calif.

WILCOX, J. B., and E. MAPLE, 1960. Audio-frequency fluctuations in the geomagnetic field. *J. Geophys. Res.,* **65**(10), 3261–72.

WILD, J. P., S. F. SMERD, and A. A. WEISS, 1963. Solar bursts. *Ann. Rev. Astron. and Astrophys.,* **1**, 291–363.

WILLARD, H. R., 1961. Two-hop 18.6 kc whistler-mode echoes received at Seattle. *J. Geophys. Res.,* **66**(6), 1976–77.

WILLIS, H. F., 1948. Audio-frequency magnetic fluctuations. *Nature,* **161**(4101), 887–88.

World Distribution of Thunderstorm Days. 1956. Geneva: World Meteorological Organization.

WRIGHT, J. W., 1960. A model of the F region above h_{max} F2. *J. Geophys. Res.*, **65**(1), 185–91. *P. 178.*

WRIGHT, J. W., and L. A. FINE, 1959. Mean electron density variations of the quiet ionosphere. NBS Tech. Note 40–1, Natl. Bureau of Standards, Central Radio Propagation Lab., Boulder, Colo.

YABROFF, I., 1961. Computation of whistler ray paths. *J. Res. NBS*, **65D**(5), 485–505. *Pp. 43, 49, 55, 176, 177, 181.*

YEH, K. C., and G. W. SWENSON, JR., 1961. Ionospheric electron content and its variations deduced from satellite observations. *J. Geophys. Res.*, **66**(4), 1061–67. *P. 202.*

YOSHIDA, S., and T. HATANAKA, 1962a. The disturbances of exosphere as seen from the VLF emission. *J. Phys. Soc. Japan*, **17**(Supplement A-II), 78-83. *Pp. 150, 293.*

———, 1962b. Variations in the VLF emissions with reference to the exosphere. *Rept. Iono. Space Res., Japan*, **16**(4), 387–409. *Pp. 150, 293.*

Index

Absorption, 61–72; QL approximation, 62; models of the ionosphere used in computing, 63–64; variation with height, 65–66; variation with wave frequency, 67–68; effect of gyro-frequency on, 68; effect of ions on, 68; variation with f_0F2, 69–70; variation with latitude, 70–71; effect of input wave direction on, 71–72, 176; effect on whistler cutoff frequencies, 126; effect on whistler-mode echo occurrence, 167; effect on emission occurrence, 293. *See also* Cyclotron damping

Absorption events, relation to emissions, 295

Alouette I satellite, vi; spectra from, 286–87; emissions observed by, 308–9; lower hybrid resonance observed by, 309

Analyzers, spectrum, 87–88, 204

Appleton's equations, 23–24

Area, effective: of whistlers, 2 3, 20, 110, 141, 144; of emissions, 291–92

"Argus" experiment, 9

Artificially generated whistlers, from nuclear explosions, 135–37. *See also* Fixed-frequency whistler-mode echoes

Artificially stimulated emissions as explanation of reduced-duration echoes, 162. *See also* Triggered emissions, artificial source

Atlas: notation system for whistler Atlas, 83, 87; of whistlers, 89–120; notation system for emission Atlas, 207; of emissions, 208–87

Atmospherics, 2; association with whistlers, 2, 21; with emissions, 269, 305

Aurora: early observations of association with VLF phenomena, 15; relation to emissions, 294–95

Auroral hiss, *see* Hiss

Auroral particles and Čerenkov radiation, 310

Backscatter, correlation with whistler-mode echoes, 169

Čerenkov radiation, 310. *See also* Emission generation mechanisms

Chorus: sound of, 9; early observation of, 15; production by solar particles, 21; defined, 207; model spectral forms, 206; spectra, 240–48, 274–78; field strength, 288–91, 296; bursts, 296; relation to periodic emissions, 307; observed in satellites, 308–9

Chorus, occurrence: correlation with magnetic variations, 21; correlation with whistlers, 21; diurnal variation, 21, 292; latitude variation, 293

Classification of whistlers as one- or two-hop, 123–24

Cluster of emissions: defined, 205; spectra, 218

Collision frequency, models for absorption calculations, 63–64

Combinations of discrete emissions: defined, 207; spectra, 219–22, 280

Communication using whistler-mode, 8

Conjugate point: observations of whistlers and atmospherics, 19; locations for receiving stations, 86; whistler spectra, 91, 93, 106, 110, 258, 260, 263, 266, 267; emission spectra, 212, 218, 223, 225, 227, 231–32, 249, 250, 256, 258, 260, 263, 266, 267, 280–85; observations of emissions, 292, 300–304

Constant-density model of electron density, 189

Coupling: to ducts, 55, 56–59; from ducts, 56–59; conditions producing echoing, 56; losses, 60–61; observational results, 179

Critical angle, 52–53

Cutoff frequencies, as affected by source spectra, 121, 125

Cutoff frequencies of whistlers, 2, 125–28; spectra demonstrating lower cutoff, 117; absence of waveguide effect, 126; affected by ducts, 126–27, 128; due to absorption, 126; affected by cyclotron damping, 127

Cyclotron damping, 125, 127, 179

Cyclotron radiation, 310; doppler-shifted, 314–15

D region, effect on VLF propagation, *see* Absorption

Dawn chorus, *see* Chorus

Detection of whistlers, methods for, 3, 11, 12

Diffuseness of whistlers, 129

Dipole latitude, 181

Direction of arrival of whistlers, 129–31; of emissions, 292

Discrete emissions, 205; model spectral forms, 206; maximum duration of, 313–14

Dispersion: effect of magnetic storms on, 4; defined, 4, 32; effect on amplitude, 7; Eckersley, 16, 32; range of, 18, 112; due to earth-ionosphere waveguide, 78; comparison of theory and measurements, 104, 185–86; temporal variations of, 109, 133–34, 197; effect